Lecture Notes in Mathematics

Edited by J.-M. Morel, F. Takens and B. Teissier

Editorial Policy for Multi-Author Publications: Summer Schools / Intensive Courses

1. Lecture Notes aim to report new developments in all areas of mathematics and their applications – quickly, informally and at a high level. Mathematical texts analysing new developments in modelling and numerical simulation are welcome. Manuscripts should be reasonably self-contained and rounded off. Thus they may, and often will, present not only results of the author but also related work by other people. They should provide sufficient motivation, examples and applications. There should also be an introduction making the text comprehensible to a wider audience. This clearly distinguishes Lecture Notes from journal articles or technical reports which normally are very concise. Articles intended for a journal but too long to be accepted by most journals, usually do not have this "lecture notes" character.

2. In general SUMMER SCHOOLS and other similar INTENSIVE COURSES are held to present mathematical topics that are close to the frontiers of recent research to an audience at the beginning or intermediate graduate level, who may want to continue with this area of work, for a thesis or later. This makes demands on the didactic aspects of the presentation. Because the subjects of such schools are advanced, there often exists no textbook, and so ideally, the publication resulting from such a school could be a first approximation to such a textbook.
   Usually several authors are involved in the writing, so it is not always simple to obtain a unified approach to the presentation.
   For prospective publication in LNM, the resulting manuscript should not be just a collection of course notes, each of which has been developed by an individual author with little or no co-ordination with the others, and with little or no common concept. The subject matter should dictate the structure of the book, and the authorship of each part or chapter should take secondary importance. Of course the choice of authors is crucial to the quality of the material at the school and in the book, and the intention here is not to belittle their impact, but simply to say that the book should be planned to be written by these authors jointly, and not just assembled as a result of what these authors happen to submit.
   This represents considerable preparatory work (as it is imperative to ensure that the authors know these criteria before they invest work on a manuscript), and also considerable editing work afterwards, to get the book into final shape. Still it is the form that holds the most promise of a successful book that will be used by its intended audience, rather than yet another volume of proceedings for the library shelf.

3. Manuscripts should be submitted (preferably in duplicate) either to Springer's mathematics editorial in Heidelberg, or to one of the series editors (with a copy to Springer). Volume editors are expected to arrange for the refereeing, to the usual scientific standards, of the individual contributions. If the resulting reports can be forwarded to us (series editors or Springer) this is very helpful. If no reports are forwarded or if other questions remain unclear in respect of homogeneity etc, the series editors may wish to consult external referees for an overall evaluation of the volume. A final decision to publish can be made only on the basis of the complete manuscript, however a preliminary decision can be based on a pre-final or incomplete manuscript. The strict minimum amount of material that will be considered should include a detailed outline describing the planned contents of each chapter.
   Volume editors and authors should be aware that incomplete or insufficiently close to final manuscripts almost always result in longer evaluation times. They should also be aware that parallel submission of their manuscript to another publisher while under consideration for LNM will in general lead to immediate rejection.

Continued on inside back-cover

Lecture Notes in Mathematics   1861

Editors:
J.-M. Morel, Cachan
F. Takens, Groningen
B. Teissier, Paris

Subseries:
Fondazione C.I.M.E., Firenze
Adviser: Pietro Zecca

Giancarlo Benettin
Jacques Henrard
Sergei Kuksin

Hamiltonian Dynamics Theory and Applications

Lectures given at the
C.I.M.E.-E.M.S. Summer School
held in Cetraro, Italy,
July 1–10, 1999

Editor: Antonio Giorgilli

Fondazione
C.I.M.E.

Editors and Authors

Giancarlo Benettin
Dipartimento di Matematica Pura e Applicata
Università di Padova
Via G. Belzoni 7
35131 Padova, Italy

e-mail: benettin@math.unipd.it

Antonio Giorgilli
Dipartimento di Matematica e Applicazioni
Università degli Studi di Milano Bicocca
Via Bicocca degli Arcimboldi 8
20126 Milano, Italy

e-mail: antonio@matapp.unimib.it

Jacques Henrard
Département de Mathématiques
FUNDP 8
Rempart de la Vierge
5000 Namur, Belgium

e-mail: Jacques.Henrard@fundp.ac.be

Sergei Kuksin
Department of Mathematics
Heriot-Watt University
Edinburgh
EH14 4AS, United Kingdom
and
Steklov Institute of Mathematics
8 Gubkina St.
111966 Moscow, Russia

e-mail: kuksin@ma.hw.ac.uk

Library of Congress Control Number: 2004116724

Mathematics Subject Classification (2000): 70H07, 70H14, 37K55, 35Q53, 70H11, 70E17

ISSN 0075-8434
ISBN 3-540-24064-0 Springer Berlin Heidelberg New York
DOI: 10.1007/b104338

Springer is a part of Springer Science + Business Media
http://www.springeronline.com
© Springer-Verlag Berlin Heidelberg 2005
Printed in Germany

Typesetting: Camera-ready TeX output by the authors

41/3142/ du - 543210 - Printed on acid-free paper

Preface

" *Nous sommes donc conduit à nous proposer le problème suivant:*
Étudier les équations canoniques

$$\frac{dx_i}{dt} = \frac{\partial F}{\partial y_i} \, , \quad \frac{dy_i}{dt} = -\frac{\partial F}{\partial x_i}$$

en supposant que la function F peut se développer suivant les puissances d'un paramètre très petit μ de la manière suivante:

$$F = F_0 + \mu F_1 + \mu^2 F_2 + \dots \, ,$$

en supposant de plus que F_0 ne dépend que des x et est indépendent des y; et que F_1, F_2, ... sont des fonctions périodiques de période 2π par rapport aux y. "

This is all of the contents of §13 in the first volume of the celebrated treatise *Les méthodes nouvelles de la mécanique céleste* of Poincaré, published in 1892.

In more usual notations and words, the problem is to investigate the dynamics of a canonical system of differential equations with Hamiltonian

$$(1) \qquad H(p, q, \varepsilon) = H_0(p) + \varepsilon H_1(p, q) + \varepsilon^2 H_2(p, q) + \dots \, ,$$

where $p \equiv (p_1, \dots, p_n) \in \mathcal{G} \subset \mathbf{R}^n$ are action variables in the open set $\mathcal{G}$, $q \equiv (q_1, \dots, q_n) \in \mathbf{T}^n$ are angle variables, and ε is a small parameter.

The lectures by Giancarlo Benettin, Jacques Henrard and Sergej Kuksin published in the present book address some of the many questions that are hidden behind the simple sentence above.

1. A Classical Problem

It is well known that the investigations of Poincaré were motivated by a classical problem: the stability of the Solar System. The three volumes of the

Méthodes Nouvelles had been preceded by the memoir *Sur le problème des trois corps et les équations de la dynamique; mémoire couronné du prix de S. M. le Roi Oscar II le 21 janvier 1889.*

It may be interesting to recall the subject of the investigation, as stated in the announcement of the competition for King Oscar's prize:

> " A system being given of a number whatever of particles attracting one another mutually according to Newton's law, it is proposed, on the assumption that there never takes place an impact of two particles to expand the coordinates of each particle in a series proceeding according to some known functions of time and converging uniformly for any space of time. "

In the announcement it is also mentioned that the question was suggested by a claim made by Lejeune–Dirichlet in a letter to a friend that he had been able to demonstrate the stability of the solar system by integrating the differential equations of Mechanics. However, Dirichlet died shortly after, and no reference to his method was actually found in his notes.

As a matter of fact, in his memoir and in the *Méthodes Nouvelles* Poincaré seems to end up with different conclusions. Just to mention a few results of his work, let me recall the theorem on generic non–existence of first integrals, the recurrence theorem, the divergence of classical perturbation series as a typical fact, the discovery of asymptotic solutions and the existence of homoclinic points.

Needless to say, the work of Poincaré represents the starting point of most of the research on dynamical systems in the XX–th century. It has also been said that the memoir on the problem of three bodies is "the first textbook in the qualitative theory of dynamical systems", perhaps forgetting that the qualitative study of dynamics had been undertaken by Poincaré in a *Mémoire sur les courbes définies par une équation différentielle*, published in 1882.

2. KAM Theory

Let me recall a few known facts about the system (1). For $\varepsilon = 0$ the Hamiltonian possesses n first integrals $p_1, \ldots, p_n$ that are independent, and the orbits lie on invariant tori carrying periodic or quasi–periodic motions with frequencies $\omega_1(p), \ldots, \omega_n(p)$, where $\omega_j(p) = \frac{\partial H_0}{\partial p_j}$. This is the unperturbed dynamics. For $\varepsilon \neq 0$ this plain behaviour is destroyed, and the problem is to understand how the dynamics actually changes.

The classical methods of perturbation theory, as started by Lagrange and Laplace, may be resumed by saying that one tries to prove that for $\varepsilon \neq 0$ the system (1) is still integrable. However, this program encountered major difficulties due to the appearance in the expansions of the so called *secular terms*, generated by resonances among the frequencies. Thus the problem become that of writing solutions valid for all times, possibly expanded in power series of the parameter ε. By the way, the role played by resonances is indeed at the basis of the non–integrability in classical sense of the perturbed system, as stated by Poincaré.

A relevant step in removing secular terms was made by Lindstedt in 1882. The underlying idea of Lindstedt's method is to look for *a single solution which is characterized by fixed frequencies*, $\lambda_1, \ldots, \lambda_n$ say, and which is close to the unperturbed torus with the same frequencies. This allowed him to produce series expansions free from secular terms, but he did not solve the problem of the presence of small denominators, i.e., denominators of the form $\langle k, \lambda \rangle$ where $0 \neq k \in \mathbf{Z}^n$. Even assuming that these quantities do not vanish (i.e., excluding resonances) they may become arbitrarily small, thus making the convergence of the series questionable.

In tome II, chap. XIII, § 148–149 of the *Méthodes Nouvelles* Poincaré devoted several pages to the discussion of the convergence of the series of Lindstedt. However, the arguments of Poincaré did not allow him to reach a definite conclusion:

> " ... *les séries ne pourraient–elles pas, par example, converger quand ... le rapport n_1/n_2 soit incommensurable, et que son carré soit au contraire commensurable (ou quand le rapport n_1/n_2 est assujetti à une autre condition analogue à celle que je viens d'énoncer un peu au hasard)?*
>
> *Les raisonnements de ce chapitre ne me permettent pas d'affirmer que ce fait ne se présentera pas. Tout ce qu'il m'est permis de dire, c'est qu'il est fort invraisemblable. "*

Here, n_1, n_2 are the frequencies, that we have denoted by λ_1, λ_2.

The problem of the convergence was settled in an indirect way 60 years later by Kolmogorov, when he announced his celebrated theorem. In brief, *if the perturbation is small enough, then most (in measure theoretic sense) of the unperturbed solutions survive, being only slightly deformed*. The surviving invariant tori are characterized by some strong non–resonance conditions, that in Kolmogorov's note was identified with the so called *diophantine condition*, namely $|\langle k, \lambda \rangle| \geq \gamma |k|^{-\tau}$ for some $\gamma > 0$, $\tau > n - 1$ and for all non–zero $k \in \mathbf{Z}^n$. This includes the case of the frequencies chosen "un peu au hasard" by Poincaré. It is often said that Kolmogorov announced his theorem without publishing the proof; as a matter of fact, his short communication contains a sketch of the proof where all critical elements are clearly pointed out. Detailed proofs were published later by Moser (1962) and Arnold (1963); the theorem become thus known as KAM theorem.

The argument of Kolmogorov constitutes only an indirect proof of the convergence of the series of Lindstedt; this has been pointed out by Moser in 1967. For, the proof invented by Kolmogorov is based on an infinite sequence of canonical transformations that give the Hamiltonian the appropriate normal form

$$H(p, q) = \langle \lambda, p \rangle + R(p, q) ,$$

where $R(p, q)$ is at least quadratic in the action variables p. Such a Hamiltonian possesses the invariant torus $p = 0$ carrying quasi–periodic motions with frequencies λ. This implies that the series of Lindstedt must converge, since they give precisely the form of the solution lying on the invariant torus. However, Moser failed to obtain a *direct* proof based, e.g., on Cauchy's classical method of majorants applied to Lindstedt's expansions in powers of ε. As discovered by Eliasson, this is due to the presence in Lindstedt's classical series of terms that grow too fast, due precisely to the small denominators, but are cancelled out by internal compensations (this was written in a report of 1988, but was published only in 1996). Explicit constructive algorithms taking compensations into account have been recently produced by Gallavotti, Chierchia, Falcolini, Gentile and Mastropietro.

In recent years, the perturbation methods for Hamiltonian systems, and in particular the KAM theory, has been extended to the case of PDE's equations. The lectures of Kuksin included in this volume constitute a plain and complete presentation of these recent theories.

3. Adiabatic Invariants

The theory of adiabatic invariants is related to the study of the dynamics of systems with slowly varying parameters. That is, the Hamiltonian $H(q, p ; \lambda)$ depends on a parameter $\lambda = \varepsilon t$, with ε small. The typical simple example is a pendulum the length of which is subjected to a very slow change – e.g., a periodic change with a period much longer than the proper period of the pendulum. The main concern is the search for quantities that remain close to constants during the evolution of the system, at least for reasonably long time intervals. This is a classical problem that has received much attention at the beginning of the the XX–th century, when the quantities to be considered were identified with the actions of the system.

The usefulness of the action variables has been particularly emphasized in the book of Max Born *The Mechanics of the Atom*, published in 1927. In that book the use of action variables in quantum theory is widely discussed. However, it should be remarked that most of the book is actually devoted to Hamiltonian dynamics and perturbation methods. In this connection it may be interesting to quote the first few sentences of the preface to the german edition of the book:

> " The title "Atomic Mechanics" given to these lectures ... was chosen
> to correspond to the designation "Celestial Mechanics". As the
> latter term covers that branch of theoretical astronomy which deals

with with the calculation of the orbits of celestial bodies according to mechanical laws, so the phrase "Atomic Mechanics" is chosen to signify that the facts of atomic physics are to be treated here with special reference to the underlying mechanical principles; an attempt is made, in other words, at a deductive treatment of atomic theory. "

The theory of adiabatic invariants is discussed in this volume in the lectures of J. Henrard. The discussion includes in particular some recent developments that deal not just with the slow evolution of the actions, but also with the changes induced on them when the orbit crosses some critical regions. Making reference to the model of the pendulum, a typical case is the crossing of the separatrix. Among the interesting phenomena investigated with this method one will find, e.g., the capture of the orbit in a resonant regions and the sweeping of resonances in the Solar System.

4. Long–Time Stability and Nekhoroshev's Theory

Although the theorem of Kolmogorov has been often indicated as the solution of the problem of stability of the Solar System, during the last 50 years it became more and more evident that it is not so. An immediate remark is that the theorem assures the persistence of a set of invariant tori with relative measure tending to one when the perturbation parameter ε goes to zero, but the complement of the invariant tori is open and dense, thus making the actual application of the theorem to a physical system doubtful, due to the indeterminacy of the initial conditions. Only the case of a system of two degrees of freedom can be dealt with this way, since the invariant tori create separated gaps on the invariant surface of constant energy. Moreover, the threshold for the applicability of the theorem, i.e., the actual value of ε below which the theorem applies, could be unrealistic, unless one considers very localized situations. Although there are no general definite proofs in this sense, many numerical calculations made independently by, e.g., A. Milani, J. Wisdom and J. Laskar, show that at least the motion of the minor planets looks far from being a quasi–periodic one.

Thus, the problem of stability requires further investigation. In this respect, a way out may be found by proving that some relevant quantities, e.g., the actions of the system, remain close to their initial value for a long time; this could lead to a sort of "effective stability" that may be enough for physical application. In more precise terms, one could look for an estimate $\left| p(t) - p(0) \right| = O(\varepsilon^a)$ for all times $|t| < T(\varepsilon)$, were a is some number in the interval $(0, 1)$ (e.g., $a = 1/2$ or $a = 1/n$), and $T(\varepsilon)$ is a "large" time, in some sense to be made precise.

The request above may be meaningful if we take into consideration some characteristics of the dynamical system that is (more or less accurately) described by our equations. In this case the quest for a "large" time should be interpreted as *large with respect to some characteristic time of the physical system, or comparable with the lifetime of it*. For instance, for the nowadays accelerators a characteristic time is the period of revolution of a particle of the beam and the typical lifetime of the beam during an experiment may be a few days, which may correspond to some 10^{10} revolutions; for the solar system the lifetime is the estimated age of the universe, which corresponds to some 10^{10} revolutions of Jupiter; for a galaxy, we should consider that the stars may perform a few hundred revolutions during a time as long as the age of the universe, which means that a galaxy does not really need to be much stable in order to exist.

From a mathematical viewpoint the word "large" is more difficult to explain, since there is no typical lifetime associated to a differential equation. Hence, in order to give the word "stability" a meaning in the sense above it is essential to consider the dependence of the time T on ε. In this respect the continuity with respect to initial data does not help too much. For instance, if we consider the trivial example of the equilibrium point of the differential equation $\dot{x} = x$ one will immediately see that if $x(0) = x_0 > 0$ is the initial point, then we have $x(t) > 2x_0$ for $t > T = \ln 2$ no matter how small is x_0; hence T may hardly be considered to be "large", since it remains constant as x_0 decreases to 0. Conversely, if for a particular system we could prove, e.g., that $T(\varepsilon) = O(1/\varepsilon)$ then our result would perhaps be meaningful; this is indeed the typical goal of the theory of adiabatic invariants.

Stronger forms of stability may be found by proving, e.g., that $T(\varepsilon) \sim 1/\varepsilon^r$ for some $r > 1$; this is indeed the theory of complete stability due to Birkhoff. As a matter of fact, the methods of perturbation theory allow us to prove more: in the inequality above one may actually choose r depending on ε, and increasing when $\varepsilon \to 0$. In this case one obtains the so called *exponential stability*, stating that $T(\varepsilon) \sim \exp(1/\varepsilon^b)$ for some b. Such a strong result was first stated by Moser (1955) and Littlewood (1959) in particular cases. A complete theory in this direction was developed by Nekhoroshev, and published in 1978.

The lectures of Benettin in this volume deal with the application of the theory of Nekhoroshev to some interesting physical systems, including the collision of molecules, the classical problem of the rigid body and the triangular Lagrangian equilibria of the problem of three bodies.

Acknowledgements

This volume appears with the essential contribution of the Fondazione CIME. The editor wishes to thank in particular A. Cellina, who encouraged him to organize a school on Hamiltonian systems.

The success of the school has been assured by the high level of the lectures and by the enthusiasm of the participants. A particular thankfulness is due

to Giancarlo Benettin, Jacques Henrard and Sergej Kuksin, who accepted
not only to profess their excellent lectures, but also to contribute with their
writings to the preparation of this volume

Milano, March 2004   Antonio Giorgilli
                                  Professor of Mathematical Physics
                                  Department of Mathematics
                                  University of Milano Bicocca

CIME's activity is supported by:

Ministero dell' Università Ricerca Scientifica e Tecnologica;
Consiglio Nazionale delle Ricerche;
E.U. under the Training and Mobility of Researchers Programme.

Contents

Physical Applications of Nekhoroshev Theorem and Exponential Estimates

Giancarlo Benettin [*]

Università di Padova, Dipartimento di Matematica Pura e Applicata,
Via G. Belzoni 7, 35131 Padova, Italy
benettin@math.unipd.it

1 Introduction

The purpose of these lectures is to discuss some physical applications of Hamiltonian perturbation theory. Just to enter the subject, let us consider the usual situation of a nearly-integrable Hamiltonian system,

$$H(I,\varphi) = h(I) + \varepsilon f(I,\varphi) \;, \qquad I = (I_1,\dots,I_n) \in \mathcal{B} \subset \mathbb{R}^n$$
$$\varphi = (\varphi_1,\dots,\varphi_n) \in \mathbb{T}^n \;, \tag{1.1}$$

$\mathcal{B}$ being a ball in $\mathbb{R}^n$. As we shall see, such a framework is often poor and not really adequate for some important physical applications, nevertheless it is a natural starting point. For $\varepsilon = 0$ the phase space is decomposed into invariant tori $\{I\} \times \mathbb{T}^n$, see figure 1, on which the flow is linear:

$$I(t) = I^o \;, \qquad \varphi(t) = \varphi^o + \omega(I^o)t \;,$$

with $\omega = \frac{\partial h}{\partial I}$. For $\varepsilon \neq 0$ one is instead confronted with the nontrivial equations

$$\dot{I} = -\varepsilon \frac{\partial f}{\partial \varphi}(I,\varphi) \;, \qquad \dot{\varphi} = \omega(I) + \varepsilon \frac{\partial f}{\partial I}(I,\varphi) \;. \tag{1.2}$$

Different stategies can be used in front of such equations, all of them sharing the elementary idea of "averaging out" in some way the term $\frac{\partial f}{\partial \varphi}$, to show that, in convenient assumptions, the evolution of the actions (if any) is very slow. In perturbation theory, "slow" means in general that $\|I(t) - I(0)\|$ remains small, for small ε, at least for $t \sim 1/\varepsilon$ (that is: the evolution is slower than the trivial *a priori* estimate following (1.2)). Throughout these lectures, however,

---

[*] Gruppo Nazionale di Fisica Matematica and Istituto Nazionale di Fisica della Materia

"slow" will have the stronger meaning of "exponentially slow", namely (with reference to any norm in $\mathbb{R}^n$)

$$\|I(t) - I(0)\| < \mathcal{I} \, (\varepsilon/\varepsilon_*)^b \qquad \text{for} \qquad |t| < \mathcal{T} e^{(\varepsilon_*/\varepsilon)^a} \, , \qquad (1.3)$$

$\mathcal{T}, \mathcal{I}, a, b, \varepsilon_*$ being positive constants. It is worthwhile to mention that stability results for times long, though not infinite, are very welcome in physics: indeed every physical observation or experiment, and in fact every physical model (like a frictionless model of the Solar System) are sensible only on an appropriate time scale, which is possibly long but is hardly infinite.[2] Results of perpetual stability are certainly more appealing, but the price to be paid — like ignoring a dense open set in the phase space, as in KAM theory — can be too high, in view of a clear physical interpretation.

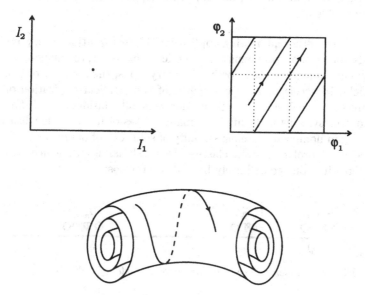

Fig. 1. *Quasi periodic motion on invariant tori.*

Poincaré, at the beginning of his *Mèthodes Nouvelles de la Méchanique Céleste* [Po1], stressed with emphasis the importance of systems of the form (1.1), using for them the strong expression *"Problème général de la dynamique"*. As a matter of fact, systems of the form (1.1), or natural generalizations of them, are met throughout physics, from Molecular Physics to Celestial Mechanics. Our choice of applications — certainly non exhausting — will be the following:

---

[2] Littlewood in '59 produced a stability result for long times, $t \sim \exp(\log \varepsilon)^2$, in connection with the triangular Lagrangian points, and his comment was: "this is not eternity, but is a considerable slice of it" [Li].

- Boltzmann's problem of the specific heats of gases: namely understanding why some degrees of freedom, like the fast internal vibration of diatomic molecules, are essentially decoupled ("frozen", in the later language of quantum mechanics), and do not appreciably contribute to the specific heats.

- The fast-rotations of the rigid body (equivalently, a rigid body in a weak force field, that is a perturbation of the Euler–Poinsot case). The aim is to understand the conditions for long-time stability of motions, with attention, on the opposite side, to the possible presence of chaotic motions. Some attention is deserved to "gyroscopic phenomena", namely to the properties of motions close to the (unperturbed) stationary rotations.

- The stability of elliptic equilibria, with special emphasis on the "triangular Lagrangian equilibria" L_4 and L_5 in the (spatial) circular restricted three body problem.

There would be other interesting applications of perturbation theory, in different fields: for example problems of magnetic confinement, the numerous stability problems in asteroid belts or in planetary rings, the stability of bounches of particles in accelerators, the problem of the physical realization of ideal constraints. We shall not enter them, nor we shall consider any of the recent extensions to systems with infinitely many degrees of freedom (localization of excitations in nonlinear systems; stability of solutions of nonlinear wave equations; selected problems from classical electrodynamics...), which would be very interesting, but go definitely bejond our purposes.

Fig. 2. *An elementary one–dimensional model of a diatomic gas.*

As already remarked, physical systems, including those we shall deal with, typically do not fit the too simple form (1.1), and require a generalization: for example

$$H(I, \varphi, p, q) = h(I) + \varepsilon f(I, \varphi, p, q) \; , \qquad (1.4)$$

or also

$$H(I, \varphi, p, q) = h(I) + \mathcal{H}(p, q) + \varepsilon f(I, \varphi, p, q) \; , \qquad (1.5)$$

the new variables (q, p) belonging to $\mathbb{R}^{2m}$ (or to an open subset of it, or to a manifold). In problems of molecular dynamics, for the specific heats, the new degrees of freedom represent typically the centers of mass of the molecules (see figure 2), and the Hamiltonian fits the form (1.5). Instead in the rigid body dynamics, as well as in many problems in Celestial Mechanics, p, q are still action–angle variables, but the actions do not enter the unperturbed Hamiltonian, and this makes a relevant difference. The unperturbed Hamiltonian, if it does not depend on all actions, is said to be *properly degenerate,* and the absent actions are themselves called degenerate. For the Kepler problem, the degenerate actions represent the eccentricity and the inclination of the orbit; for the Euler-Poinsot rigid body they determine the orientation in space of the angular momentum. The perturbed Hamiltonian, for such systems, fits (1.4). Understanding the behavior of degenerate variables is physically important, but in general is not easy, and requires assumptions on the perturbation.[3] Such an investigation is among the most interesting ones in perturbation theory.

As a final introductory remark, let us comment the distinction, proposed in the title of these lectures, between "exponential estimates" and "Nekhoroshev theorem".[4] As we shall see, some perturbative problems concern systems with essentially constant frequencies. These include isochronous systems, but also some anisochronous systems for which the frequencies stay nevertheless almost constants during the motion, as is the case of molecular collisions. Such systems require only an analytic study: in the very essence, it is enough to construct a single normal form, with an exponentially small remainder, to prove the desired result. We shall address these problems with the generic expression "exponential estimates". We shall instead deserve the more specific expression "Nekhoroshev theorem", or theory, for problems which are effectively anisochronous, and require in an essential way, to be overcome, suitable geometric assumptions, like convexity or "steepness" of the unperturbed Hamiltonian h (and occasionally assumptions on the perturbation, too). The geometrical aspects are in a sense the heart of Nekhoroshev theorem, and certainly constitute its major novelty. As we shall see, geometry will play an absolutely essential role both in the study of the rigid body and in the case of the Lagrangian equilibria.

These lectures are organized as follows: Section 2 is devoted to exponential estimates, and includes, after a general introduction to standard perturbative methods, some applications to molecular dynamics. It also includes an account of an approximation proposed by Jeans and by Landau and Teller, which looks alternative to standard methods, and seems to work excellently in connection with molecular collisions. Section 3 is fully devoted to the Jeans–Landau–Teller approximation, which is revisited within a mathematically well posed perturbative scheme. Section 4 contains an application of exponential estimates to Statistical Mechanics, namely to the Boltzmann question about the possible existence of long equilibrium times in classical gases. Section 5 contains a general introduction to Nekhoroshev theorem. Section 6 is devoted

---

[3] This is clear if one considers, in (1.4), a perturbation depending only on (p, q): these variables, for suitable f, can do anything on a time scale $1/\varepsilon$.

[4] Such a distinction is not common in the literature, where the expression "Nekhoroshev theorem" is often ued as a synonymous of stability results for exponentially long times.

to the applications of Nekhoroshev theory to Euler–Poinsot perturbed rigid body, while Section 7 is devoted to the application of the theory to elliptic equilibria, in particular to the stability of the so–called Lagrangian equilibrium points L_4, L_5 in the (spatial) circular restricted three body problem.

The style of the lectures will be occasionally informal; the aim is to provide a general overview, with emphasis when possible on the connections between different applications, but with no possibility of entering details. Proofs will be absent, or occasionally reduced to a sketch when useful to explain the most relevant ideas. (As is well known to researchers active in perturbation theory, complete proofs are long, and necessarily include annoying parts, so for them we forcely demand to the literature.) Besides rigorous results, we shall also produce heuristic results, as well as numerical results; understanding a physical system requires in fact, very often, the cooperation of all of these investigation tools.

Most results reported in these lectures, and all the ideas underlying them, are fruit on one hand of many years of intense collaboration with Luigi Galgani, Antonio Giorgilli and Giovanni Gallavotti, from whom I learned, in the essence, all I know; on the other hand, they are fruit of the intense collaboration, in the last ten years, with my colleagues Francesco Fassò and more recently Massimiliano Guzzo. I wish to express to all of them my gratitude. I also wish to thank the director of CIME, Arrigo Cellina, and the director of the school, Antonio Giorgilli, for their proposal to give these lectures. I finally thank Massimiliano Guzzo for having reviewed the manuscript.

2 Exponential Estimates

We start here with a general result concerning exponential estimates in exactly isochronous systems. Then we pass to applications to molecular dynamics, for systems with either one or two independent frequencies.

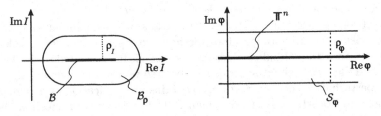

Fig. 3. *The complex extended domains of the action–angle variables.*

A. Isochronous Systems

Let us consider a system of the form (1.1), with linear and thus isochronous h:

$$H(I, \varphi) = \omega \cdot I + \varepsilon f(I, \varphi) \ . \tag{2.1}$$

Given an "extension vector" $\varrho = (\varrho_I, \varrho_\varphi)$, with positive entries, we define the extended domains (see figure 3)

$$\Delta_\varrho(I) = \{I' \in \mathbb{C}^n : |I'_j - I_j| < \varrho_I, \; j = 1, \ldots, n\} \qquad \mathcal{B}_\varrho = \bigcup_{I \in \mathcal{B}} \Delta_\varrho(I)$$

$$\mathcal{S}_\varrho = \{\varphi \in \mathbb{C}^n : |\operatorname{Im} \varphi_j| < \varrho_\varphi, \; j = 1, \ldots, n\} \qquad \mathcal{D}_\varrho = \mathcal{B}_\varrho \times \mathcal{S}_\varrho \, .$$

$$\text{(2.2)}$$

Given two extension vectors ϱ and ϱ', inequalities of the form $\varrho' \leq \varrho$ are intended to hold separately on both entries. All functions we shall deal with, will be real analytic (that is analytic and real for real variables) in $\mathcal{D}_{\varrho'}$, for some $\varrho' \leq \varrho$. Concerning norms, we make here the most elementary and common choices,[5] and denote

$$\|u\|_{\varrho'}^\infty = \sup_{(I,\varphi) \in \mathcal{D}_{\varrho'}} |u(I, \varphi)| \, , \qquad \|v\|^\infty = \max_{1 \leq j \leq n} |v_j| \, , \qquad |\nu| = \sum_j |\nu_j| \, ,$$

respectively for $u : \mathcal{D}_{\varrho'} \to \mathbb{C}$, for $v \in \mathbb{C}^n$ and for $\nu \in \mathbb{Z}^n$. By $\langle . \rangle_\varphi$ we shall denote averaging on the angles.

A simple statement introducing exponential estimates for the isochronous system (2.1) is the following:

Proposition 1.   *Consider Hamiltonian (2.1), and assume that:*

(a) f is analytic and bounded in $\mathcal{D}_\varrho$;
(b) ω satisfies the "Diophantine condition"

$$|\nu \cdot \omega| > \frac{\gamma}{|\nu|^n} \qquad \forall \nu \in \mathbb{Z}^n, \; \nu \neq 0 \, , \qquad \text{(2.3)}$$

for some positive constant γ;
(c) ε is small, precisely

$$\varepsilon < \varepsilon_* = \frac{C \|f\|_\varrho^\infty}{\gamma \varrho_I \varrho_\varphi^n} \, ,$$

for suitable $C > 0$.

Then there exists a real analytic canonical transformation $(I, \varphi) = \mathcal{C}(I', \varphi')$, $\mathcal{C} : \mathcal{D}_{\frac{1}{2}\varrho} \to \mathcal{D}_\varrho$, which is small with ε:

$$\|I' - I\|^\infty < c_1 \varepsilon \varrho_I \, , \qquad \|\varphi' - \varphi\|^\infty < c_2 \varepsilon \varrho_\varphi$$

(with suitable $c_1, c_2 > 0$), and gives the new Hamiltonian $H' := H \circ \mathcal{C}$ the normal form

---

[5] Obtaining good results requires in general the use of more sophisticated norms. But final results can always be expressed (with worse constants) in terms of these norms.

$$H'(I', \varphi') = \omega \cdot I' + \varepsilon g(I', \varepsilon) + \varepsilon \, e^{-(\varepsilon_*/\varepsilon)^a} \mathcal{R}(I', \varphi', \varepsilon) \,, \qquad (2.4)$$

with $a = 1/(n+1)$ and

$$g = \langle f \rangle_\varphi + \mathcal{O}(\varepsilon) \,, \qquad \|g\|_{\frac{1}{2}\varrho}^\infty \le 2 \|f\|_\varrho^\infty \,, \qquad \|\mathcal{R}\|_{\frac{1}{2}\varrho}^\infty \le \|f\|^\infty.$$

Such a statement (with some differences in the constants) can be found for example in [Ga1,BGa,GG,F1]; see also [B]. The optimal value $1/(n+1)$ of the exponent a, which is the most crucial constant, comes from [F1]. The interest of the proposition is that the new actions I' are "exponentially slow",

$$\|\dot{I}'\|^\infty \sim \varepsilon e^{-(\varepsilon_*/\varepsilon)^a} \,,$$

and consequently up to the large time $|t| \sim e^{(\varepsilon_*/\varepsilon)^a}$, also recalling $\|I' - I\|^\infty \sim \varepsilon$, it is

$$\|I'(t) - I'(0)\|^\infty < (\text{const})\,\varepsilon \,, \qquad \|I(t) - I(0)\|^\infty < (\text{const})\,\varepsilon \,. \qquad (2.5)$$

The behavior of I and I', as resulting from the proposition, is illustrated in figure 4.

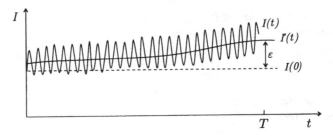

Fig. 4. *A possible behavior of I and I' as functions of time, according to Proposition 1; $T \sim e^{(\varepsilon_*/\varepsilon)^a}$*

Remark: As is well known (and easy to prove), Diophantine frequencies are abundant in measure: in any given ball, the set of frequencies which do not satisfy (2.3) has relative measure bounded by $(\text{const})\sqrt{\gamma}$. Non Diophantine frequencies, however, form a dense open set.

Sketch of the proof. The proof of proposition 1 includes lots of details, but the scheme is simple; we outline it here both to introduce a few useful ideas and to provide some help to enter the not always easy literature. Proceding recursively, one performs a sequence of $r \ge 1$ elementary canonical transformations $\mathcal{C}_1, \ldots, \mathcal{C}_r$, with $\mathcal{C}_s : \mathcal{D}_{(1-\frac{s}{2r})\varrho} \to \mathcal{D}_{(1-\frac{s-1}{2r})\varrho}$, posing then $\mathcal{C} = \mathcal{C}_r \circ \cdots \circ \mathcal{C}_1$. The progressive reduction of the analyticity domain is necessary to perform, at each step, Cauchy estimates of derivatives of functions, as well as to prove convergence of series. After s steps one deals with a Hamiltonian H_s in normal form up to the order $s \leq r - 1$, namely

$$H_s(I, \varphi) = h(I) + \varepsilon g_s(I, \varepsilon) + \varepsilon^{s+1} f_s(I, \varphi, \varepsilon) , \qquad (2.6)$$

and operates in such a way to push the remainder f_s one order further, that is to get $H_{s+1} = H_s \circ C_{s+1}$ of the same form (2.6), but with $s + 1$ in place of s. To this end, the perturbation f_s is split into its average $\langle f_s \rangle$, which does not depend on the angles and can be progressively accumulated into g, and its zero-average part $f_s - \langle f_s \rangle$; the latter is then "killed" (at the lowest order $s + 1$) by a suitable choice of C_{s+1}. No matter how one decides to perform canonical transformations — the so-called Lie method is here recommended, but the traditional method of generating functions with inversion also works — one is confronted with the Hamilton–Jacobi equation, in the form

$$\omega \cdot \frac{\partial \chi}{\partial \varphi} = f_s - \langle f_s \rangle , \qquad (2.7)$$

the unknown χ representing either the generating function or the the generator of the Lie series (the auxiliary Hamiltonian entering the Lie method). Let us recall that in the Lie method canonical transformations are defined as the time–one map of a convenient auxiliary Hamiltonian flow, the new variables being the initial data. In the problem at hand, to pass from order s to order $s + 1$, we use an auxiliary Hamiltonian $\varepsilon^s \chi$, and so, denoting its flow by $\Phi^t_{\varepsilon^s \chi}$, the new Hamiltonian $H_{s+1} = H_s \circ \Phi^1_{\varepsilon^s \chi}$ is

$$H_{s+1} = h + \varepsilon g_s + \varepsilon^{s+1} f_s + \varepsilon^{s+1} \{\chi, h\} + \mathcal{O}(\varepsilon^{s+2}) ;$$

developing the Poisson bracket, and recalling that $\frac{\partial \chi}{\partial \varphi}$ has zero average, (2.7) follows.

Equation (2.7) is solved by Fourier series,

$$\chi(I, \varphi) = \sum_{\nu \in \mathbb{Z}^n \setminus \{0\}} \frac{\hat{f}_{s,\nu}(I) \, e^{i\nu \cdot \varphi}}{i\nu \cdot \omega} ,$$

where $\hat{f}_{s,\nu}(I)$ are the Fourier coefficients of f_s; assumption (b) is used to dominate the "small divisors" $\nu \cdot \omega$, and it turns out ,that the series converges and is conveniently estimated in the reduced strip $S_{(1 - \frac{s}{2r})\varrho}$.

This procedure works if ε is sufficiently small, and it turns out that at each step the remainder reduces by a factor $\varepsilon \lambda$, with

$$\lambda = \frac{c \, \|f\|_\varrho^\infty \, r^{n+1}}{\gamma \varrho_I \varrho_\varphi^n} ,$$

c being some constant. (One must be rather clever to get here the optimal power r^{n+1}, and not a worse higher power. Complicated tricks must be introduced, see [F1].) The size of the last remainder f_r is then, roughly,

$$\varepsilon^{r+1}\lambda^r \sim \varepsilon \left(\varepsilon r^{n+1}\right)^r \|f\|_\varrho^\infty .$$

Quite clearly, raising r at fixed ε would produce a tremendous divergence.[6] But clearly, *it is enough to choose r dependent on ε, in such a way that (for example)* $\varepsilon\lambda \simeq e^{-1}$,

$$r \sim \varepsilon^{-1/(n+1)} ,$$

to produce an exponentially small remainder as in the statement of Proposition 1. It can be seen [GG] that this is nearly the optimal choice of r as a function of ε, so as to minimize, for each ε, the final remainder. The situation resembles nonconvergent expansions of functions in asymptotic series. The "elementary" idea of taking r to be a function of ε, growing to infinity when ε goes to zero, is the heart of exponential estimates and of the analytic part of Nekhoroshev theorem.

Remark: As we have seen, one proceeds as if the gain per step were a reduction of the perturbation by a factor ε (see (2.6)). This is indeed the prescription, but the actual gain at each step is practically much less, just a factor e^{-1}. The point is that, due to the presence of small divisors, and to the necessity of making at each step Cauchy estimates with reduction of the analyticity domain, the norm of f_r grows very rapidly with r. The essence of the proof is to show that $\|f_r\|$ grows "only" as $r^{r/a}$, with some positive a (as large as possible, to improve the result). Such an apparently terrible growth gives rise to the desired exponential estimates, the final remainder decreasing as e^{-1/ε^a}.

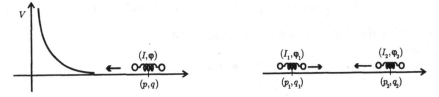

Fig. 5. *Elementary molecular collisions*

B. One Frequency Systems: Preliminary Results

For $n = 1$ the above proposition becomes trivial — systems with one degree of freedom are integrable — but it is not if we introduce additional degrees of freedom, and pass from Hamiltonians of the form (1.1) to Hamiltonians of the form (1.5). The model we shall consider here represents the collision of a molecule with a fixed smooth wall in one dimension, or equivalently the

---

[6] By the way: the condition in ε which allows performing up to r elementary canonical transformations, has the form $\varepsilon\lambda < 1$: that is, raising r, before than leading to a divergence, would be not allowed.

collinear collision of a point particle with a diatomic molecule, see figure 5; a simple possible form for the Hamiltonian is the following:

$$H(\pi,\xi,p,q) = \tfrac{1}{2}(\pi^2 + \omega^2\xi^2) + \tfrac{1}{2}p^2 + V(q - \tfrac{1}{2}\xi) , \qquad (2.8)$$

where $q \in \mathbb{R}^+$ and $p \in \mathbb{R}$ are position and momentum of the center of mass of the molecule, while ξ is an internal coordinate (the excess length with respect to the rest length of the molecule) and π is the corresponding momentum. The potential V is required to have the form outlined in the figure, namely to decay to zero (in an integrable way, see later) for $q \to \infty$ and, in order to represent a wall, to diverge at $q = 0$. For given finite energy and large ω, ξ is small, namely is $\mathcal{O}(\omega^{-1})$; to exploit this fact it is convenient to write

$$V(q - \tfrac{1}{2}\xi) = V(q) + \omega^{-1}\mathcal{V}(q,\xi) ,$$

with $\mathcal{V}(q,\xi)$ bounded for finite energy and large ω. Passing to the action-angle variables (I,φ) of the oscillator, defined by

$$\pi = \sqrt{2I\omega}\cos\varphi , \qquad \xi = \omega^{-1}\sqrt{2I\omega}\sin\varphi ,$$

the Hamiltonian (for which we mantain the notation H) takes finally the form

$$H(I,\varphi,p,q) = \omega I + \mathcal{H}(p,q) + \omega^{-1}f(I,\varphi,p,q) , \qquad (2.9)$$

with

$$\mathcal{H} = \tfrac{1}{2}p^2 + V(q) .$$

The physical quantity to be looked at, for each motion, is the energy exchange between the two degrees of freedom due to the collision, namely

$$\Delta E = \omega \cdot (I(+\infty) - I(-\infty)) ; \qquad (2.10)$$

this is indeed the main quantity which is responsible of the approach to thermal equilibrium in physical gases.

The natural domain of H is a real set $\mathcal{D} = \mathcal{I} \times \mathbb{T} \times \mathcal{B}$, where $\mathcal{I}$ and $\mathcal{B}$ are defined by conditions on the energy of the form

$$E_0 < \omega I < 2E_0 , \qquad \mathcal{H}(p,q) < E_1 . \qquad (2.11)$$

Given now a four-entries extension vector $\varrho = (\omega^{-1}\varrho_I, \varrho_\varphi, \varrho_p, \varrho_q)$, the complex extended domain $\mathcal{D}_\varrho$ is defined in obvious analogy with (2.2). Due to the decay of the coupling term f at infinity, it is convenient to introduce, in addition to the uniform norm $\|f\|_\varrho^\infty$, the q–dependent "local norm"

$$\mathcal{F}(q) = \sup_{\substack{(I,\varphi,p,\tilde{q})\in\mathcal{D}_\varrho \\ |\tilde{q}-q|<\varrho_q}} f(I,\varphi,p,\tilde{q}) .$$

The next proposition is a revisitation of a result contained in [Nei1], explicitly stated and proved in [BGG1,BGG2]; the improvement in [F1] is also taken into account.

Proposition 2.   *Assume that:*

i. H is analytic and bounded in $\mathcal{D}_\varrho$;
ii. $\mathcal{F}(q)$, as defined above, dacays to zero in an integrable way for $|q| \to \infty$;
iii. ω is large, say $\omega > \omega_*$ with suitable ω_*.

Then there exists a canonical transformation $(I, \varphi, p, q) = \mathcal{C}(I', \varphi', p', q')$, $\mathcal{C} :$
$\mathcal{D}_{\frac{1}{2}\varrho} \to \mathcal{D}_\varrho$, small with ω^{-1} and reducing to the identity at infinity:

$$|I' - I| < \omega^{-2}\mathcal{F}(q)\varrho_I , \qquad |\alpha' - \alpha| < \omega^{-1}\mathcal{F}(q)\varrho_\alpha \quad for \; \alpha = \varphi, p, q,$$

which gives the new Hamiltonian $H' = H \circ \mathcal{C}$ the normal form

$$\begin{aligned} H'(I', \varphi', p', q') = \; & \omega I' + \mathcal{H}(p', q') + \omega^{-1} g(I', p', q', \omega) \\ & + \omega^{-1} e^{-\omega/\omega_*} \mathcal{R}(I', \varphi', p', q') , \end{aligned} \qquad (2.12)$$

with $g = \langle f \rangle_\varphi$, and g, $\mathcal{R}$ bounded by

$$|g(I', \varphi', p', q')|, \; |\mathcal{R}(I', \varphi', p', q')| < (const)\,\mathcal{F}(q) .$$

The consequence of this proposition on ΔE is immediate: consider any real motion $(I(t), \varphi(t), p(t), q(t))$, $-\infty < t < \infty$, representing a bounching of the molecule on the wall, so that $q(t) \to \infty$ for $t \to \pm\infty$. Let (2.11) be satisfied initially, that is asymptotically at $t \to -\infty$. Then $\frac{\partial \mathcal{R}}{\partial \varphi}(I(t), \varphi(t), p(t), q(t))$ is dominated by $(const)\,\mathcal{F}(q(t))$, which vanishes at infinity, and thanks to the fact that asymptotically $\mathcal{C}$ is the identity, it is

$$|\Delta E| = |\omega \cdot (I(\infty) - I(-\infty))| = |\omega \cdot (I'(\infty) - I'(-\infty))|$$

$$= e^{-\omega/\omega_*} \left| \int_{-\infty}^{\infty} \frac{\partial \mathcal{R}}{\partial \varphi'}(I'(t), \varphi'(t), p'(t), q'(t)) \, \mathrm{d}\,t \right| \qquad (2.13)$$

$$< (const)\, e^{-\omega/\omega_*} \left| \int_{-\infty}^{\infty} \mathcal{F}(q(t)) \, \mathrm{d}\,t \right| < (const)\, e^{-\omega/\omega_*} .$$

The behavior of I and I' is illustrated in figure 6. In the very essence: due to the local character of the interaction, exploited through the use of the local norm $\mathcal{F}$, "slow evolution" of the action acquires, in such a scattering problem, a specially strong meaning, namely the change in the action is exponentially small after an infinite time interval. As is remarkable, the canonical transformation and the oscillation of the energy are large, namely of order $\mathcal{O}(\omega^{-1})$, during the collision, and only at the end of it they become exponentially small.

C. Boltzmann's Problem of the Specific Heats of Gases

The above result is relevant, in particular, for a quite foundamental question raised by Boltzmann at the and of 19th century, and reconsidered by Jeans a

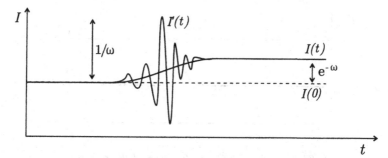

Fig. 6. *I and I' as functions of t, in molecular collisions*

few years later, concerning the classical values of the specific heats of gases. One should recall that at Boltzmann's time the molecular theory of gases was far from being universally accepted. In some relevant questions the theory was indubitably succesful: in particular, via the equipartition principle, it provided the well known mechanical interpretation of the temperature as kinetic energy per degree of freedom, and led to the celebrated link $C_V = \frac{f}{2} R$ (R denoting the usual constant of gases) between the constant-volume specific heat, which charachterizes the thermodynamics of an ideal gas, and the number f of degrees of freedom of each molecule, thought of as a small mechanical device; more precisely, f is the number of quadratic terms entering the expression of the energy of a molecule.

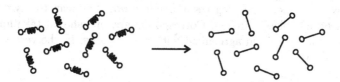

Fig. 7. *Vibrating molecules, $C_V = \frac{7}{2}R$, and rigid ones, $C_V = \frac{5}{2}R$*

The situation, however, was still partially contradictory: on the one hand, the above formula explained in a quite elementary way why the specific heats of gases generally occur in discrete values, and why gases of different nature, whenever their molecules have the same mechanical structure, also exhibit the same specific heat. On the other hand, some questions remained obscure: in particular, in order to recover the experimental value $C_V = \frac{5}{2}R$ of diatomic gases, it was necessary to ignore the two energy contributions (kinetic plus potential) of the internal vibrational degree of freedom, and treat diatomic molecules as rigid ones; see figure 7. In addition, in some cases the specific heats of gases were known to depend on the temperature, more or less as in figure 8, as if f was increasing with the temperature: and this is apparently meaningless.

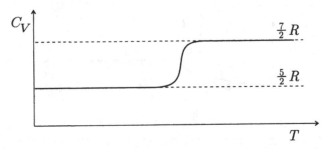

Fig. 8. *The specific heat C_V as function of the diatomic gas.*

As is well known, these phenomena were later explained by means of quantum mechanics: they were called "freezing" of the high–frequency degrees of freedom, and interpreted as a genuine quantum effect. As is less known Boltzmann, already in 1895 before Plank's work, was able to imagine a completely classical mechanism to explain, at least qualitatively, the freezing phenomenon [Bo1,Bo2]. The idea is quite elementary: take a diatomic gas in equilibrium, and give it energy, for example by compressing it. In principle, in agreement with the equipartition theorem, energy goes eventually uniformly distributed among all degrees of freedom (with a double contribution, kinetic and potential, for the vibrational ones), so one should count $f = 7$. However — according to Boltzmann — in ordinary conditions the time scale one should wait in order for the vibrational degrees of freedom to be effectively involved in the energy sharing, might be so large, compared to the experimental times, that in any experiment such degrees of freedom would appear, to any practical extent, to be completely frozen. Correspondingly, one should take for f the "effective value" $f = 5$, in agreement with experiments. In the very words of Boltzmann [Bo1]:

"But how can the molecules of a gas behave as rigid bodies? Are they not composed of smaller atoms? Probably they are; but the *vis viva* of their internal vibration is transformed into progressive and rotatory motion so slowly, that when a gas is brought to a lower temperature the molecules may retain for days, or even for years, the higher *vis viva* of their internal vibration corresponding to the original temperature."

Only at higher temperatures the frequency of the molecules slowers (as in a pendulum, when the amplitude grows), and moreover the translational time scale, which provides the time unit in the problem, shortens: the fast degrees of freedom are no more fast nor frozen, and the experimental value $f = 7$ is recovered.

A few years later, namely immediately after Plank's work, Jeans [J1,J2,J3], surprisingly unaware of Boltzmann's suggestion, reconsidered the question, and studied heuristically both the collision of a diatomic molecule with an unstructured atom, to understand the anomalous specific heats, and the related problem of the lack of the "ultraviolet catastrophe" in the blackbody radiation.[7] Jeans' purpose is to show that, in both cases, Plank's quantization was unnecessary.[8] Let us restrict ourselves to the former problem, forgetting the too complicated question of the blackbody radiation. The heuristic conclusion, or perhaps the convinciment reached by Jeans, is the following: if φ^o denotes the asymptotic phase of the oscillator,

$$\varphi^o = \lim_{t \to -\infty} \varphi(t) - \omega t , \qquad (2.14)$$

then the average $\langle \Delta E \rangle_{\varphi^o}$ of ΔE on φ^o follows an exponential law of the form

$$\langle \Delta E \rangle_{\varphi^o} \sim e^{-\tau \omega} , \qquad (2.15)$$

where τ is a convenient constant, not well defined but of the order of the collision time. According to (2.15), for large ω — large "elasticity", in Jeans' own words — equilibrium times could get enormously long:

"In other words, the 'elasticity' could easily make the difference between dissipation of energy in a fraction of a second and dissipation in billions of years."

(dissipation means here transfer of energy to the internal degrees of freedom).

D. The Jeans-Landau-Teller (JLT) Approximation for a Single Frequency

Further contributions to the problem of the energy exchanges with fast degrees of freedom in classical systems, came from Rutgers [Ru] and Landau and Teller [LT], around 1936.[9] Quite surprisingly, these authors are unaware of both

---

[7] As is known, in conflict with experience and with the common sense, C_V for the blackbody was theoretically predicted to be infinite, with a diverging contribution of the high frequencies, simply because of the infinite number of degrees of freedom.

[8] Later on, however, Jeans reconsidered his point of view. Chapter XVI of his book on gas theory [J3], where he better explains his point of view, is still present in the 1916 second edition, but not in the 1920 third edition.

[9] The very fundamental problem of quantization is obviously no more in discussion in 1936, but other problems, like the possible dependence of the velocity of sound on the frequency, were leading to the same question. In the very essence: the velocity of sound depends on C_V, and so if the effective C_V depends on the time scale of the experiment, then the velocity of the low and of the high frequency sound waves (time scales of 10^{-1} and 10^{-4} sec respectively) could be different, with a possibly observable dispersion. By the way: most of the consideration contained in [LT], concerning the dispersion of sound, are nearly identical to those reported by Jeans in the first two editions of his book [J3].

Boltzmann and Jeans ideas. It is worthwhile to reconsider here [LT], although in a somehow revisited form (see also [Ra]). The approximation scheme of [LT] follows rather closely the ideas by Jeans, so we shall refer to it as to the Jeans-Landau-Teller (JLT) approximation.

Consider again the Hamiltonian

$$H(I, \varphi, p, q) = \omega I + \mathcal{H}(p, q) + \varepsilon f(I, \varphi, p, q) , \qquad (2.16)$$

which coincides with (2.9), but for the fact that ω^{-1} in front of the perturbation f is here replaced by the small parameter ε. As we shall see, it is very useful to treat ω and ε as independent parameters, recalling only at the end $\varepsilon = \omega^{-1}$. Consider a motion $(I(t), \varphi(t), p(t), q(t))$, with asymptotic data for $t \to -\infty$

$$I(t) \to I^o , \quad \varphi(t) - \omega t \to \varphi^o , \quad p(t) \to -p^o , \quad q(t) + p^o t \to q^o = 0 . \ (2.17)$$

Taking $q^o = 0$ is not restrictive: it corresponds to fix the time origin, and gives meaning to φ^o. One has obviously

$$\Delta E = \omega \Delta I = \omega \varepsilon \int_{-\infty}^{\infty} \frac{\partial f}{\partial \varphi}(I(t), \varphi(t), p(t), q(t)) \, \mathrm{d} t . \qquad (2.18)$$

The idea is that for small ε the motion is somehow close to the unperturbed motion

$$I_0(t) = I^o , \qquad \varphi_0(t) = \varphi^o + \omega t , \qquad p_0(t) , \qquad q_0(t) , \qquad (2.19)$$

where $(p_0(t), q_0(t))$ is a solution of the (integrable) Hamiltonian problem $\mathcal{H}$, with asymptotic data as in (2.17). Replacing (2.19) into (2.18) gives a kind of "first order" approximation

$$\Delta E \simeq \omega \Delta I = \omega \varepsilon \int_{-\infty}^{\infty} \frac{\partial f}{\partial \varphi}(I^o, \varphi^o + \omega t, p_0(t), q_0(t)) \, \mathrm{d} t .$$

In some special cases the integral can be explicitly computed. But quite generally, see [BCS] for details, if $p_0(t)$, $q_0(t)$ are analytic, as functions of the complex time t, in a strip $|\operatorname{Im} t| < \tau$ (this of course requires $\mathcal{H}$ to be analytic), then it is

$$\Delta E = E_0 + \sum_{\nu > 0} E_\nu \cos(\nu \varphi^o + \alpha_\nu) , \qquad (2.20)$$

with exponentially small E_ν, namely

$$E_\nu = \varepsilon \mathcal{E}_\nu \, e^{-\nu \tau \omega} \qquad \text{for } \nu \neq 0 , \qquad E_0 = 0 . \qquad (2.21)$$

The coefficients $\mathcal{E}_\nu$ in principle depend on ω, but in a way much weaker than exponential, and are practically treated as constants (the precise dependence of E_ν on ω is related to the nature of the singularities of $p_0(t)$, $q_0(t)$).

Since E_0 is the average, that is the most important quantity in the physical problem, the second of (2.21) is not satisfactory, and some inspection to higher order contributions is mandatory; the result turns out to be,[10] see Section 2,

$$E_0 = \mathcal{O}(\varepsilon^2 e^{-2\tau\omega}) . \tag{2.22}$$

The JLT approximation is in agreement with the Proposition 2 above, but the result sounds *much* better: it has the form of an equality, though approximate, rather than a less useful inequality; the exponential law appears already at first order, rather than at the end of a complicated procedure; the crucial coefficient τ in the exponent has a clear definition, and is connected in a simple way to the unperturbed problem, while the constant ω_* entering the proposition is more obscure (ω_*, precisely as ε_* in Proposition 1, expresses the divergence rate of the best perturbative series one is able to produce). As is also remarkable and new, the JLT approximation provides different exponential laws for the different Fourier components of ΔE. The most important components are E_0, namely the average, and E_1, which provides the dominant contribution to the fluctuations. For large ω, however, fluctuations are relatively large, that is $E_1 \gg E_0$; this will be important, see section 4 below. Finally, it is worthwhile to mention that the JLT approximation naturally extends to other systems, for example a system with a rotator in place of the oscillator [BCS],

$$H(I,\varphi,p,q) = \tfrac{1}{2}I^2 + \mathcal{H}(p,q) + \varepsilon f(I,\varphi,p,q) ; \tag{2.23}$$

the results for ΔE are practically identical to (2.20,2.21,2.22).

In front of such an appealing result, a natural question arises: is the heuristic procedure meaningful, and in some sense reliable? Before discussing theoretically the approximation, and try to make it rigorous in suitable assumptions, let us compare the results with accurate numerical computations. As a matter of fact, see [BGi,BF1,BChF1], the use of symplectic integration algorithms in scattering problems allows to compute reliably *very small* energy exchanges, as is necessary to test the exponential laws (2.21) and (2.22) on a sufficiently wide range.[11]

---

[10] On this point, both [LT] and its revisitation [Ra] are somehow weak: due to the fact that Cartesian coordinates are used instead of the action–angle ones, some second order terms spuriously enter the first order calculation, and are taken as the result. This is surprising, since these terms are positive definite, as if the oscillator could continuously gain energy. A better procedure [BCG] shows that all second order terms are indeed $\mathcal{O}(\varepsilon^2 e^{-2\tau\omega})$, but their coefficients can have any sign.

[11] We cannot enter here the delicate problem of the accuracy of symplectic integrators, and demand for this point to the literature, in particular to [BGi,BF1]. But it is worthwhile to recall here that the main tool to understand the behavior of symplectic integration algorithms, in particular for scattering problems, comes precisely from perturbation theory, and is a question of exponential estimates.

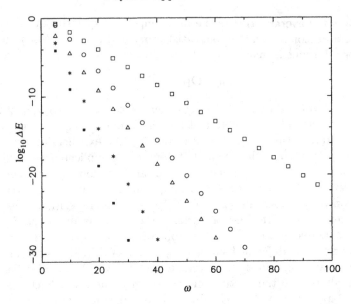

Fig. 9. *The Fourier components E_ν of ΔE, $\nu = 1, 0, 2, 3, 4$ (top to bottom), as functions of ω, for model (2.16). Quadruple precision (33 decimal digits).*

Figure 9 reports E_ν as function of ω for $\nu = 0, 1, 2, 3$. The figure refers to the Hamiltonian (2.8), with $V(x) = (\text{const}) \, e^{-x^2}/x$. The lines in semilog scale represent the exponential laws; the computed values λ_ν of the slopes agree with the theoretical values $\lambda_\nu = \nu\tau$ for $\nu \neq 0$, $\lambda_0 = 2\tau$, within approximately 1%; τ is also computed numerically, with great accuracy, in an independent way. It is worthwhile to observe that the measured energy exchanges range over more than 30 orders of magnitude, and that it is possible to separate, for example, E_3 from E_1 even when the former is *much* less than the latter (see [BCS,BF1] for a discussion on this point). Even better results were obtained for the rotator, that is for the system (2.23), which turns out to be easier to be handled numerically. Multiprecision arithmetics allows increasing the accuracy; the result, *for ΔE ranging over about 100 orders of magnitudes*, is in figure 10,[12] and the computed slopes turn out to agree with the theoretical prediction within approximately 0.1%.

E. The JLT Approximation for Two Independent Frequencies

The case of two or more identical frequencies, entering the problem of the collision of two or more identical molecules, easily reports to the case of a

---

[12] Such a computation goes far beyond Physics, and was made only to test the reliability of symplectic integrators. Aa is also remarkable, for large ω the ratio between E_1 and E_3 is tremendously large — it exceeds 10^{60} — and nevertheless E_3 is computed reliably, see [BF1].

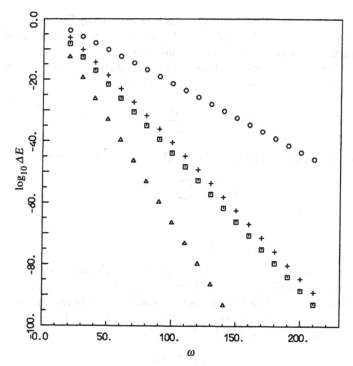

Fig. 10. *The Fourier components E_ν of ΔE, $\nu = 1, 0, 2, 3$ (top to bottom), as functions of ω, for model (2.23). Multiprecision (110 decimal digits).*

single frequency; we shall discuss this point in Section 4, when we shall need it. Here instead we consider the extension of the JLT approximation to the delicate case of more than one independent frequencies. To be definite, we shall refer to a specific model, namely

$$H(I, \varphi) = \sum_{j=1}^{n} \frac{I_j^2}{2} + f(t)\, g(\varphi) , \qquad I \in \mathbb{R}^n , \quad \varphi \in \mathbb{T}^n , \qquad (2.24)$$

with the special choice

$$f(t) = \frac{e^{-t^2}}{t^2 + \tau^2} , \qquad g(\varphi) = \mathcal{G} \sum_{\nu \in \mathbb{Z}^2} e^{-\varrho|\nu|}\, e^{i\nu \cdot \varphi} . \qquad (2.25)$$

This is a problem of adiabatic invariance, actually the simplest problem with more than one frequency to which the JLT approximation applies. The relevant features of the model are: (i) f has an analyticity strip of finite size τ, and decays (in an integrable way) to zero for $|t| \to \infty$; (ii) g is also analytic in a strip of finite size ϱ, and has a full Fourier series with nonvanishing coefficients. The fast decay $\sim e^{-t^2}$ of the interaction is useful for numerical computations, but has no other motivation; the very regular decay of the Fourier components of g simplifies the analysis. System (2.25) should be regarded as a simplified model for the collision of two rotating molecules.

The JLT approximation for this model is straightforward, namely, denoting as before by I^o, φ^o the asymptotic data, it reads

$$\Delta I_j = -\int_{-\infty}^{\infty} f(t) \frac{\partial g}{\partial \varphi_j} (\varphi^o + I^o t) \, \mathrm{d}t \ .$$

The integration, for f, g as in (2.24), is also easy, and one finds

$$\Delta I_j = \sum_{\nu \in \mathbb{Z}^n} \mathcal{I}_\nu \, e^{i\nu \cdot \varphi} \ , \tag{2.26}$$

with

$$\mathcal{I}_\nu = c\,\nu\, e^{-\tau|\nu \cdot I^o| - \varrho|\nu|} \ , \qquad c = \pi \tau^{-1} e^{\tau^2} \ . \tag{2.27}$$

What is *not* easy instead is the analysis of such result, namely understanding which terms are small or large in (2.26). It must be stressed that in absence of such analysis, the result is essentially formal and nearly empty. We are able to proceed only in the simple case $n = 2$, $I^o = \lambda \Omega$, for fixed $\Omega \in \mathbb{R}^2$ and large $\lambda \in \mathbb{R}^+$, so that the expression for $\mathcal{I}$ takes the form

$$\mathcal{I}_\nu = c\,\nu\, e^{-\lambda\tau|\nu \cdot \Omega| - \varrho|\nu|} \ . \tag{2.28}$$

Similar expressions can be found in [Ga2,S,DGJS] (in connection with the splitting of separatrices, a problem which turns out to be strongly related), and in [BCG,BCaF]. Still, for a generic $\Omega \in \mathbb{R}^2$, the analysis is too difficult, and the situation gets clear only under additional assumptions on Ω, of arithmetic character. Following [BCaF], we consider here the special case $\Omega = (1, \sqrt{2})$, and proceed heuristically (for a rigorous treatement of a similar situation, focused on the asymptotic behavior of the series for large λ, see [DGJS]).

A little reflection shows that, for large λ, the coefficients $\mathcal{I}_\nu$ entering the sum (2.26) have *very* different size. The largest ones are those for which $\nu \cdot \Omega$ is small, that is the corresponding $\nu = (\nu_1, \nu_2)$ are such that $-\nu_1/\nu_2$ is a good rational approximation of $\sqrt{2}$. The theory of continued fraction provides then the following sequence[13] of ν's:

$$(1, -1), \quad (3, -2), \quad (7, -5), \quad (17, -12), \quad (41, -29), \quad \cdots$$

For each ν in such a "resonant sequence", it is convenient to report $\log \|\mathcal{I}_\nu\|$ (euclidean norm) versus λ in logarithmic scale; this gives for each ν a straight line

$$\log \|\mathcal{I}_\nu\| = -\alpha_\nu \lambda - \beta_\nu \ ,$$

---

[13] The rule, for $\Omega = (1, \sqrt{2})$, is that the sequence starts with $(1, -1)$ and $(\nu_1, -\nu_2)$ is followed by $(\nu_1 + 2\nu_2, -\nu_1 - \nu_2)$.

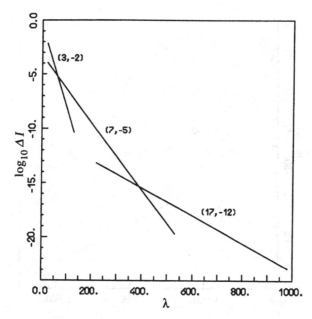

Fig. 11. *The amplitudes $\|\mathcal{I}_\nu\|$ vs. λ, for ν in the resonant sequence, according to the JLT approximation.*

with

$$\alpha_\nu = |\nu \cdot \varOmega| \ , \qquad \beta_\nu = \varrho|\nu| + \log\|\nu\| + \log c \ .$$

Note that, proceding in the sequence, α_ν lowers, while β_ν increases, so the lines are as in figure 11 (the terms $\mathcal{I}_\nu$, with ν out of the sequence, would produce much lower lines, and correspondingly negligible contributions). Quite clearly, even inside the sequence, the different terms have very different size, and practically, for each λ, just one of them dominates, with the only exception of narrow crossover regions around the intersection of the lines, where two nearby terms are comparable. The conclusion is that, if we forget crossover and denote by $\overline\nu(\lambda)$ the ν giving for each λ the dominant contribution, then the quantity of physical interest

$$\varDelta_{\max} I = \max_{\varphi^\circ \in \mathbb{T}^2} \|\varDelta I\|$$

follows the elementary law

$$\varDelta_{\max} I \simeq \|\mathcal{I}_{\overline\nu(\lambda)}\| \ . \tag{2.29}$$

This is practically a brocken line. Such a behavior is illustrated in figure 12, where $\varDelta_{\max} I$, computed numerically on the basis of (2.26), is plotted versus λ in semilog scale, for $\tau = \varrho = 1$.

In front of such an uncommon behavior, a numerical check of the theoretical results, to test the reliability of the approximation, looks mandatory.

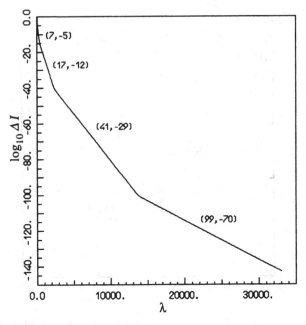

Fig. 12. *A numerical plot of* $\Delta_{\max}I$. *The curve resembles a brocken line, thoug it is not.*

The best test is computing numerically $\Delta_{\max}I$, as function of λ, from the dynamics, and compare the numerical outcome with the theoretical brocken line. The result is shown in figure 13, for two different choices of the parameter τ and $\varrho = 1$; the crosses represent the numerical data, while the solid line is

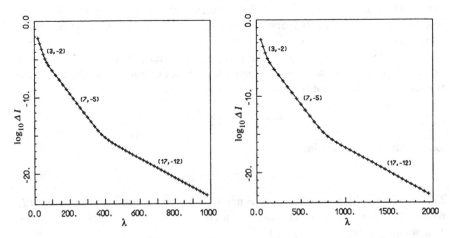

Fig. 13. *Plot of* $\max_{\varphi^{\circ}} \|\Delta I\|$. *The crosses are the numerical results, while the line is the theoretical expectation according JLT. Left:* $\tau = 1$, $\varrho = 1$; *right:* $\tau = 0.5$, $\varrho = 1$.

the theoretical expectation. The agreement looks pretty good. Let us stress that all constants in (2.26) and (2.27) are determined, with no free parameters to be adjusted. For a more quantitative test, one can compare the measured values of the constants α_ν and β_ν, obtained by a least square fit of the experimental data, with the theoretical expressions above; another quantity which can be tested is the ratio $\gamma_\nu = \Delta I_2/\Delta I_1$, which, according to (2.28), should be ν_2/ν_1 when $\mathcal{I}_\nu$ dominates. The results of the test are reported in the Table, for different values of the constants τ and ϱ, and for different dominant ν; α, β and γ are there the theoretical values, while α', β' and γ' are the corresponding computed values. The agreement between theoretical and computed quantities looks excellent, in some cases (for γ) even impressive.

Also in this case of two frequencies, one can compare the outcome of the JLT approximation with rigorous inequalities obtained within traditional perturbation theory. What it is easily proved rigorously is a proposition like the following:

Proposition 3.   *Let H be as in (2.24), with f, g as in (2.25). Consider a motion with $I(-\infty) = \lambda\Omega$, and $\Omega \in \mathbb{R}^2$ such that, for some $\gamma > 0$,*

$$|\nu \cdot \Omega| > \frac{\gamma}{|\nu|} \ . \tag{2.30}$$

Then there exists $\lambda_* > 0$ such that, if $\lambda > \lambda_*$, it is

$$\|I(+\infty) - I(-\infty)\| < (\text{const}) \, \lambda^{-1} e^{-(\frac{\lambda}{\lambda_*})^{1/2}} \ . \tag{2.31}$$

The Table

τ	ϱ	ν	α	α'	β	β'	γ	γ'
1.0	1.0	(7,-5)	0.0711	0.0709	7.70	7.76	1.400000	1.400003
		(17,-12)	0.02942	0.02943	23.82	23.83	1.416666	1.416666
0.5	1.0	(7,-5)	0.03554	0.03551	7.76	7.78	1.40000	1.40001
		(17,-12)	0.01472	0.01473	23.87	23.88	1.4166666	1.4166666
1.0	0.5	(17,-12)	0.02944	0.02945	9.320	9.325	1.416666	1.416666
		(41,-29)	0.0122	0.0124	28.9	28.4	1.4193793	1.4193793
1.0	0.25	(17,-12)	0.0294	0.0296	2.07	2.10	1.4166	1.4165
		(41,-29)	0.0122	0.0122	11.4	11.1	1.4137931	1.4137931

The strong Diophantine condition (2.30) is satisfied by a zero measure uncountable set[14] in $\mathbb{R}^2$, including $\Omega = (1, \sqrt{2})$. Such a restriction allows to get $(\lambda/\lambda_*)^a$ with $a = \frac{1}{2}$ in (2.31).

---

[14] To have a positive measure set in the space of frequencies, the denominator at the r.h.s. of (2.30) needs to be $|\nu|^{n-1+\vartheta}$, $\vartheta > 0$, n being the number of frequencies ($n = 2$ in the problem at hand). The optimal exponent of λ in the exponential law is then $a = 1/(n + \vartheta)$.

The inequality (2.31) can be compared with the asymptotic behavior, for large λ, of (2.24). The latter is studied rigorously in [DGJS], and heuristically in [S,BCaF]; the result is

$$\|\Delta I\| \simeq A \frac{e^{\tau^2}}{\varrho\tau} \sqrt{\frac{\lambda}{\lambda_0}} \left(1 + \mathcal{O}(\sqrt{\lambda})\right) e^{-\sqrt{\lambda/\lambda_0}}, \qquad \lambda_0^{-1} = (2+\sqrt{2})\varrho\tau,$$

with $A = \sqrt{3}(\sqrt{2}-1)\pi/2$. Quite clearly, the JLT approximation is compatible with rigorous perturbation theory. But clearly, there is no comparison in the accuracy and power of results.

The next Sections 3 and 4 are fully devoted to further considerations on the JLT approximation.

3 A Rigorous Version of the JLT Approximation in a Model

A. Lindstedt Series Versus Von Zeipel Series

It is practically impossible, using the standard procedure of classical perturbation theory outlined in Section 2-A, to go beyond results in the form of upper bounds like (2.5) or (2.13), for the obvious reason that the higher order terms in g and in the remainder $\mathcal{R}$, in the normal forms (2.4) or (2.12), are hardly known exactly, and only their norms are easily controlled. To produce "exact estimates", that is narrow two-sided inequalities, it is mandatory to avoid chains of canonical transformations, and look directly at the behavior of the solutions, specifically of $I(t)$. This however is difficult: as is clear for example from figure 6 (for definiteness, we refer here to molecular collisions) $\dot{I}$ is "large", namely is $\mathcal{O}(\varepsilon)$ or $\mathcal{O}(\omega^{-1})$, and a final exponential estimate, with no accumulation of deviations, requires taking into consideration compensations among deviations.

As a matter of fact, a branch of perturbation theory based on series expansions of the solution in the original variables, without canonical transformations, does exits, and is known in the literature as "Lindstet method", or method of Lindstet series. It is among the oldest branches of perturbation theory, but it was soon abandoned in favor of the "von Zeipel method", namely the method based on canonical transformations and normal forms, because the series developments appeared to conduce quite rapidly to huge amounts of terms, rather difficult to handle, and to apparently unavoidable divergences.

Nowadays, after the work of Eliasson [E] who showed how to overcome these difficulties, Lindsted series had a kind of revival, and are presently used both in KAM theory and in the related problem of the "splitting of separatrices" in forced pendula or similar systems. A rigorous analysis of the JLT approximation by means of Lindstet series was produced in [BCG]; as a matter of fact, the example there treated seems to be the simplest possible application of the Lindsted method. In this section we shall explain such result.

The Hamiltonian studied in [BCG] is

$$H(I,\varphi,p,q) = \omega I + \mathcal{H}(p,q) + \varepsilon g(\varphi)V(q) , \qquad \mathcal{H}(p,q) = \frac{p^2}{2m} + U(q) ,$$

with

$$I \in \mathbb{R} , \qquad \varphi \in \mathbb{T}^1 , \qquad (p,q) \in \mathbb{R}^2 .$$

Thanks to the fact that the perturbation is independent of I, so that the motion of φ is, trivially,

$$\varphi(t) = \varphi^o + \omega t , \tag{3.1}$$

such a model does not really represent the behavior of a diatomic molecule in an external potential, rather the behavior of a point mass, with a superimposed periodic force $F = -\varepsilon g(\varphi^o + \omega t)V'(q)$. However, as shown in [BCG], the generalization to a generic perturbation $V(I,\varphi,p,q)$ is possible, and even easy, as well as the generalization to the case $(I,\varphi) \in \mathbb{R}^n \times \mathbb{T}^n$. But the language and the notation get complicated, while no new ideas are added, so we prefer to treat here only the simplest case. Concerning the choice of the potentials U and V, we shall make here, as in [BCG], the easy choice

$$U(q) = V(q) = U_0 \, e^{-q/d} , \tag{3.2}$$

which allows explicit computations. The constants U_0, d and m will be taken respectively as units of energy, length and mass, and so put equal to one from now on.

The quantity of interest, we recall, is

$$\Delta E = \omega I(t)\Big|_{t=-\infty}^{\infty} = -\mathcal{H}(p(t),q(t))\Big|_{t=-\infty}^{\infty}$$

as function of the asymptotic data of the trajectory at $t = -\infty$.

B. The Energy–Time Variables

First of all, it is convenient to introduce for the translational degree of freedom new canonical variables in place of (p,q), precisely the energy–time variables (η,ξ); these are the analog, for unbounded motions, of the more familiar action–angle variables. To this purpose, consider any solution

$$p_0(\eta,t) , \qquad q_0(\eta,t)$$

of the Hamilton equations for $\mathcal{H}$, such that asymptotically the translational energy is η, i.e. $p(-\infty) = -\sqrt{2\eta}$. Solutions with the same η are identical up to the choice of the time origin; the one symmetric in time turns out to be

$$p_0(\eta,t) = \sqrt{2\eta} \tanh \sqrt{\frac{\eta}{2}} t , \qquad q_0(\eta,t) = \log \frac{(\cosh \sqrt{\eta/2}\, t)^2}{\eta} . \tag{3.3}$$

We interpret these expressions as a change of variables, namely we pass from (p, q) to the new variables (η, ξ) by the (canonical) substitution

$$p = p_0(\eta, \xi) , \qquad q = q_0(\eta, \xi) .$$

It is obviously $\mathcal{H}(p_0(\eta, \xi), q_0(\eta, \xi)) = \eta$, while correspondingly the new Hamiltonian $K(I, \varphi, \eta, \xi) = H(I, \varphi, p_0(\eta, \xi), q_0(\eta, \xi))$ takes the form

$$K(I, \varphi, \eta, \xi) = \omega I + \eta + \varepsilon g(\varphi) f(\eta, \xi) ,$$

with

$$f(\eta, \xi) = \frac{\eta}{(\cosh \sqrt{\eta/2}\, \xi)^2} . \tag{3.4}$$

An inspection to (3.3) shows that the domain of analyticity of the transformation, and thus of f, is for any $\eta > 0$

$$|\operatorname{Im} \xi| < \tau(\eta) = \pi / \sqrt{2\eta} \tag{3.5}$$

(the singularities nearest to the real axis are second order poles in $\xi = \pm i\tau$). The energy exchange ΔE reads, in these new notations,

$$\Delta E = -\Delta \eta = -\eta(+\infty) + \eta(-\infty) .$$

Using (3.1), the Hamilton equations associated to K practically reduce to only one pair of time–dependent equations for η and ξ, namely

$$\dot{\eta} = \varepsilon g(\varphi^o + \omega t) f_\eta(\eta, \xi) , \qquad \dot{\xi} = \varepsilon g(\varphi^o + \omega t) f_\xi(\eta, \xi) , \tag{3.6}$$

with

$$f_\eta = -\frac{\partial f}{\partial \xi} , \qquad f_\xi = \frac{\partial f}{\partial \eta} . \tag{3.7}$$

Such form of f_η, f_ξ reflects the Hamiltonian character of the problem. This, however, plays no role in the construction of Linstedt series, which are naturally more general, and is useful only occasionally, to show that a huge set of individually large terms, entering $\Delta \eta$, exactly vanish. So, for the only sake to be clear, we shall proceed with generic f_η, f_ξ, and recall (3.7) only when necessary. The functions f_η, f_ξ will be characterized by their analyticity properties, and for the fact that they vanish, in an integrable way, for $\xi \to \infty$, so as to represent a collision.

C. The Result

Consider a motion $\eta(t)$, $\xi(t)$ such that, asymptotically for $t \to -\infty$,

$$\eta(t) \to \eta^o , \qquad \xi(t) - t \to 0 ,$$

and expand it in power series of ε around the unperturbed motion $\eta_0(t) = \eta^o$, $\xi_0(t) = t$:

$$\eta(t) = \eta^o + \sum_{h=1}^{\infty} \varepsilon^h \eta_h(t) \ , \qquad \xi(t) = t + \sum_{h=1}^{\infty} \varepsilon^h \xi_h(t) \ . \qquad (3.8)$$

The series (in such a collisional problem) turn out to be convergent, for small ε, uniformly in t. Denote by $\eta_{h,\nu}$, $\xi_{h,\nu}$, $\nu \in \mathbb{Z}$, the Fourier components, with respect to φ^0, respectively of $\eta_h(+\infty)$ and $\xi_h(+\infty)$. In these notations it is then

$$\Delta E = -\sum_{\nu \in \mathbb{Z}} \tilde{E}_\nu \, e^{i\nu\varphi^o} \ , \qquad \tilde{E}_\nu = \sum_{h=1}^{\infty} \varepsilon^h \eta_{h,\nu} \ . \qquad (3.9)$$

By replacing (3.8) into the equations of motions (3.6), one finds a hierarchy of equations for η_h, ξ_h, complicated to write but conceptually easy. The first order is straightforward: one just uses inside f_η and f_ξ, in the equations of motion (3.6), the unperturbed motion $\eta(t) = \eta^o$, $\xi(t) = t$, thus getting, for example for η,

$$\dot{\eta}_1 = f_\eta(\eta^o, t)g(\varphi^o + \omega t) \ , \qquad \eta_1(t) = \int_{-\infty}^{t} f_\eta(\eta^o, t')g(\varphi^o + \omega t') \, dt' \ . \quad (3.10)$$

This is precisely the JLT approximation, rewritten in the (η, ξ) variables. Actually if

$$g(\varphi) = \sum_{\nu \in \mathbb{Z}} g_\nu \, e^{i\nu\varphi} \ ,$$

then one immediately deduces

$$\eta_1(+\infty) = \sum_{\nu \in \mathbb{Z}} \eta_{1,\nu} \, e^{i\nu\varphi^o} \ , \qquad \eta_{1,\nu} = g_\nu \int_{-\infty}^{\infty} f_\eta(\eta^o, t)e^{i\nu\omega t} \, dt \ .$$

For $\nu \neq 0$, by simply recalling that f_η is analytic, as function of ξ, as far as (3.5) is satisfied, one then gets

$$\eta_{1,\nu} \sim g_\nu \, e^{-\tau|\nu|\omega} \ .$$

Such an exponential law is useless for $\nu = 0$: but *thanks to the Hamiltonian character of the problem*, i.e. to the first of (3.7), it turns out that $\eta_{1,0}$ exactly vanishes:

$$\eta_{1,0} = -g_0 \int_{-\infty}^{\infty} \frac{\partial f}{\partial t} \, dt = -g_0 V(q(t))\Big|_{t=-\infty}^{\infty} = 0 \ . \qquad (3.11)$$

For f as in (3.4), the integral for the dominant term $\eta_{1,1}$ can be explicitly computed, namely

$$\eta_{1,1} = 4\pi i g_1 \frac{\omega^2}{e^{\tau\omega} - e^{-\tau\omega}} \ ,$$

and so

$$\Delta E = 8\pi g_1 \frac{\varepsilon \, \omega^2}{e^{\tau\omega} - e^{-\tau\omega}} \sin \varphi^o + \cdots \ .$$

Similar expressions are found for ξ_1; the average $\xi_{1,0}$, however, in general does not vanish.

Let us now proceed beyond the first order. The complete hierarchy of equations reads, for α either η or ξ:

$$\alpha_h(t) = \int_{-\infty}^{t} F_{\alpha,h}(t') \, dt' \ , \tag{3.12}$$

with

$$F_{\alpha,1}(t) = g(\varphi^o + \omega t) f_\alpha(\eta^o, t) \ , \tag{3.13}$$

and for $h > 1$:

$$F_{\alpha,h}(t) = g(\varphi^o + \omega t) \sum_{m=1}^{h-1} \sum_{j=0}^{m} f_\alpha^{m,j}(\eta^o, t) \sum_{\substack{k_1, \ldots, k_m \geq 1 \\ |k|=h-1}} \xi_{k_1}(t) \cdots \xi_{k_j}(t) \eta_{k_{j+1}}(t) \cdots \eta_{k_m}(t),$$

$$\tag{3.14}$$

where $|k| = \sum_i k_i$, while $f_\alpha^{m,j}$ is the coefficient entering the Taylor expansion of f_α,

$$f_\alpha^{m,j} = \frac{1}{j!(m-j)!} \frac{\partial^m f_\alpha}{\partial \xi^j \partial \eta^{m-j}} \ .$$

The procedure to be followed is now this:

(a) Proving convergence of all expansions, uniformly in t, for sufficiently small ε.

(b) Working out conditions such that the lowest order term $\eta_{1,\nu}$, for $\nu \neq 0$, dominates the series (3.9) for $\tilde{E}_\nu$. This requires, in particular, that at any order h in ε the coefficients $\eta_{h,\nu}$ have at least a factor $e^{-|\nu|\tau\omega}$ in front.

(c) Proving that for $\nu = 0$ the Hamiltonian symmetry leads to a cancellation, which generalizes (3.11): among terms contributing to $\tilde{E}_0$, only those with in front a factor $e^{-2\tau\omega}$ (or smaller) survive, while individually larger terms exactly sum to zero.

The assumptions which are needed are the following: concerning g, it is supposed to be analytic and bounded in a strip $|\operatorname{Im}\varphi| < \varrho$, for some positive ϱ; without loss of generality, we can assume that g is bounded by 1 in the strip, so that

$$|g_\nu| \leq e^{-\varrho|\nu|} \ . \tag{3.15}$$

Concerning f_η, f_ξ, the technical assumption that turns out to be useful, and is satisfied by f as in (3.4), is that the coefficients $f_\alpha^{m,j}$ are analytic, as functions of ξ, in a strip $|\operatorname{Im}\xi| < \tau(\eta)$, and in any smaller strip $|\operatorname{Im}\xi| < (1-\delta)\tau(\eta)$, $\delta > 0$, they are bounded by an expression of the form

$$|f_\alpha^{m,j}(\eta, s + i\sigma)| \leq C^m \delta^{-m-m_0} w(s) \tag{3.16}$$

with some $C > 0$, $m_0 > 0$ and

$$\int_{-\infty}^{\infty} w(s)\,\mathrm{d}s = A < \infty . \qquad (3.17)$$

A little reflections shows that these hypotheses are indeed natural in this problem, and just make quantitative two elementary facts: (i) For given η, the unperturbed motion $q(t)$ is analytic for $|\operatorname{Im} t| < \tau(\eta)$, with τ as in (3.5); Cauchy estimates then easily lead to (3.16). (ii) Along any unperturbed motion, the coupling term $V(q(t))$ vanishes in an integrable way for $t \to \pm\infty$. For the potentials (3.2), one computes $m_0 = 3$.

Proposition 1. *In the above assumptions, denoting*

$$B = 8CA , \qquad m_1 = m_0 + 1 ,$$

the following holds:

i. For $|\varepsilon| < B^{-1}$ the series (3.8) converge, namely it is

$$|\eta_h(t)| , \; |\xi_h(t)| \le A B^{h-1} .$$

ii. The Fourier components $\eta_{h,\nu}$ and $\xi_{h,\nu}$, respectively of $\eta_h(+\infty)$ and $\xi_h(+\infty)$, satisfy the δ-corrected exponential estimates

$$|\eta_{h,\nu}| \, |\xi_{h,\nu}| \le A B^{h-1} \delta^{-hm_1+1} e^{-|\nu|\tau(1-\delta)\omega - \varrho|\nu|} , \qquad (3.18)$$

for any $\delta \in (0,1)$.

iii. In the Hamiltonian case, the average $\eta_{h,0}$ satisfies the special exponential estimate

$$|\eta_{h,0}| \le A B^{h-1} \delta^{-hm_1+1} e^{-2\tau(1-\delta)\omega} . \qquad (3.19)$$

Comments:

1. The presence of the correction $(1 - \delta)$ at the exponents in the estimates (3.18) shows that points (b), (c) of the above program are fulfilled only if ε is specially small, namely

$$\varepsilon < (\mathrm{const})\,\omega^{-m_1} ; \qquad (3.20)$$

indeed, in order for the correction to disappear, in such a way that the first order (which is exactly computed and has no correction) dominates, one must take $\delta \sim \omega^{-1}$, but then (3.20) is necessary to ensure convergence.

2. If instead, as in the physical problem of molecular collisions, one has only $\varepsilon = \omega^{-1}$, then only upper estimates to the energy exchange can be worked out. Such upper estimates are quite interesting, and full in agreement with numerical computations: in particular, taking $\delta = \varepsilon^{1/(2m_1)} = \omega^{-1/(2m_1)}$, for $\omega > B^2$ one gets

$$|\tilde{E}_\nu| < (\mathrm{const})\, e^{-|\nu|\omega\tau(1-\omega^{-1/(2n)})-\varrho\nu}\ ;$$

for large ω, this expression gives precisely the observed exponential laws, with the correct slopes. Such a result, even if non "exact" (it is not two–sided) is nevertheless *much* better than the results which can be obtained by the method of canonical transformation.

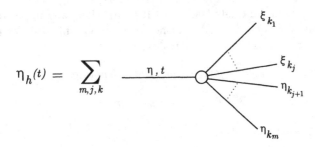

$$\eta_h(t) = \sum_{m,j,k} \underline{\quad\quad \eta,t \quad\quad}$$

Fig. 14. *The expansion of η_h in elementary trees.*

D. Sketch of the Proof

The hierarchy of equations (3.12–3.14) has the form, for α either η or ξ,

$$\alpha_h(t) = \sum_{m,j,k} \int_{-\infty}^{t} \mathcal{K}^\alpha_{m,j}(t')\, \xi_{k_1}(t')\cdots\xi_{k_j}(t')\eta_{k_{j+1}}(t')\cdots\eta_{k_m}(t')\ \mathrm{d}t'\ ,$$

where the range of the indices in the sum is as in (3.14), and the integration kernel is

$$\mathcal{K}^{m,j}_\alpha(t) = g(\varphi^\circ + \omega t) f^{m,j}_\alpha(\eta^\circ, t)$$

(the dependence of $\mathcal{K}^{m,j}_\alpha$ on φ°, η° is left implicit). To each term of such a huge sum it is natural to associate an "elementary tree", see figure 14, with a "root" labelled by α and t, and $m \geq 1$ branches labelled $\xi_{k_1},\ldots,\eta_{k_m}$. The diagram (with labels) completely identifies the term, in the following way: the number of branches gives m; the number of ξ–type branches gives j; $k_1,\ldots,k_m$ identify the integrand, and specify in particular that the tree represents a contribution to $\alpha_h(t)$, $h = |k| - 1$. The circle stays for integration on time, with kernel $\mathcal{K}^{m,j}_\alpha$. To avoid overcounting, the rule is that ξ–type branches stay above η–type branches.

From elementary trees one constructs "trees", by recursively expanding all branches $\xi_{k_1}(t) \ldots, \eta_{k_m}(t)$ in elementary trees, in all possible ways; the expansion ends when all the end–branches represent either η_1 or ξ_1, whose explicit expressions are in (3.10). Simple examples of trees are in figure 15. *Elementary rules provide a one to one correspondence between trees and contributions to $\alpha_h(t)$.* Indeed, α and t are explicitly reported on the root; h

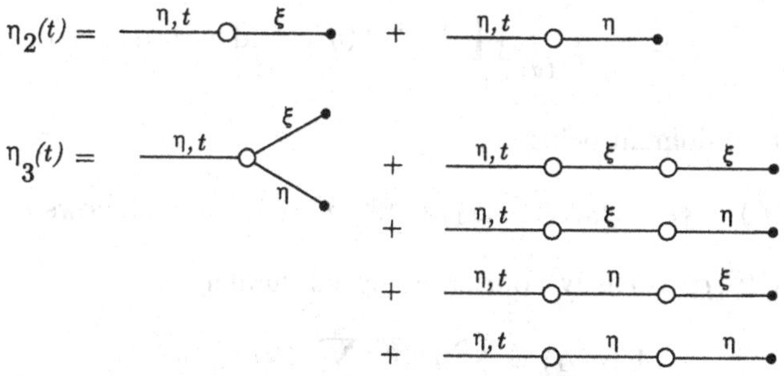

$$\eta_2(t) = \quad \underset{\eta,t}{\circ} \quad \underset{\xi}{\bullet} \quad + \quad \underset{\eta,t}{\circ} \quad \underset{\eta}{\bullet}$$

$$\eta_3(t) = \quad \underset{\eta,t}{\circ}\!\!<^{\xi}_{\eta} \quad + \quad \underset{\eta,t}{\circ} \quad \underset{\xi}{\circ} \quad \underset{\xi}{\bullet} \quad + \quad \underset{\eta,t}{\circ} \quad \underset{\xi}{\circ} \quad \underset{\eta}{\bullet} \quad + \quad \underset{\eta,t}{\circ} \quad \underset{\eta}{\circ} \quad \underset{\xi}{\bullet} \quad + \quad \underset{\eta,t}{\circ} \quad \underset{\eta}{\circ} \quad \underset{\eta}{\bullet}$$

Fig. 15. *The trees contributing to η_2 and η_3.*

is precisely the number of vertices of the tree (also equal to the number of branches, including the root); each internal vertex represents an integration over a variable t_v, $v = 0, \ldots, h-1$, with integration kernel $\mathcal{K}_\alpha^{m,j}(t_v)$, where α is the label of the outcoming (the left) branch and m, j are as in elementary trees; each end vertex v, coherently with (3.10), also represents an integration on time, with kernel

$$\mathcal{K}_\alpha^{0,0}(t_v) = g(\varphi^\circ + \omega t_v) f_\alpha(\eta^\circ, t_v) .$$

So, each tree with h vertices is a multiple integral in $t_0, \ldots, t_{h-1}$, the integration domain reflecting the partial ordering of the tree: (i) $t'_v \leq t_v$ if v' follows v in the tree,[15] and (ii) $t_0 \leq t$, if $v = 0$ denotes the root vertex. From now on, however, we shall restrict the attention to the asymptotic values $\alpha_h(+\infty)$, so condition (ii) is ineffective and t_0 extends from $-\infty$ to ∞. For example, the first two trees for $\eta_3(\infty)$ in figure 15 corrispond respectively to

$$\int_{-\infty}^{\infty} dt_0 \int_{-\infty}^{t_0} dt_1 \int_{-\infty}^{t_0} dt_2 f_\eta^{2,1}(\eta^\circ, t_0) f_\xi(\eta^\circ, t_1) f_\eta(\eta^\circ, t_2) g(\varphi^\circ + \omega t_0) g(\varphi^\circ + \omega t_1) g(\varphi^\circ + \omega t_2)$$

and to

$$\int_{-\infty}^{\infty} dt_0 \int_{-\infty}^{t_0} dt_1 \int_{-\infty}^{t_1} dt_2 \, f_\eta^{2,1}(\eta^\circ, t_0) f_\xi(\eta^\circ, t_1) f_\xi(\eta^\circ, t_2) g(\varphi^\circ + \omega t_0) g(\varphi^\circ + \omega t_1) g(\varphi^\circ + \omega t_2).$$

Let Θ denote the set of all topologically distinguishable tree–like diagrams; a tree as above, contributing to $\alpha_h(+\infty)$, is completely identified by a diagram $\vartheta \in \Theta$, and by the set of labels $\underline{\alpha} = (\alpha_0, \ldots, \alpha_{h-1})$ "decorating" its root and its branches, with $\alpha_0 = \alpha$ and $\alpha_1, \ldots, \alpha_{h-1}$ arbitrary, but for the fact that among the branches issuing from the same vertex, ξ–type ones must stay above η–type ones. One can then write

$$\alpha_h(+\infty) = \sum_{\vartheta \in \Theta} \sum_{\underline{\alpha}:\alpha_0=\alpha} V(\vartheta, \alpha) ,$$

where the "value" $V(\vartheta, \alpha)$ of the tree is given by

---

[15] In any tree, the vertices constitute in the obvious way a partially ordered set.

$$V(\vartheta, \underline{\alpha}) = \int_{T(\vartheta)} \prod_{v \in \vartheta} \mathcal{K}_{\alpha_v}^{m_v, j_v}(\eta^o, t_v) \, \mathrm{d}t_0 \cdots \mathrm{d}t_{h-1} \, ,$$

the integration domain being

$$T(\vartheta) = \left\{ \underline{t} = (t_0, \ldots, t_{h-1}) \in \mathbb{R}^h : t'_v \le t_v \quad \text{if } v' \text{ follows } v \right\} \, .$$

The value $V(\vartheta, \underline{\alpha})$ is easily Fourier–analyzed: namely

$$V(\vartheta, \underline{\alpha}) = \sum_{\nu \in \mathbb{Z}} e^{i\nu\varphi^o} \sum_{\underline{n} \in \mathbb{Z}_\nu^h} V(\vartheta, \underline{\alpha}, \underline{n}) \, ,$$

with $\mathbb{Z}_\nu^h = \{ \underline{n} \in \mathbb{Z}^h : \sum_v n_v = \nu \}$ and

$$V(\vartheta, \underline{\alpha}, \underline{n}) = \left(\prod_{v \in \vartheta} g_{n_v} \right) \int_{T(\vartheta)} \left[\prod_{v \in \vartheta} f_{\alpha_v}^{m_v, j_v}(\eta^o, t_v) \right] e^{i\omega \underline{n} \cdot \underline{t}} \, \mathrm{d}t_0 \cdots \mathrm{d}t_{h-1} \cdot$$

$$(3.21)$$

Correspondingly, it is

$$\alpha_{h,\nu} = \sum_{\vartheta \in \Theta_h} \sum_{\underline{\alpha} : \alpha_0 = \alpha} \sum_{\underline{n} \in \mathbb{Z}_\nu^h} V(\vartheta, \underline{\alpha}, \underline{n}) \, .$$

The proof of points (i) and (ii), using (3.15)–(3.17), follows rather easily. In the very essence, point (i) comes from a simple combinatorial counting of diagrams. Point (ii) follows from simultaneously raising all the integration paths to $\mathrm{Im} \, t_v = \pm(1 - \delta)\tau$, with sign equal to the sign of ν; this produces indeed the claimed exponential factor, with the $(1 - \delta)$ correction (for the way the integrals are nested, the imaginary part of all integration variables must be the same).

What is not trivial instead is point (iii), that is the cancellation mechanism leading at any order h to the special exponential estimate for the average $\eta_{h,0}$. Some manipulation and further decomposition of trees is necessary, for which we are forced to demand to [BCG]. As a result, one finds that among trees which contribute to $\eta_{h,0}$, some have the desired factor $e^{-2\tau(1-\delta)\omega}$ (or smaller) in front, some other do not and are large. But these, *in the Hamiltonian case*, exactly sum to zero. More precisely, they partition into classes according to a curious rule: two trees are in the same class iff one is obtained from the other by "moving the root" from the root vertex v_0 to any other vertex v (this changes the ordering of the tree), and moreover, along the uniquely determined path from v_0 to v, any label η is replaced by the conjugated one ξ, and conversely. Thanks to the Hamiltonian symmetry (3.7), it turns out that the sum of the values of all trees in the same class exactly vanishes; this indeed generalizes (3.11) to higher orders. See figure 16 for an elementary example of a class with zero sum; to better recognize the movement of the root, the vertices are numbered. Unfortunately, here we cannot be more precise. A complete description of the compensation mechanism is found in [BCG].

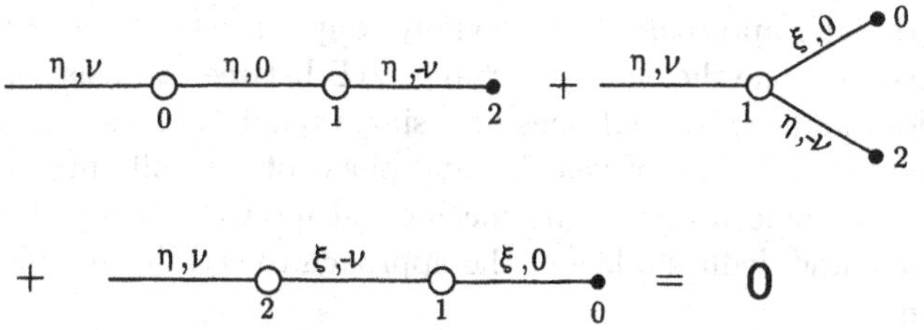

Fig. 16. *Illustrating the compensation mechanism: a class of individually large trees, obtained one from the other by "moving of the root", exactly sum to zero.*

4 An Application of the JLT Approximation

A. The Problem

In Section 2 we introduced the JLT approximation, and observed that it is in beautiful agreement with numerical results. In Section 3 we then proved on an example that the approximation is correct (in reasonable assumptions) as an upper bound to the energy exchange, while with extra assumptions it even becomes "exact". Here we shall use the JLT approximation as the basic tool to investigate the Boltzmann–Jeans problem of the time scale for equilibrium in an elementary model of a classical diatomic gas.

The model we have in mind represents a one–dimensional gas of many identical molecules, see figure 2. Molecular collisions produce large energy exchanges among the translational degrees of freedom and, separately, among the vibrational ones (equality of the frequencies is important here). Instead, as we know, for large ω the energy exchange between the translational degrees of freedom and the vibrational ones, in each collision, is difficult. In such a situation, it looks reasonable to assume that at any given moment, the two populations of degrees of freedom are separately in thermal equilibrium, with possibly different temperatures T_{tr} and T_{vib}, and ask for the law of approach to thermal equilibrium. To answer the question, we proceed as follows:

(i) We assume that the dominant contribution to the energy exchanges between translational and vibrational degrees of freedom comes from well separated two–molecules collisions (for a discussion about many molecules collisions, see [BHS]). As the Hamiltonian for the two–molecules collision, in the frame of the center of mass, we take

$$H(p, r, \pi_1, \pi_2, \xi_1, \xi_2) = \frac{p^2}{4} + U(r) + \frac{1}{2}(\pi_1^2 + \pi_2^2) + \frac{\omega^2}{2}(\xi_1^2 + \xi_2^2) + V(r, \xi_1, \xi_2) \, ;$$

$$(4.1)$$

the separation between U and V is established by requiring $V(r, 0, 0) = 0$. Both U and V are assumed to be smooth (in fact analytic) functions, and to vanish for $r \to \infty$, so as to describe a collision; as is natural, $U(r)$ will be assumed to diverge for $r \to 0$.

(ii) We use the JLT approximation, trivially adapted to the above Hamiltonian (4.1), to determine the energy exchange ΔE between translational degrees of freedom and vibrational ones in a single binary collision, as a function of the asymptotic data of velocity and phase of the colliding molecules;

(iii) We then combine together the mechanical model and the statistical assumptions, and deduce a law of the approach to equilibrium in the gas, of the form

$$\frac{\mathrm{d}}{\mathrm{d}t}(T_{vib} - T_{tr}) = -(T_{vib} - T_{tr})\, F(\omega, T_{tr}) \, , \qquad (4.2)$$

where F is a positive function which depends on the choice of the potentials entering the Hamiltonian of the two–molecules collision. In very reasonable assumptions, F turns out to decrease with ω as a stretched exponential; in particular, if $U(r)$ behaves, for small r, as r^{-s}, it is

$$F(\omega) \sim e^{-a\omega^{\alpha}} \, , \quad \text{where} \quad \alpha = \frac{2}{3 + 2/s} \, . \qquad (4.3)$$

Such a study, reported in [BHS], follows rather closely the study reported in [OH,OHBFM] on a closely related problem, namely the approach to equilibrium in a strongly magnetized pure electron plasma. In place of the internal vibration of molecules one has, in the plasma, the Larmor rotation of the electrons around the magnetic field lines, see figure 17. The essence of the problem, and its mathematical structure, are indeed quite similar.

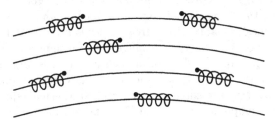

Fig. 17. *A model of a pure electron plasma. The fast Larmor rotation plays the same role as the molecular vibrations.*

B. Revisiting the JLT Approximation

We show here how the JLT approximation adapts to the problem at hand of the two–molecules collision. To this purpose we introduce the action–angle variables of the two oscillators,

$$\pi_i = \sqrt{2I_i\omega}\cos\varphi_i \, , \quad \xi_i = \omega^{-1}\sqrt{2I_i\omega}\sin\varphi_i \, , \quad i = 1, 2 \, , \qquad (4.4)$$

which give the Hamiltonian the form

$$\hat{H}(r, p, I_1, I_2, \varphi_1, \varphi_2) = \omega(I_1 + I_2) + \mathcal{H}(r, p) + \hat{V}(r, I_1, I_2, \varphi_1, \varphi_2) \, . \qquad (4.5)$$

Because of the exact resonance, it is convenient to introduce the further canonical change of variables $(I_1, I_2, \varphi_1, \varphi_2) \mapsto (J, \Gamma, \psi, \gamma)$ defined by

$$J = I_1 + I_2 , \quad \Gamma = I_2 , \quad \psi = \varphi_1 , \quad \gamma = \varphi_2 - \varphi_1 .$$

Notice that the angles now appear as one fast angle, ψ, and one slow angle, γ. The coupling term now becomes of order $\omega^{-1}\sqrt{\omega J}$, and for given vibrational energy (given temperature) and large ω, it is as small as ω^{-1}. The final Hamiltonian is thus of the form

$$K(r, p, J, \Gamma, \psi, \gamma) = \omega J + \mathcal{H}(r, p) + \omega^{-1}\sqrt{\omega J} f(r, J, \Gamma, \psi, \gamma) , \qquad (4.6)$$

with

$$\mathcal{H}(r, p) = \frac{p^2}{4} + U(r) .$$

Consider now any solution $p_0(t), r_0(t)$ of the Hamilton equations for $\mathcal{H}$, such that asymptotically it is $p(t) \to p^o$, $r(t) - p^o t \to 0$, and denote by τ the width of its analyticity strip as function of the complex time. Following closely the prescription of Section 2, it is easy to apply to such an Hamiltonian the JLT approximation scheme, and compute the energy exchange $\Delta E = \omega \Delta J$ just by integration along the unperturbed motion

$$p = p_0(t) , \quad r = r_0(t) , \quad J = J^o , \quad \Gamma = \Gamma^o , \quad \psi = \psi^o + \omega t , \quad \gamma = \gamma^o .$$

Taking into account only the dominant terms, that is the first Fourier component and the average, as a result of the approximation one finds

$$\Delta E \simeq E_0 + E_1 \cos(\psi^o + \alpha) ,$$

where E_1 is exactly known, namely

$$E_1 = A\sqrt{\omega J^o}\, e^{-\omega\tau} , \qquad A = \left| \int_{-\infty}^{\infty} f_1(r_0(t + i\tau), J^o, \Gamma^o, \gamma^o)e^{i\omega t}\, dt \right| , \quad (4.7)$$

$f_1(r, J, \Gamma, \gamma)$ denoting the first coefficient of the Fourier series of F in the phase ψ, while E_0 (which is a second order quantity) is known only approximately,

$$E_0 = \mathcal{O}(e^{-2\omega\tau}) \ll E_1 .$$

The coefficient A is not exactly constant, but it depends on ω and on the asymptotic data in a very smooth way; later on, it will be treated as a constant.

Accurate numerical cheks [BHS] show that, as is not surprising, the JLT approximation works very well in this problem, too.

C. The Statistical Part of the Problem

Following the prescription of point (iii) above, we assume now that the asymptotic data of the colliding molecules at $t = -\infty$ are distributed according to the Boltzmann rule, and on the basis of this statistical assumption we compute the average energy exchange per unit time and per molecule. It is convenient to eliminate the variable r, by introducing a Poincaré section $r = r^*$, with r^* so large that the interaction f is negligible. The number dn of pairs of molecules which cross the section $r = r^*$ (with $\dot{r} < 0$) in time dt is given by

$$\mathrm{d}n = n\,\mu\,C\,e^{-\beta_{tr}E_{tr}(p) - \beta_{vib}E_{vib}(J)}\,|p|\,\mathrm{d}p\,\mathrm{d}J\,\mathrm{d}\Gamma\,\mathrm{d}\psi\,\mathrm{d}\gamma\,\mathrm{d}t\,,$$

where

$$\beta_{tr} = 1/(k_B T_{tr})\,,\qquad \beta_{vib} = 1/(k_B T_{vib})\,,$$

$$E_{tr}(p) = \frac{p^2}{4}\,,\qquad E_{vib}(J) = \omega J\,,$$

while n is the total number of molecules and μ is the density. The domain $\mathcal{D}$ of the different variables is

$$p \in (-\infty, 0)\,,\quad J \in (0, \infty)\,,\quad \Gamma \in (-J, J)\,,\quad \psi, \gamma \in (0, 2\pi)\,.$$

The quantity we are interested in, is the average energy exchange per unit time and per molecule,

$$\langle \dot{E_{vib}} \rangle = C\mu \int_{\mathcal{D}} \Delta E(p, J, \Gamma, \psi, \gamma)\,e^{-\beta_{tr}E_{tr}(p) - \beta_{vib}E_{vib}(J)}|p|\,\mathrm{d}p\,\mathrm{d}J\,\mathrm{d}\Gamma\,\mathrm{d}\psi\,\mathrm{d}\gamma\,,\quad (4.8)$$

and this might disorient: indeed the very detailed expression of E_1 produced by the JLT approximation is apparently useless, since the term $E_1 \cos(\psi + \alpha)$ is trivially averaged out by the integration over ψ, while the average E_0 is known only approximately.

Fortunately, the two terms are not independent: *due to very elementary properties of the dynamics, namely the preservation of the phase space volume and the time–reversal, it is, exactly,*

$$\langle \dot{E_{vib}} \rangle = \frac{1}{2}\langle \Delta E\big(1 - e^{-(\beta_{vib} - \beta_{tr})\Delta E}\big) \rangle\,,\qquad (4.9)$$

and for small ΔE

$$\langle \dot{E_{vib}} \rangle \simeq \frac{1}{2}\,(\beta_{vib} - \beta_{tr})\langle (\Delta E)^2 \rangle\,.\qquad (4.10)$$

The proof of (4.9) is straightforward: denote by $x = (p, J, \Gamma, \psi, \gamma)$ the asymptotic state before collision, and by $x' = (p', J', \Gamma', \psi', \gamma')$ the state after collision (that is, again at $r = r^*$), time–reversed. The Jacobian of the map $\Psi : x \mapsto x'$ is $|p|/|p'|$, and of course $\Delta E(x') = -\Delta E(x)$. We can then proceed as follows: first we change the dummy integration variable x in (4.8) by x', then we go back to x by the substitution $x' = \Psi(x)$. The result is

$$\langle \dot{E_{vib}} \rangle = C\mu \int_{\mathcal{D}} (-\Delta E)\,e^{-\beta_{tr}(E_{tr} - \Delta E) - \beta_{vib}(E_{vib} + \Delta E)}\,|p|\mathrm{d}p\,\mathrm{d}J\,\mathrm{d}\Gamma\,\frac{\mathrm{d}}{\mathrm{d}t}\psi\,\mathrm{d}\gamma\,,$$

and so, summing with (4.9), (4.10) follows.

The above expression (4.10) for $\langle \dot{E}_{vib} \rangle$ is nice: in particular, it shows that *it is enough to assume that the average E_0 of ΔE is much smaller than the fluctuation E_1, to deduce that*

$$\langle \dot{E}_{vib} \rangle = \frac{1}{4}(\beta_{vib} - \beta_{tr})\langle E_1^2 \rangle .$$

So, since $E_1 \sim e^{-\tau\omega}$, $\langle \dot{E}_{vib} \rangle$ is necessarily of order $e^{-2\tau\omega}$. Using the expression (4.7) of E_1, the integration in J, Γ, ψ, γ is straightforward. As a result, also using the obvious relations

$$\frac{\mathrm{d}}{\mathrm{d}t}T_{vib} = \frac{2}{k_B}\langle \dot{E}_{vib} \rangle , \qquad \frac{\mathrm{d}}{\mathrm{d}t}T_{tr} = \frac{1}{k_B}\langle \dot{E}_{tr} \rangle = -\frac{1}{k_B}\langle \dot{E}_{vib} \rangle ,$$

one finds (4.2), with

$$F(\omega, T_{tr}) = \frac{(\text{const})}{T_{tr}} \int_0^\infty e^{\beta_{tr} E_{tr}} e^{-2\tau(E_{tr})\omega} \, \mathrm{d}E_{tr} . \tag{4.11}$$

Further details can be found in [BHS].

Some remarkable features of (4.2)–(4.11) are the following:

o It does describe an approach to equilibrium, with $\frac{\mathrm{d}}{\mathrm{d}t}(T_{vib} - T_{tr})$ proportional to the difference $T_{tr} - T_{vib}$.

o The expression is complete and explicit but for a multiplicative constant, if one is able to determine the coefficient $\tau(E_{tr})$. *This is a zero–order quantity depending only on the properties of the unperturbed motion $r_0(t)$,* and for not too complicated potentials, it can be at least roughly estimated.

The characteristic time to reach equilibrium

$$\mathcal{T}(T_{tr}, \omega) \sim \frac{1}{F(T_{tr}, \omega)}$$

is certainly a rapidly increasing function of ω, as expected by Jeans, but *is not a pure exponential of ω* (By reading [J1,J2,J3] one gets the impression that on this point the intuition of Jeans failed). For instance, if for small r

$$U(r) \sim \frac{1}{r^s} , \qquad s \geq 1 ,$$

then a rough estimate based on dimensional considerations gives for large ω

$$\tau \sim E_{tr}^{-(s+2)/(2s)} , \qquad \mathcal{T} \sim \exp \omega^{\frac{2}{3+2/s}} . \tag{4.12}$$

This less than exponential dependence on ω arises through the statistical averaging, namely to the fact that now we are not working at fixed energy, rather at fixed translational temperature. The point is that, because of the factor $e^{-\tau\omega}$ in the function to be integrated, with τ decreasing for increasing translational energy, the most significant contributions to energy equipartition come from collisions involving molecules with large translational energy. But according to the Boltzmann distribution, there are very few collisions with large E_{tr}. The compromise between these two scaling laws results in the above functional dependence on ω. Such a mechanism is also illustrated in the next paragraph, devoted to a numerical check of the exponential law (4.12).

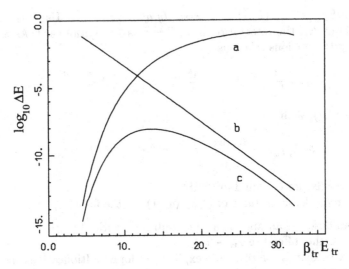

Fig. 18. *Illustrating the numerical computation of $\langle \dot{E}_{vib} \rangle$. Curves (a)–(c) represent respectively $W(E_{tr})$, the Boltzmann factor $e^{-\beta_{tr}E_{tr}}$, and their product (semi-log scale), vs. $\beta_{tr}E_{tr}$. Data: $\beta_{tr} = 4$, $\beta_{vib} = 0.6$, $\omega = 40$.*

D. A Numerical Check

The law to be checked can be written in the form

$$\langle \dot{E}_{vib} \rangle = C \int_0^\infty W(E_{tr}) e^{-\beta_{tr}E_{tr}} \, \mathrm{d}E_{tr} \,, \qquad (4.13)$$

with

$$W(E_{tr}) = \int_D \Delta E \, e^{-\beta_{vib}E_{vib}} \, \mathrm{d}J \, \mathrm{d}\Gamma \, \mathrm{d}\psi \, \mathrm{d}\gamma \,;$$

D denotes here the domain of J, Γ, ψ, γ. The idea is to compute numerically $\langle \dot{E}_{vib} \rangle$, for fixed β_{tr}, β_{vib} and ω, by regularly scanning the E_{tr} axis, and to compute the integral for $W(E_{tr})$, for each E_{tr}, by a "Monte–Carlo" method (averaging over many initial data extracted randomly, with the correct probability distribution). For numerical details, see [BHS]. As for the Hamiltonian, a simple choice, convenient for numerical integration, is H of the form (4.1), with

$$U(r) + V(r, \xi_1, \xi_2) = \frac{e^{-\varrho^2}}{\varrho} \,, \qquad \varrho = r - \frac{\xi_1 + \xi_2}{2} \,.$$

The result of such a computation is reported in figure 18. Curve (a) is the computed value of W as function of E_{tr} (in units β_{tr}^{-1}, and in semi–log scale). The line (b) represents the Boltzmann factor $e^{-\beta_{tr}E_{tr}}$. Curve (c) is the product $W(E_{tr})e^{-\beta_{tr}E_{tr}}$, and according to (4.13), the integral of this last curve gives $\langle E_{vib}\rangle$. The figure refers to $\beta_{tr} = 4$, $\beta_{vib} = 0.6$, and $\omega = 40$. Curve (c), if represented in a linear vertical scale, gets the shape of a well defined peak, around the maximum at $\beta_{tr}E_{tr} \simeq 14$; this peak is represented in figure 19, left curve (left vertical scale). If one increases ω, the peak moves to the right and its value decreases: for example, for $\omega = 160$, the peak is around $\beta_{tr}E_{tr} \simeq 26$, see the right curve of figure 19 (right vertical scale). As shown by the scales, the equal height of the peaks is a graphic artifact; their height, and area, are indeed *very* different. It is perhaps worthwhile to remark that, already for $\omega = 40$, practically all contributions to the energy exchanges come from *very few* collisions with large E_{tr} (the Boltzmann factor of such collisions is $e^{-14} < 10^{-6}$). For $\omega = 160$, the situation is even more dramatic (Boltzmann factor $e^{-26} < 10^{-11}$).

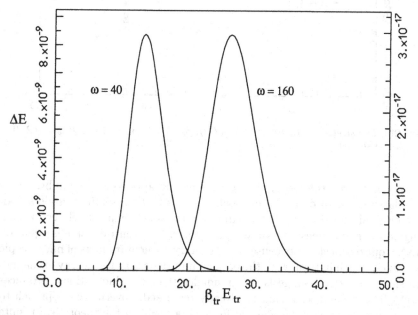

Fig. 19. *The curve (c) of the previous figure 3, with vertical linear scale. Same temperatures. Left (and left scale): $\omega = 40$; right (and right scale): $\omega = 160$.*

By varying ω at fixed temperatures, one expects to obtain the stretched exponential (4.3), the coefficient a depending on β_{tr} but not on β_{vib}. The result is represented in figure 20, where $\langle E_{vib}\rangle$ is reported vs. $\omega^{2/5}$ (logarithmic vertical scale), for fixed $\beta_{tr} = 4$ and three different values of β_{vib}. The straight lines are consistent with the exponential law (4.3), for $s = 1$; the nearly perfect parallelism of the lines indicates that the coefficient a is indeed independent of β_{vib}, as theoretically expected. The proportionality of the r.h.s. of (4.3) to $T_{vib} - T_t$ is also confirmed, though for large temperature differences a deviation from linearity is observed.

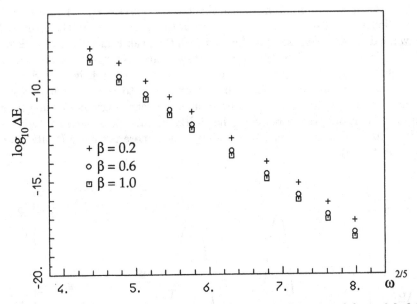

Fig. 20. *The stretched exponential law (4.3), for $s = 1$; $\beta_{tr} = 4$ and $\beta_{vib} = 0.2, 0.6$, 1 (top to bottom).*

In conclusion, the mechanism governing the approach to equilibrium, in our classical gas of diatomic molecules, seems to be essentially understood. The original intuitions by Boltzmann and Jeans get qualitatively confirmed: long equilibrium times, for large ω, do occur. The central point is equation (4.9), a quite robust one because based on very elementary facts of microscopic dynamics, which in turn, with the only assumptions that the energy exchanges are small and the average is much smaller than the fluctuations, produces (4.11). The same mechanism, as already remarked, governs the approach to equilibrium in an electron plasma; for such a problem the theoretical results are also confirmed by real experiments.

5 The Essentials of Nekhoroshev Theorem

A. The Statement

Nekhoroshev theorem, in its standard and original formulation [Nek1,Nek2], concerns Hamiltonian systems of the form (1.1), with suitable non isochronous

h. The aim, as reminded in the Introduction, is to prove that, under suitable hypotheses, exponential estimates of the form (1.3) hold. Hypotheses obviously include, as in the isochronous case discussed in Section 3, analyticity of H and smallness of ε. The arithmetic assumption on ω instead becomes meaningless, and must be replaced by some other assumption on h, of geometric nature.

The simplest assumption on h under which the theorem can be proven, moreover with the best results for the exponents a and b entering (1.3), is quasi–convexity. A function $h : \mathcal{B} \to \mathbb{R}$ is said to be *quasi convex* in $\mathcal{B}$, if for any $I \in \mathcal{B}$, denoting by $h' = \omega$ the n–tuple of the first derivatives and by h'' the matrix of the second derivatives, the equations

$$h'(I) \cdot \xi = 0 \ , \qquad h''(I)\xi \cdot \xi = 0 \tag{5.1}$$

admit only the trivial solution $\xi = 0$. A possible statement of Nekhoroshev theorem (qualitative, i.e. not specifying constants), is the following:

Proposition 2 (Nekhoroshev Theorem). *Consider the Hamiltonian*

$$H(I,\varphi) = h(I) + \varepsilon f(I,\varphi) \ , \qquad (I,\varphi) \in \mathcal{B} \times \mathbb{T}^n \ , \tag{5.2}$$

and assume that

i. H is analytic in a complex neighborhood $\mathcal{D}_\varrho$ of the real domain $\mathcal{D} = \mathcal{B} \times \mathbb{T}^n$;
ii. h is quasi–convex.

Then there exist constants $\mathcal{I}$, $\mathcal{T}$, a, b, ε_* such that, if $\varepsilon < \varepsilon_*$, then any motion with initial data in $\mathcal{D}$ satisfies the exponential estimates

$$\|I(t) - I(0)\| < \mathcal{I}\,(\varepsilon/\varepsilon_*)^b \qquad for \qquad |t| < \mathcal{T}e^{(\varepsilon_*/\varepsilon)^a} \ . \tag{5.3}$$

Possible values of a and b are $a = b = 1/(2n)$, as well as $a = 1/(4n)$, $b = 1/4$.

The best values of the exponents a and b come from [Lo1,LN,Pö]. The necessity of some geometric assumption on h, stronger than pure anisochronicity (i.e. $\det h'' \neq 0$, as in KAM theorem), is evident by the elementary counterexample

$$H(I_1, I_2, \varphi_1, \varphi_2) = \frac{I_1^2}{2} - \frac{I_2^2}{2} + \varepsilon \sin(\varphi_1 + \varphi_2) \ , \tag{5.4}$$

for which one immediately checks that the "fast" motion

$$I_1(t) = I_2(t) = I^\circ + \varepsilon t \ , \qquad \varphi_1(t) = -\varphi_2(t) = \varphi^\circ + I^\circ t + \frac{1}{2}\varepsilon t^2 \ , \tag{5.5}$$

incompatible with (5.3), does exist. An easy way to assure quasi–convexity is to assume that h is a convex function (i.e., h'' is positive); a typical model example with convex h, frequently used in the literature to illustrate Nekhoroshev theorem, is a set of rotators coupled by positional forces,

$$H(I,\varphi) = \sum_{j=1}^{n} \frac{p_j^2}{2} + \varepsilon f(\varphi) \ . \tag{5.6}$$

B. Sketch of the Proof

We shall not produce a complete proof of Nekhoroshev theorem, which is not really difficult, but is somehow long and complicated. We shall limit ourselves to a sketch of the proof, with the purpose to to illustrate the most relevant ideas: which are the main difficulties to be solved in the anisochronous case, and why a geometric assumption, like quasi–convexity, naturally enters the theorem. The reader is suggested to follow the different steps, having in mind the above model example (5.6).

Let us consider Hamiltonian (5.2), and try to make the first perturbative step, to eliminate "as far as possible" the dependence of the perturbation on the angles φ at order ε. Using (for example) the Lie method, we introduce an "auxiliary Hamiltonian" $\varepsilon\chi$, and define the canonical transformation as the time–one map $\Phi^1_{\varepsilon\chi}$, where Φ^t_F denotes, as is common, the flow of the Hamiltonian F. The new Hamiltonian $H^{(1)}(I', \varphi') = H(\Phi^1_{\varepsilon\chi}(I', \varphi'))$ is immediately found to have the form

$$H^{(1)} = h + \varepsilon(\{\chi, h\} + f) + \varepsilon^2 f^{(1)}(I, \varphi, \varepsilon) ,$$

with

$$f^{(1)} = \frac{1}{2}\{\chi, \{\chi, h\}\} + \{\chi, f\} + \mathcal{O}(\varepsilon) . \tag{5.7}$$

So, to accomplish our purpose we should determine the unknown function χ, in such a way that $\{\chi, h\} + f$ is "as independent as possible" of the angles. Getting a complete independence of φ is (for generic f) impossible: since $\{\chi, h\} = \omega \cdot \frac{\partial h}{\partial \varphi}$, so that $\langle\{\chi, h\}\rangle = 0$, the equation for χ is

$$\omega(I) \cdot \frac{\partial \chi}{\partial \varphi}(I, \varphi) = f(I, \varphi) - \langle f\rangle(I) \tag{5.8}$$

(the unessential primes have been dropped). Projecting on Fourier components, it then follows, for each $\nu \in \mathbb{Z}^n \setminus \{0\}$ and any $I \in \mathcal{B}$,

$$i(\nu \cdot \omega(I))\hat{\chi}_\nu(I) = \hat{f}_\nu(I) , \qquad \hat{\chi}_\nu(I) = \frac{\hat{f}_\nu(I)}{i\nu \cdot \omega(I)} . \tag{5.9}$$

But this is (generically) impossible, since for anisochronous h some denominators vanish on a dense subset of $\mathcal{B}$.[16]

---

[16] Exercise: show that, if $\det h'' \neq 0$, then the set

$$\mathcal{B}^{(r)} = \{I \in \mathcal{B} \,|\, \exists \nu^{(1)}, \ldots, \nu^{(r)} \in \mathbb{Z}^n : \nu^{(s)} \cdot \omega(I) = 0, s = 1, \ldots, r\}$$

for $1 \leq r \leq n - 1$ is dense in $\mathcal{B}$. The difficulty we are facing is the one raised by Poincaré in his well known theorem on the generic non existence of integrals of motion in nearly integrable anisochronous Hamiltonian systems [Po1].

The way out of this difficulty proceeds as follows:

(a) *The "ultraviolet cut–off"*.   It is not necessary to take care of all Fourier components. Having in mind that, eventually, the remainder must be exponentially small, it is possible to introduce an ε–dependent cut-off N, and separate from f an "ultraviolet" part, i.e. to introduce the decomposition

$$f = f^{\leq N} + f^{>N} , \qquad f^{>N} = \sum_{\nu \in \mathbb{Z}^n : |\nu| > N} \hat{f}_\nu(I) e^{i\nu \cdot \varphi} .$$

Thanks to the analyticity of f, the size of the single Fourier components f_ν decreases exponentially with $|\nu|$, and correspondingly the ultraviolet part $f^{>N}$ decreases exponentially with the cut-off N: $\|f^{>N}\| < C e^{-cN}, C, c > 0$.[17] Quite clearly, it is enough to take $N \sim \varepsilon^{-a}$, in order for $f^{>N}$ to be exponentially small, and to give a small contribution to the drift of the actions, as required by (5.3). Having introduced the cut-off, we are left with a finite number of resonances $\nu \cdot \omega(I)$ to take care.

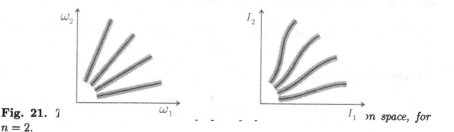

Fig. 21. ⟨ ... ⟩n space, for
$n = 2$.

(b) *The "geometry of resonances"*.   Let Λ be any r–dimensional sublattice of $\mathbb{Z}^n$, $r = 1, \dots, n$, which admits a basis $\nu^{(1)}, \dots, \nu^{(r)}$ with $|\nu^{(s)}| < N$ for any s. The *resonant manifold* M_Λ is defined, as is natural, by

$$M_\Lambda = \{ I \in \mathcal{B} : \nu \cdot \omega(I) = 0 \; \forall \nu \in \Lambda \} ;$$

r is called the *multiplicity* of the resonance, and is the codimension[18] of M_Λ. For any ε, one must take care of a finite set of resonant manifolds, which form a web in $\mathcal{B}$ (a finite one, though finer and finer as ε decreases). The solution (5.9) is appropriate far from resonances, but it has no meaning on the different M_Λ,

---

[17] Exercise: prove this inequality, also computing C, c, assuming that f is analytic in a strip $|\operatorname{Im} \varphi_j| \leq \varrho_\varphi$. As norm of f, use either the sup–norm or the "Fourier norm", i.e. the sum of the sup–norms of the Fourier components.

[18] From quasi–convexity it follows that the determinant of h'' restricted to the plane orthogonal to ω is different from zero; in turn, this implies that the r equations defining M_Λ are independent.

where some denominators exactly vanish, nor it is sensible in neighborhoods of such manifolds of size, at least, $\mathcal{O}(\sqrt{\varepsilon})$: indeed, the remainder $f^{(1)}$ in (5.7), due to the derivative with respect to the actions which is present in the Poisson bracket, contains the squares of the small denominators $\nu \cdot \omega(I)$, and if any of them is $\mathcal{O}(\sqrt{\varepsilon})$, then the new perturbation $\varepsilon^2 f^{(1)}$ is just of order ε, and nothing is gained.[19] Formally, for each lattice Λ one defines[20] a *resonant region* R_Λ, as the subset of $\mathcal{B}$ such that

$$|\omega(I) \cdot \nu^{(s)}| < \delta_r , \quad s = 1, \ldots, r \tag{5.10}$$

for at least one basis $\nu^{(1)}, \ldots, \nu^{(r)}$ of Λ. The constants δ_r must be such that

$$\delta_1 < \delta_2 < \ldots < \delta_n , \tag{5.11}$$

and a convenient choice turns out to be

$$\delta_r \sim \varepsilon^{b_r} , \quad \frac{1}{2} > b_1 > \ldots > b_r > 0 . \tag{5.12}$$

Finally, one defines the *resonant zones* Z_Λ by posing $Z_\Lambda = R_\Lambda$ for $\Lambda = \mathbb{Z}^n$, and then recursively, for $\dim \Lambda = r = n-1, \ldots, 1$,

$$Z_\Lambda = R_\Lambda \setminus \bigcup_{\Lambda' : \dim \Lambda' = r+1} R_{\Lambda'} .$$

The nonresonant domain

$$Z_0 = \mathcal{B} \setminus \bigcup_{\Lambda' : \dim \Lambda' = 1} R_{\Lambda'}$$

is also defined. Figure 21 represents the resonant manifolds (the lines) and the resonant zones (the corridors around them), in the simple case $n = 2$; zones and domains coincide, in this elementary example, if a neighborhood of the origin is excluded. A symbolic picture of the higher dimensional case is provided by figure 22, which shows the intersection of two resonant manifolds M_Λ and $M_{\Lambda'}$ in $M_{\Lambda \oplus \Lambda'}$, and the resonant zones Z_Λ, $Z_{\Lambda'}$ and $Z_{\Lambda \oplus \Lambda'}$ around them; according to (5.11), (5.12), $Z_{\Lambda \oplus \Lambda'}$ is larger than Z_Λ and $Z_{\Lambda'}$. (The figure is realistic for $n = 3$, if it is regarded as a section of the action space $\mathcal{B}$, for example a section by a surface of constant h where the motion is approximately confined.) The four dashed corners in the figure belong both to Z_0 and to $Z_{\Lambda \oplus \Lambda'}$ (only zones of nearby multiplicity are by definition disjoint).

---

[19] Even more: the canonical transformation is not small with ε, and might be not even defined. Exercise: compute exactly $f^{(1)}$ for the Hamiltonian (5.6), for $f(\varphi)$ with a finite Fourier development.

[20] We are following here the original definitions by Nekhoroshev, though the names are not identical. Pöscel introduced some improvements in the geometrical construction, which however are not necessary for our purposes.

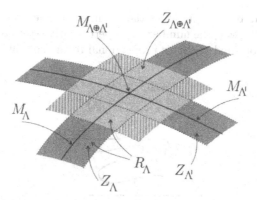

Fig. 22. *Resonant manifolds and resonant zones, for $n > 2$.*

In the nonresonant zone, the small divisors are controlled by δ_1, and the φ–dependence of the perturbation can be "killed" at first order. Correspondingly, the new Hamiltonian can be given the first–order normal form[21]

$$H^{(1)}(I, \varphi) = h(I) + \varepsilon g(I) + \varepsilon^2 f^{(1)}(I, \varphi) .$$

Inside a resonant zone Z_Λ, instead, the harmonics $\nu \in \Lambda$ cannot be killed, and the best normal form one can produce is the *resonant normal form adapted to Λ*,

$$H_\Lambda^{(1)}(I, \varphi) = h(I) + \varepsilon g_\Lambda(I, \varphi) + \varepsilon^2 f^{(1)}(I, \varphi) ,$$

g_Λ having Fourier components only in Λ:

$$g(I, \varphi) = \sum_{\nu \in \Lambda} \hat{g}_\nu(I) e^{i\nu \cdot \varphi} \tag{5.13}$$

($\hat{g}_\nu = \hat{f}_\nu$, at this first step). Notice that this includes, as special case, the non resonant zone, for which it is $\Lambda = \{0\}$.

(c) *The "plane of fast drift".*   Now, let us imagine that we are very skilled, namely are able to proceed perturbatively far beyond the first step, and produce in each Z_Λ a normal form with an exponentially small remainder:

$$H_\Lambda(I, \varphi) = h(I) + \varepsilon g_\Lambda(I, \varphi) + \mathcal{O}(e^{-1/\varepsilon^a}) , \tag{5.14}$$

with g_Λ as in (5.13). This is not at all trivial, but it does not contain additional difficulties with respect to the isochronous case. We shall assume that such

---

[21] The smallness of $\delta_r(\varepsilon)$, and other technical facts (reduction of domains by quantities small with ε, to estimate derivatives and Poisson brackets), imply that the new perturbation is not of order ε^2 but larger. These are technical facts, that unfortunately we cannot discuss here. The only important point is the perturbation reduces.

analytic work can be done, to focus the attention on the geometric aspects of the proof.[22] By the way, the number N_0 of perturbative steps to be performed, which gives the optimal result, is proportional to the cut–off N.

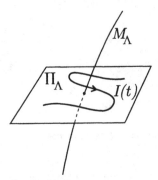

Fig. 23. *The movement of the actions is flattened on the plane of fast drift Π_Λ.*

The normal form is used for motions with initial datum in Z_Λ. One immediately recognizes that, as far as (5.14) can be used, that is as far as, during the motions, new rresonances are not acquired, the motion of the actions is almost flattened on the hyperplane $\Pi_\Lambda(I^o) \in \mathcal{B}$ generated by Λ, passing through I^o; see figure 23. Indeed, the Hamilton equations for the actions are

$$\dot{I} = \varepsilon \sum_{\nu \in \Lambda} \mathcal{I}_\nu(I, \varphi)\,\nu + \mathcal{O}(e^{-1/\varepsilon^a}) \,, \qquad \mathcal{I}_\nu = -ig_\nu(I)e^{i\nu \cdot \varphi} \,,$$

so that $\dot{I}$ is almost parallel to Λ, and dist $(I(t), \Pi_\Lambda(I^o))$ stays small for an exponentially large time.

(d) *Using quasi–convexity.*   Quasi–convexity implies two basic facts:

i.   The plane of fast drift Π_Λ and the resonant manifold M_Λ intersect transversally. Indeed, a loss of transversality would require that some vector $\xi = \sum_j c_j \nu^{(j)} \in \Pi_\Lambda$ is tangent to M_Λ, and so orthogonal to all vectors $h''\nu^{(s)}$, $s = 1, \ldots r$, which are orthogonal to M_Λ. In particular, it should be $h''\xi \cdot \xi = 0$, and simultaneously $\omega \cdot \xi = 0$, but this is in conflict with quasi–convexity. Due to the complementary dimensions, the intersection is a point I^*.

---

[22] In the 1977 reference paper by Nekhoroshev [Nek2], a paper long more than 50 pages, the "analytic lemmma" concerning the possibility of producing the normal forms (5.14), is just stated and not proved, while all of the attention is devoted to the geometric part of the proof.

ii. The unperturbed Hamiltonian h, restricted to Π_Λ, has an extremum in I^*. Indeed, for ξ parallel to Λ, it is

$$h(I^* + \xi) = h(I^*) + \omega(I^*) \cdot \xi + \frac{1}{2}h''(I^*)\xi \cdot \xi + \mathcal{O}(\|\xi\|^3) \; ;$$

the linear term vanishes, and the quadratic one has definite sign.

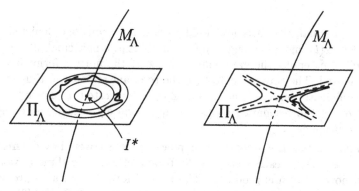

Fig. 24. *Illustrating the role of quasi-convexity of h for the confinement of actions in Π_Λ: (a) in the quasi-convex case, actions are trapped inside an elliptic structure; (b) in the hyperbolic case, the asymptots provide possible escape directions.*

This situation is represented in figure 24, left: around I^*, the surfaces of constant h form an elliptic structure on Π_Λ. But since the energy $H = h + \mathcal{O}(\varepsilon)$ is conserved, h oscillates, during the motion, at most of quantities of order ε. Correspondingly $I(t)$ (for $I(0) \in Z_\Lambda$, and as long as the normal form (5.8) can be used) must approximately follow the level lines of h; the quantity $\|I(t) - I^*\|$ then oscillates at most of $\sqrt{\varepsilon}$, and $\|I(t) - I^\circ\|$ is bounded, essentially, by the diameter of $\Pi_\Lambda \cap Z_\Lambda$, which according to (5.12) is small with ε. Let us remark that this elementary mechanism of confinement, based on energy conservation, fails if, in place of the elliptic structure, there is an hyperbolic structure in Π_Λ around I^*, as in figure 24, right: quite clearly, the asymptots constitute possible direction of escape compatible with energy conservation. Escape along the asymptots is precisely what happens in the counterexample (5.4), see (5.5).

(e) *Non overlapping of resonances.* As a final step, we must solve a consistency problem. Indeed, in step (c) we used in an essential way the resonant normal form. This however is possible only if, during the motion (up time $\sim e^{1/\varepsilon^a}$) new resonances, *within the same δ_r used to construct the normal form*, are not introduced: that is, if no other resonant region *of the same multiplicity* is entered. Here it gets clear why resonant regions of larger multiplicity are required to have larger diameter. Indeed, should all constants

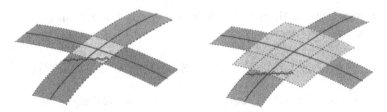

Fig. 25. *Illustrating the question of non–overlapping of resonances.*

δ_r be taken equal, the situation could be the dangerous one depicted in figure 25, left: $I(t)$, moving along $\Pi_\Lambda(I^o)$, enters $R_{\Lambda'}$; a new small denominator $|\omega(I) \cdot \nu'| < \delta_r$ enters the game, and the use of the normal form (5.8) is no longer allowed. The way out is to take the resonant region and thus the zone $Z_{\Lambda \oplus \Lambda'}$ sufficiently larger than Z_Λ and $Z_{\Lambda'}$: as suggested by figure 25, right, if the sizes of the resonant regions are appropriately scaled, the dangerous situation disappears.

(f) *Comments.* Let us summarize: the phase space is covered by different resonant zones, and in each zone, thanks to analytic and arithmetic work, an adapted normal form is produced. The normal form provides (approximate) confinement of the actions onto the plane of constant drift $\Pi_\Lambda(I^o)$. Quasi–convexity, via the simple mechanism of energy conservation, provides confinement inside $\Pi_\Lambda(I^o)$. A well designed geometry of resonances keeps different resonant zones (of the same multiplicity) sufficiently well separated, so as to assure that the above procedure is consistent.

It is worthwhile to remark that the use of energy conservation is not the only way to prove confinement of the actions inside the plane of constant drift. An alternative idea, as good as energy conservation in the quasi–convex case, but more general, is the so called *trapping* mechanism, introduced by Nekhoroshev in his 1977 paper. The idea, in principle, is simple: if the geometry of resonances is designed as above, then the (possible) exit from a resonant zone is such that resonances are lost, but never gained (see again figure 25, right). In other words: the multiplicity of the resonance, in the course of time, can only decrease. In the worst case, $I(t)$ looses one after the other all resonances, and arrives in the nonresonant zone, where it stops.[23] We shall come back on this mechanism in Section 7, when we shall deal with a system for which the quasi–convexity assumption is not satisfied.

General references on Nekhoroshev theorem include: (i) The original papers by Nekhoroshev [Nek1,Nek2]; the exponents, in the convex case, are $a, b \sim 1/n^2$. (ii) Paper [BGG3], dedicated to the convex case (similar exponents). (iii) papers [Ga1,BGa], where the idea of energy conservation was

---

[23] This one–way behavior might seem in conflict with the reversibility of Hamiltonian dynamics. A little reflection shows it is not.

first fully exploited; possible exponents include $a = 1/8$, $b \sim 1/n^2$. (iv) papers [Lo1,LN], very interesting both for the result, namely $a = b = 1/(2n)$ (a much longer time scale), and for a revolutionary technique.[24] (v) paper [Pöl], where the geometry of resonances was improved; the result is $a = b = 1/(2n)$, as well as $a = 1/2$, $b = 1/(4n)$. Other papers concern applications and extensions to special systems, including systems with infinitely many degrees of freedom.

C. Pathologies in Physical Systems

According to the purpose outlined in the Introduction, we shall now focus the attention to physical applications of Nekhoroshev theorem. Applications, however, are far from trivial, since most interesting systems to which one would like to apply the theorem, do not fit the assumptions. Two pathologies typically occur:

i.   The integrable system is *properly degenerate,* namely the number m of constants of motion exceeds the number n of degrees of freedom. Well known examples are the Euler–Poinsot rigid body (the rigid body with a fixed point, in absence of external torques), for which $n = 3$ and $m = 4$, and the Kepler system, for which $n = 3$ and $m = 5$. The result of degeneracy is that the number of actions effectively entering the unperturbed Hamiltonian h is $n_0 = 2n - m < n$, and quasi–convexity (as well as *steepness,* see later) is violated. Using the notation I, φ for the actions effectively present in the unperturbed Hamiltonian and their conjugated angles, and p, q for the remaining variables, the perturbed Hamiltonian has the form

$$H(I, \varphi, p, q) = h(I) + \varepsilon f(I, \varphi, p, q) \ .$$

For such a system, using the standard techniques of perturbation theory, it is not difficult to produce resonant or nonresonant normal forms, up to an exponentially small φ–dependent remainder, say

$$H_\Lambda(I, \varphi, p, q) = h(I) + \varepsilon g_\Lambda(I, \varphi, p, q) + \mathcal{O}(e^{-1/\varepsilon^a})$$
$$g_\Lambda(I, \varphi, p, q) = \sum_{\nu \in \Lambda} \hat{g}_\nu(I, p, q)e^{i\nu \cdot \varphi} \ ,$$

so as to keep control of $I_1, \ldots, I_{n_0}$ (in case of convex h). But this is a poor result, for two reasons: first of all, the p, q variables are typically very interesting (for the rigid body, they determine the spatial orientation of the angular momentum; for the Kepler problem, they include the eccentricity and inclination of the Keplerian ellipsis). Moreover, these variables could approach a singularity in a short time: the normal form gets then useless, and long time stability of the actions cannot be deduced.

---

[24] The geometric part, in particular, is highly semplified, since only resonances of multiplicity $n - 1$ are considered. A quick easier proof, unfortunately strictly limited to the convex case.

ii. The action–angle coordinates get singular somewhere in the phase space, often in correspondence to the most interesting motions. Examples include the proper rotations of the rigid body around a symmetry axis, the circular orbits of the Kepler problem, and a set of harmonic oscillators whenever any of them is at rest. From a geometric point of view, singular motions are motions on singular lower dimensional leaves of the foliation into invariant tori: an n–dimensional torus (n_0–dimensional, for degenerate systems) shrinks to a lower dimensional one, and correspondingly an angle gets undefined (the angle giving the orientation of the pericenter, for the Keplerian ellipses; the angle giving the precession of the symmetry axis of the body around the direction of the angular momentum, for the rigid body; the phase of the oscillator at rest, in the last example). The question to be solved (more technical, but not completely technical) is how to proceed perturbatively without using the action–angle variables.

Both difficulties are present in the examples that we are going to study in the remaining part of these lectures.

6 The Perturbed Euler–Poinsot Rigid Body

The Euler–Poinsot rigid body is a rigid body with a fixed point, in absence of external torques. We shall restrict ourselves to the symmetric case, i.e. when two inertia moments are equal, though most results could be adapted to the triaxial case. Before entering the perturbative study, we must shortly review from a geometric point of view the behaviour of the unperturbed system.

A. The Unperturbed System

Let (e_x, e_y, e_z) be a basis fixed in the space, and (e_1, e_2, e_3) be a proper basis of the body, with inertia moments $A_1 = A_2 \neq A_3$. The phase space of the system is the cotangent boundle $\mathcal{M} = T^*SO(3)$, which however is trivial and can be identified with $SO(3) \times \mathbb{R}^3$. A point of $\mathcal{M}$ is identified by a pair (R, M), where $R \in SO(3)$ is the matrix such that $Re_x = e_1$ and so on, while $M = (M_x, M_y, M_z) \in \mathbb{R}^3$ is the angular momentum in the space.[25] Alternatively, one can use $m = (m_1, m_2, m_3) = R^{-1}M$ (the so-called body representation of the angular momentum) in place of M; the pair (R, m) also provides a good parametrization of $T^*_R SO(3)$.

The Euler–Poinsot rigid body has four independent integrals of motion. A possible choice is given by

---

[25] The triviality of $T^*SO(3)$ precisely expresses the fact that the angular momentum M exists, as vector in $\mathbb{R}^3$, regardless of the configuration R of the body. In a similar way, the triviality of the tangent bundle $TSO(3)$ expresses geometrically the well known existence of the angular velocity as a vector of $\mathbb{R}^3$.

$$K , \quad \|M\| , \quad M_z , \quad M_{z'} ,$$

where K is the kinetic energy

$$K = \frac{m_1^2}{2A_1} + \frac{m_2^2}{2A_2} + \frac{m_3^2}{2A_3} ,$$

and z' is any direction non parallel to z. In the symmetric case it is

$$K = \frac{1}{2A_1}(M^2 + \eta \, m_3^2) , \qquad \eta = \frac{A_1}{A_3} - 1 ,$$

so that m_3 is also an integral of motion, which can be used with some advantage in place of K.

Both $(\|M\|, m_3, M_z)$ and $(\|M\|, m_3, M_{z'})$ are triples of independent integrals of motion in involution, so the Liouville–Arnold theorem applies in two independent ways, giving rise to two independent foliations of the phase space in tori $\mathbb{T}^3$. Such foliations, however, are not intrinsic, as is obvious since reference is made to arbitrary chosen z axes, and so they are not useful to understand the structure of the phase space. In particular, each foliation gets singular when e_3 gets parallel to the z axis at hand, as is obvious since m_3 and M_z loose independence; but the singularity is spurious: due to the arbitrariness of the z axis, there cannot be anything special in the phase space when $e_3 = \pm e_z$.

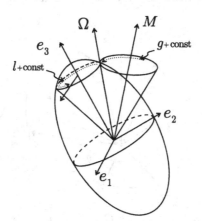

Fig. 26. *Illustrating the movement of the Euler–Poinsot rigid body. Poinsot cones roll without sliding, as in gear.*

To understand the real structure of the phase space of the Euler–Poinsot rigid body, it is convenient to recall the classical Poinsot description (though the description is more general, we refer here to the symmetric rigid body; see, for details, any standard book on theoretical mechanics). This is essentially as follows: (i) The angular momentum M, due to the absence of torques, stays constant. (ii) Denoting by $\Omega \in \mathbb{R}^3$ the angular velocity of the body (Ω is related to the angular momentum by $\Omega_i = m_i/A_i$), the three vectors e_3, M and Ω are coplanar, and the angles between them stay constant. (iii) During the motion, the vector Ω traces two circular cones, in the body around e_3 and in the space around M, and the cones roll without sliding, as in a gear, with constant velocity; see figure 26.

A good choice of action–angle coordinates, adapted to describe in a simple way the Euler–Poinsot motion, is the following (see figure 27). Let $G = \|M\|$; assume that the spatial frame is such that $n_1 := M \times e_z \neq 0$, and denote $J = M_z$, $j =$ angle from e_x to n_1 in the $e_x e_y$ plane. G, J, j clearly determine M. To specify the configuration of the body, let $L = m_3$ (L determines the angle between e_3 and the already fixed vector M); assume that $n_2 := M \times e_3 \neq 0$ (warning: proper rotations around e_3 are here excluded), and let $g =$ angle from n_1 to n_2 in the plane orthogonal to M; L and g determine e_3. The configuration is then completely determined by a last coordinate, which establishes the orientation of the body around e_3, and a convenient choice turns out to be the angle l from n_2 to e_1 in the plane $e_1 e_2$.

From the very construction, it turns out that G, L, J, g, l, j are coordinates in the domain $\mathcal{M}'$, depending on the spatial frame, such that $M \times e_z \neq 0$, $M \times e_3 \neq 0$. It can be proven that

Proposition 3 (Andoyer–Deprit): G, L, J, g, l, j are canonical coordinates on $\mathcal{M}'$, with canonical 2-form $dG \wedge dg + dL \wedge dl + dJ \wedge dj$.

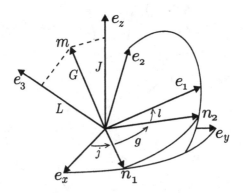

Fig. 27. *The action-angle coordinates G, L, J, g, l, j for the symmetric rigid body.*

The Hamiltonian, that is the kinetic energy, in these coordinates depends only on G and L, and is easily found to be

$$h(G, L) = \frac{1}{2A_1}(G^2 + \eta L^2) ; \tag{6.1}$$

correspondingly, G, L, J, j stay constant, while g, l advance uniformly with angular velocity

$$\omega(G, L) = \frac{1}{A_1}(G, \eta L) \ .$$

This is in complete agreement with the Poinsot description; note that g and l are angles on the Poinsot cones (compare with figure 26).

The singularity of the construction for $M \times e_z = 0$, that is for $J = \pm G$, is an inessential chart singularity. As is evident, two charts of action angle coordinates

$$G, \quad L, \quad J^{(i)}, \quad g^{(i)}, \quad l, \quad j^{(i)}, \qquad i = 1, 2 \ ,$$

relative to two different spatial frames with different z axis, are sufficient to cover

$$\mathcal{M}_0 := \{(R, M) \in \mathcal{M} : M \times e_3 \neq 0\} \ .$$

It is worthwhile to observe that G, L, l are intrinsic (they do not depend on the frame), and for this reason the chart index has been omitted. The other coordinates are instead chart dependent, and their transition functions are of the special form (look at the figure)

$$g^{(2)} = g^{(1)} + g_{12}\left(\frac{J^{(1)}}{G}, j^{(1)}\right), \qquad J^{(2)} = J_{12}\left(\frac{J^{(1)}}{G}, j^{(1)}\right), \qquad j^{(2)} = j_{12}\left(\frac{J^{(1)}}{G}, j^{(1)}\right) .$$
$$(6.2)$$

As is remarkable, $g^{(1)}$ and $g^{(2)}$ differ only by the origin. This is relevant in the perturbative developments for two reasons: first, the set obtained by fixing $G, L, J^{(i)}, j^{(i)}$, namely the four integrals of motion, is a torus $\mathbb{T}^2$ independent of the chart; moreover, given any function $F : \mathcal{M}_0 \to \mathbb{R}$, its average on $g^{(i)}$ is well defined, independently of the chart. *Averaging on the "fast angles" g and l, which is the basic tool of perturbation theory, is a chart independent geometric operation.*

The geometric structure of the phase space now clearly emerges. First of all we can identify an action space $\mathcal{A}$, namely the sector

$$\mathcal{A} = \{(G, L) \in \mathbb{R}^2 : G \geq 0, |L| \leq G\} \ ,$$

whose border $L = \pm G$ corresponds to the border of $\mathcal{M}_0$ (the proper rotations around e_3). To each point of $\mathcal{A}$ such that $G > 0$, a sphere S^2 is attached, where $\mu := M/\|M\|$ runs; $J^{(i)}/G, j^{(i)}$ are local coordinates on the sphere, determining respectively the latitude and the longitude of μ (singularities on the polar axis are clearly unavoidable). Finally, for each (G, L) in the interior $\mathcal{A}_0$ of $\mathcal{A}$ and each $\mu \in S^2$, we have a two dimensional torus $\mathbb{T}^2$, and $g^{(i)}, l$ are coordinates on it.

For (L, G) on the border of $\mathcal{A}$, if $G > 0$, μ still runs on S^2, but one of the Poinsot cones degenerates in a line, so the two dimensional torus is replaced by a circle. Finally for $G = L = 0$ we have a manifold $SO(3)$, and each point of it is an equilibrium.

Formally, see [BF2] for details, one can introduce in $\mathcal{M}_0$ a double fibration: a first fibration has four dimensional basis $\mathcal{B}_0 = \mathcal{A}_0 \times S^2$, and two dimensional fiber $\mathbb{T}^2$; a second fibration has instead two dimensional basis $\mathcal{A}_0$, and four dimensional fiber, namely the level set on which the kinetic energy and the modulus of the angular momentum are constant; the fibre has in turn the structure of a fiber bundle, with basis S^2 and fibre $\mathbb{T}^2$ (this is not the product $S^2 \times \mathbb{T}^2$ only because the origin of $g^{(i)}$ depends on the point on S^2 in a chart dependent way). A pictorial, but rather realistic, representation of $\mathcal{M}_0$ is produced in figure 28 (after [F2,BF2]). The picture continues on the border $L = \pm G \neq 0$, with the only difference that the petals of the daisy[26] are thiner, namely $\mathbb{T}^1$ in place of $\mathbb{T}^2$.

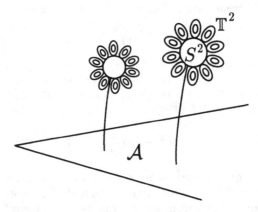

Fig. 28. *A pictoric illustration of the double fibration of $T^*SO(3)$: the action space $\mathcal{A}$; in each point of $\mathcal{A}$ a spere S^2, where $\mu = m/\|m\|$ stays; in each point of the spere a torus $\mathbb{T}^2$.*

With reference to the figure, the unperturbed motion, with Hamiltonian (6.1), is described as follows: the stem of the daisy stays fixed on the ground ($\|M\|, m_3$ stay constant); the motion takes place on a single petal (μ stays constant), and is linear quasi periodic with frequency ω ($g^{(i)}, l$ advance uniformly).

Remark: The double fibration is typical of all properly degenerate systems, see [F3]. The description provided by the Liouville–Arnold theorem, with a single fibration, for such systems is instead rough and misleading (though correct, since the assumptions of the theorem are satisfied). For the rigid body, applying the Liouville–Arnold theorem, with reference to ($\|M\|, m_3, M_z$) as to the set of the independent integrals of motion in involution, means excluding from consideration the poles of the sphere (M_z and m_3 there loose independence). The sphere is thus replaced by a cylinder, say $(-G, G) \times \mathbb{T}^1$, and the interval

---

[26] Un uncommon spherically symmetric daisy.

$(-G, G)$ is attached to $\mathcal{A}$ to form a three dimensional basis, while $\mathbb{T}^1$ is attached to $\mathbb{T}^2$ to form $\mathbb{T}^3$. This is a legitime but not sensible operation, which introduces spurious singularities in the foliation in correspondence of the arbitrarily chosen poles of the sphere. (By the way: dynamically, it is impossible to stay consistently out of the poles, since nothing special is there.)

As a final comment on the unperturbed problem, it is worthwhile to notice that h, as defined in (6.1), is always a quasi–convex function in $\mathcal{A}$, though for negative η it might appear similar to the counterexample (5.5). Indeed, an elementary computation shows that quasi–convexity of h is lost for (G, L) : $L = \pm G/\sqrt{-\eta}$, but since $\eta > -\frac{1}{2}$, these points do not belong to $\mathcal{A}$.

B. Results for Non Gyroscopic Motions

Now we enter the perturbed problem, namely the rigid body in a small positional potential. Positional means that the potential depends only on the configuration $R \in SO(3)$ of the body; correspondingly, the representative of the potential in each coordinate system is a homogeneous function of degree zero of the actions. From now on, it will be important to distinguish between functions defined intrinsically on the manifold, and their representatives in local coordinates. Local representatives will have an upper index (i), just as local coordinates; intrinsic functions will not. However, functions like the kinetic energy h, which depend only on global coordinates, and therefore have the same form in the different charts, with innocent abuse of the convention will have no index, and will be confused with the corresponding function $\mathcal{M}_0 \to \mathbb{R}$. So, we have an intrinsic Hamilton function $H = h + \varepsilon f : \mathcal{M}_0 \to \mathbb{R}$, which is represented locally by

$$H^{(i)}(G, L, J^{(i)}, g^{(i)}, l, j^{(i)}) = h(G, L) + \varepsilon f^{(i)}(G, L, J^{(i)}, g^{(i)}, l, j^{(i)}), \qquad i = 1, 2.$$
$$(6.3)$$

It is worthwhile to remark that (due to the homogeneity property of f) the system has an elementary scaling property: indeed the change of variables

$$G = \alpha \tilde{G}, \qquad L = \alpha \tilde{L}, \qquad J^{(i)} = \alpha \tilde{J}^{(i)}$$

(the angles being unchanged), canonically conjugates $H^{(i)}$ to

$$\tilde{H}^{(i)}(\tilde{G}, \tilde{L}, \tilde{J}^{(i)}, g^{(i)}, l, j^{(i)}) = h(\tilde{G}, \tilde{L}) + \alpha^{-2} \varepsilon f^{(i)}(\tilde{G}, \tilde{L}, \tilde{J}^{(i)}, g^{(i)}, l, j^{(i)}) ;$$

this shows that it is equivalent to consider a rigid body in a small potential, that is a potential proportional to a small parameter ε, and a fast rigid body with initial actions G^o, L^o, J^o multiplied by $1/\sqrt{\varepsilon}$, in an ε–independent potential. In these lectures (at variance with [BF2,BFG1], and for homogeneity with the other applications) we shall deal with initial actions of order one, and potential proportional to ε.

In each chart it is not difficult to work perturbatively, along the lines outlined in Section 5, to eliminate "as far as possible" the dependence of the

Hamiltonian on the angles g and l, that is producing suitable (resonant or nonresonant) normal forms.

The procedure, exactly as in the standard Nekhoroshev theorem, is the following:

i. To stay far from the singularity at $L = \pm G$, one restricts the attention to

$$\mathcal{A}_\delta = \{(G, L) \in \mathcal{A} : |G - L| > \delta\sqrt{\varepsilon}\} \,,$$

and correspondingly to $\mathcal{M}_\delta = \{(R, M) \in T^*SO(3) : (G, L) \in \mathcal{A}_\delta\}$ (at the end, it will be necessary to show, for consistency, that the point $(G(t), L(t))$ does not escape $\mathcal{A}_\delta$, if initially $(G^o, L^o) \in \mathcal{A}_{\delta_0}$ for some $\delta_0 > \delta$).

ii. One introduces a cut–off N, and it turns out that a good choice is $N = c\varepsilon^{-1/4}$, with suitable c. *The same N is chosen for both charts.*

iii. For all $\nu \in \mathbb{Z}^2$, $0 < |\nu| \le N$, one introduces resonant manifolds lines $M_\nu \in \mathcal{A}_\delta$, defined by $\nu \cdot \omega(G, L) = 0$, and resonant zones Z_ν; a convenient choice for the zones is

$$Z_\nu = \{(G, L) \in \mathcal{A}_\delta : |\nu \cdot \omega(G, L)| < G/(2N|\nu|)\} \,.$$

If a neighborhood of the origin $G = 0$ is excluded, and is ε is sufficiently small, different resonant zones are easily seen to be disjoint (zones coincide here with regions). So, the "geography of resonances" in this problem is very simple: points of $\mathcal{A}_\delta$ are either nonresonant or resonant only once, and no overlapping occurs. We shall denote by $\mathcal{Z}_\nu$ (including $\nu = 0$) the subset of $\mathcal{M}_\delta : (G, L) \in Z_\nu$. As is relevant, *The resonant lines and zones are the same in both charts*, and so $\mathcal{Z}_\nu$ is well defined as a subset of $\mathcal{M}_\delta$.

iv. Out of the resonant zones, one performs a number $N_0 \sim \varepsilon^{-1/4}$ perturbative steps, thus producing a nonresonant normal form

$$H_0^{(i)} = h(G, L) + \varepsilon u_0^{(i)}(G, L, J^{(i)}, j^{(i)}) + \mathcal{O}(e^{-1/\varepsilon^{1/4}}) \,, \qquad (6.4)$$

with

$$u_0^{(i)} = \langle f^{(i)} \rangle + \mathcal{O}(\varepsilon) \,;$$

$\langle . \rangle$ denotes averaging on $g^{(i)}$ and l. Inside $\mathcal{Z}_\nu$ one instead produces the resonant normal form

$$H_\nu^{(i)} = h(G, L) + \varepsilon u_\nu^{(i)}(G, L, J^{(i)}, j^{(i)}, \nu_1 g^{(i)} + \nu_2 l) + \mathcal{O}(e^{-1/\varepsilon^{1/4}}) \quad (6.5)$$

(pay attention on the dependence of $u_\nu^{(i)}$ on the combination $\nu \cdot \varphi$, $\varphi = (g, l)$). *The same N_0 is chosen for both charts.* As a result, the construction is such that *the normal forms $H_\nu^{(i)}$, $i = 1, 2$, are the local representatives of a function H_ν defined intrinsically in $\mathcal{Z}_\nu$.* It is not obvious that such a chart independent construction is possible. The essential point is that, at each perturbative step, the terms accumulating into $u^{(i)}$ are defined by means of averaging operations on $g^{(i)}$ and l; as already remarked, though

$g^{(i)}$ does depend on the chart, averaging on $g^{(i)}$ is a chart independent operation. More precisely, it turns out that the averages $\langle f^{(i)} \rangle (G, L, J^{(i)}, j^{(i)})$, $i = 1, 2$, are the local representatives of a function $\langle f \rangle : \mathcal{M}_0 \to \mathbb{R}$, and similarly $u_0^{(i)}(G, L, J^{(i)}, j^{(i)})$, $u_\nu^{(i)}(G, L, J^{(i)}, j^{(i)}, \nu_1 g^{(i)} + \nu_2 l)$ are local representatives of functions $u_0, u_\nu : \mathcal{M}_0 \to \mathbb{R}$.

It is very important to have a chart independent construction. Indeed, due to the proper degeneracy of the system, it is not possible to work consistently inside a single chart, since for a generic potential there is no way to exclude that $(J^{(i)}, j^{(i)})$ approaches a chart singularity (M parallel to e_z), and correspondingly the system escapes the domain in which the normal forms are defined.[27]

The results of such a work is summarized in the following proposition, where for simplicity of notation $G_t, L_t, \ldots$ stay for $G(t), L(t), \ldots$ The statement is not as detailed as it could be; for a more detailed statement, see [BF2].

Proposition 4: *Consider $H = h + \varepsilon f$, with h as in (6.1) and f positional and analytic in $T^*SO(3)$, and let $H^{(i)}$ as in (6.3), $i = 1, 2$, be the representatives of H in the local coordinates $(G, L, J^{(i)}, g^{(i)}, l, j)$. Fix any $\delta > 0$.*
There exist $c, \varepsilon_* > 0$ such that, if $\varepsilon < \varepsilon_*$, then up to

$$|t| \leq (\text{const}) \, e^{(\varepsilon_*/\varepsilon)^{1/4}} \qquad (6.6)$$

i) any initial datum in $\mathcal{M}_{2\delta}$ does not escape $\mathcal{M}_\delta$;
ii) G, L stay almost constant, while $g^{(i)}, l$ preceed almost regularly:

$$|G_t - G_0|, \, |L_t - L_0| \, \leq (\text{const}) \sqrt{\varepsilon}$$
$$|\dot{g}_t^{(i)} - G_0/A_1|, \, |\dot{l}_t - \eta L_0/A_1| \leq (\text{const}) \sqrt{\varepsilon} \; ;$$

iii) if the initial datum is nonresonant up to the cut-off $N = c(\varepsilon_*/\varepsilon)^{1/4}$, then the average $\langle f \rangle$ stays also almost constant,

$$|\langle f \rangle (R_t, M_t) - \langle f \rangle (R_0, M_0)| < (\text{const}) \, \varepsilon^{1/4} \; .$$

The meaning of point ii) is immediate: for small perturbation (equivalently: for given perturbation and large initial angular velocity, with $\|\omega(0)\| \sim 1/\sqrt{\varepsilon}$), and up to a long time, the body performs an approximate Euler–Poinsot precession around the instant direction of the angular momentum M, which in

---

[27] This is evident if, for example, the external potential is a small gravity, in a direction e_0 forming with e_z an angle $\alpha \neq 0$. As is well known, in such a case M precedes regularly around e_0, with speed $\mathcal{O}(\varepsilon)$, so if initially M also forms an angle α with e_0, it will reach a singularity in a time of order ε^{-1}.

turn moves slowly in space, with speed $\mathcal{O}(\varepsilon)$. In particular, the angle between e_3 and M stays almost constant. Point iii), concerning only nonresonant motions, tells in addition that in each chart $\langle f^{(i)} \rangle (G, L, J^{(i)}, j^{(i)})$ stays constant up quantities of order $\varepsilon^{1/2}$. From point i) it then follows that for any G_0, L_0 the function $\hat{f}^{(i)}_{G_0,L_0}$, defined by

$$\hat{f}^{(i)}_{G_0,L_0}(J^{(i)}, j^{(i)}) = \langle f^{(i)} \rangle (G_0, L_0, J^{(i)}, j^{(i)}),$$

also stays almost constant. But $\hat{f}^{(i)}_{G_0,L_0}$, $i = 1, 2$, are representatives of a function $\hat{f}_{G_0,L_0}$ on the sphere $\|M\| = G_0$, and generically the level sets $\hat{f}_{G_0,L_0} = (\text{const})$ are regular lines on such a sphere; they are precisely the level lines of the averaged potential. The consequence is that *the tip of the angular momentum M stays near such lines for long times*. See figure 29, left, where the trace of $\mu = M/\|M\|$ on the unit sphere is represented. Such a result generalizes, in a sense, the familiar case of the rigid body in a small gravitational field: the only difference is that the lines of constant gravitational potential, namely the horizontal circles, are replaced by other equipotential lines, namely the level lines of the potential, averaged on the fast motion on the Poinsot cones (moreover, the motion is regular only up to small deviations). The regularity of the motion of M, in the nonresonant case, appears obvious if one looks at the normal form (6.4), and neglects the small remainder. Indeed, in this approximation the behavior of $J^{(i)}, j^{(i)}$ is determined, in each chart, by the Hamiltonian $u^{(i)}(G, L, J^{(i)}, j^{(i)})$, in which G, L are parameters. The system has only one degree of freedom, and the motion is necessarily regular; moreover, $u^{(i)}$ is close to $\langle f^{(i)} \rangle$.

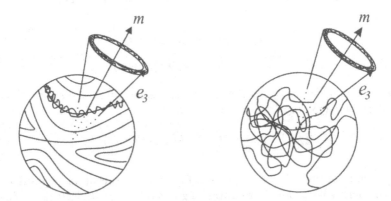

Fig. 29. *Different motions of $\mu = M/\|M\|$ on S^2: almost regular motion close to a level curve of the averaged potential energy (left); chaotic motion filling a two dimensional portion of S^2 (right). In both cases e_3 preceeds almost regularly about M.*

Nothing can be said, instead, concerning the motion of M in space, in case of resonant initial data. In fact, if one looks at the resonant normal form (6.5), it is clear that there is, at least, a chance that the motion of M is chaotic, and invades a two dimensional region of the sphere which does not shrink to a line for $\varepsilon \to 0$, see figure 29, right. This is clearly suggested, in the approximation in which the small remainder in (6.5) is neglected. Indeed in such a case (see [BF2] for details), due to the presence of the "slow angle" $\nu_1 g^{(i)} + \nu_2 l$ inside $u_\nu^{(i)}$, the problem remains essentially a two degrees of freedom one, and two degrees of freedom Hamiltonians are known to admit chaotic motions. A relevant improvement to the above proposition [Gu] tells however that, for a mechanism that is too complicated to be explained here, such chaotic motions are possible only for low order resonances, more precisely up to a cut-off $N' = \mathcal{O}(\log \varepsilon^{-1})$.

A numerical study of a possible normal form Hamiltonian in the resonance $\nu = (0, 1)$, that is $L = 0$, is produced in [BF2]. The Hamiltonian there considered is

$$\tilde{H} = \frac{G^2}{2A_1} + \frac{\eta L^2}{2A_1} + \varepsilon \tilde{f} \,,$$

with $\eta, A_1 = 1$ and

$$\tilde{f} = \frac{J}{G} \sin l - \frac{1}{2}\left(1 - \frac{J^2}{G^2} \sin^2 j\right) \,;$$

G is here a parameter, practically set equal to one.[28] Chaotic motions are shown to exist, also for quite small ε (up to 2.5×10^{-5}), in a neighborhood of the exact resonance, namely for $L \simeq \sqrt{\varepsilon}$; in particular, for such motions M/G invades a relevant portion of the unit sphere.

Observing such chaotic motions in the real three dimensional problem of the rigid body with a fixed point, is a not easy task, both because of the presence of quite different time scales for the different variables and for the accuracy needed, and for some technical reasons[29] which we cannot enter here. Recent numerical calculations, however, suggest that chaotic motions in low resonances, with M/G invading a two dimensional portion of the unit sphere, do exist [BChF2].

C. Results for Gyroscopic Motions

The above proposition does not concern directly gyroscopic motions, that is motions near to proper rotations around the symmetry axis e_3. Point (i) of the proposition implies idirectly that motions with initial datum δ–close to the proper rotation, namely in

---

[28] In [BF2] the language is different, namely ε is set to one and G is large. But as already remarked, there is complete equivalence, with $\varepsilon = G^{-2}$.

[29] Accurate computations require a symplectic integration scheme, which however needs to be implemented on a manifold, and not only inside single charts, see [BChF1].

$$\overline{\mathcal{M}_\delta} = \mathcal{M} \setminus \mathcal{M}_\delta \,,$$

cannot escape $\overline{\mathcal{M}_{2\delta}}$ for the long time scale (6.6). That is: gyroscopic motions remain gyroscopic for long time. But this is a poor result, since it does not tell anything on the motion of the angular momentum M in space, though it states that e_3 in any case closely follows M.

To understand the behavior of M, and prove the equivalent of points (ii) and (iii) for gyroscopic motions, one must learn to work perturbatively around singularities of the action–angle variables, or in geometric words, around singularities of the foliation of the phase space into invariant tori. As already remarked, this is a rather general problem in perturbation theory. We are here confronted with it in connection with the gyroscopic motions of the rigid body, but we shall be confronted with it in the next sections too, dealing with the problem of the stability of the Lagrangian equilibrium points L_4, L_5 in the circular restricted three body problem.

For the rigid body, the perturbative construction goes through the following steps:

i. One introduces new canonical action - angle variables $(\Gamma, \Lambda, \gamma^{(i)}, \lambda)$ "adapted to the singlularity", namely

$$\Gamma = G, \qquad \Lambda = G - L, \qquad \gamma^{(i)} = g^{(i)} + l, \qquad \lambda = -l,$$

$(J^{(i)}, j^{(i)})$ remaining unchanged. The singularity $L = G$ (for symmetry, we can restrict the attention only to it) corresponds now to $\Lambda = 0$, and one easily sees that only the pair (Λ, λ) is there singular, while $(\Gamma, \gamma^{(i)})$ is regular; in particular (look at figure 27), the angle $\gamma^{(i)}$ becomes equal, on the singularity, to the angle of proper rotation, usually called ψ, of the familiar Euler coordinates (in the same limit, $j^{(i)}$ gets equal to the precession φ of e_3 about e_z).

ii. The polar–like coordinates Λ, λ are replaced by Cartesian–like coordinates x, y, via

$$x = \sqrt{2\Lambda} \cos\lambda \,, \qquad y = \sqrt{2\Lambda} \sin\lambda \,,$$

and it turns out [NL] (see also [BFG1]) that $(\Gamma, \gamma^{(i)}, x, y, J^{(i)}, j^{(i)})$, $i = 1, 2$, provide an analytic atlas in the "North emisphere"

$$\mathcal{M}_+ = \{(R, M) \in T^*SO(3) : m_3 > 0\}$$

(the chart singularity moved to the equator). It turns out that

$$x = \frac{\sqrt{2}\, m_2}{\sqrt{\Gamma - \Lambda}} \,, \qquad y = \frac{\sqrt{2}\, m_1}{\sqrt{\Gamma - \Lambda}} \,.$$

The Hamiltonian, in each chart, gets the form

$$K^{(i)}(\Gamma, \gamma^{(i)}, x, y, J^{(i)}, j^{(i)}) = k(\Gamma, \Lambda(x, y)) + \varepsilon \Phi^{(i)}(\Gamma, \gamma^{(i)}, x, y, J^{(i)}, j^{(i)}) \,,$$

with $\Lambda(x, y) = \frac{1}{2}(x^2 + y^2)$ and

$$k(\Gamma, \Lambda) = \frac{1}{2A_3}[\Gamma^2 + \beta\Lambda^2 - 2\beta\Gamma\Lambda] \, ,$$

with

$$\beta = 1 - \frac{A_3}{A_1} \, , \qquad -1 < \beta < 1 \, . \tag{6.7}$$

The domain of $K^{(i)}$ is such that

$$G > 0 \, , \qquad 0 \le \Lambda(x, y) < G \, , \qquad |J^{(i)}| < G \, , \qquad g^{(i)}, j^{(i)} \in \mathbb{T}^2 \, .$$

It should be stressed that Λ here is not a coordinate, but a (nonsingular) function of x and y. A further change of coordinates, widely used after Birkhoff in connection with perturbation theory in Cartesian coordinates, turns out to be useful, namely the passage to the complex canonical coordinates

$$w = \frac{y - ix}{i\sqrt{2}} \, , \qquad z = \frac{y + ix}{\sqrt{2}} \, ;$$

out of the singularity it is

$$w = \sqrt{\Lambda} \, e^{-i\lambda} \, , \qquad z = \sqrt{\Lambda} \, e^{i\lambda} \, , \qquad \Lambda = -iwz \, .$$

With little abuse of notation, though we changed variables from x, y to w, z, we do not change the names of functions.

iii. Resonant and nonresonant normal forms are constructed. The construction of normal forms in Cartesian coordinates is a well established procedure in the isochronous case (in our notations, for k linear in Λ). In the non isochronous case, however, some care must be paid, due to the presence of non constant small denominators, which alter in an essential way the Birkhoff construction. The procedure to be followed, see [SM] and [BGF], is conceptually simple: in the very essence, the idea is to use coordinates w, z, but to proceed perturbatively — with Fourier developments, ultraviolet cut-off and so on — as if Λ, λ were coordinates.

To this purpose, one first introduces the frequency

$$\omega(\Gamma, \Lambda) = \frac{1}{A_3}(\Gamma - \beta\Lambda, -\beta(\Gamma - \Lambda)) \, ,$$

which is well defined on the singularity, too, where

$$\omega \to \omega_0 = \frac{\Gamma}{A_3}(1, -\beta) \, .$$

As is remarkable, gyroscopic motions are resonant or nonresonant (for a given cut-off) depending only on β, that is on the geometry of the body, and on ε. The two components of ω_0 are easily interpreted as the frequency of the rotation about e_3, and of the small oscillations of e_3 around M in the Euler–Poinsot motion. For the perturbation, as well as for any analytic function $F : \mathcal{M} \to \mathbb{R}$, $F^{(i)}(\Gamma, g^{(i)}, w, z, J^{(i)}, j^{(i)})$, one defines the "Fourier series",

$$F^{(i)} = \sum_{\nu \in \mathbb{Z}^2} \hat{F}_\nu^{(i)}(\Gamma, \Lambda, J^{(i)}, j^{(i)}) \, E_\nu^{(i)}(g^{(i)}, w, z) \,,$$

(Λ stays now for the product iwz), with $\hat{F}^{(i)}$ analytic, and

$$E_\nu^{(i)} = \begin{cases} e^{i\nu_1 \gamma^{(i)}} \, w^{\nu_2} & \text{for } \nu_2 < 0 \\ e^{i\nu_1 \gamma^{(i)}} \, z^{\nu_2} & \text{for } \nu_2 \geq 0. \end{cases}$$

As is quite important, *the above development in Fourier series is intrinsic:* namely, although $\hat{F}_\nu^{(i)}$ and $E_\nu^{(i)}$ are only local, the product $\hat{F}_\nu^{(i)} E_\nu^{(i)}$ is nevertheless the representative of an intrinsic "Fourier component", and a Fourier series is well defined on the manifold (see [BFG1] for details). Once the Fourier series is defined, it is sensible to introduce the ultraviolet cut-off N, and the resonant and nonresonant zones, as in the case of nonresonant motions. However, having in mind to work only in a small neighborhood $\overline{\mathcal{M}}_\delta$ of the proper rotation, of size $\varepsilon^{1/2}$, it is enough to introduce just a single zone, either resonant or nonresonant depending on ω_0, and work consistently inside it. So, *for gyroscopic motions, being resonant or nonresonant does not depend on the initial datum, but on β, that is on the geometry of the body.*

The nonresonant normal form, for example, looks in each chart

$$K_0^{(i)} = k(\Gamma, \Lambda(x, y)) + \varepsilon u_0^{(i)}(\Gamma, \Lambda(x, y), J^{(i)}, j^{(i)}) + \mathcal{O}(e^{-1/\varepsilon^{1/4}}) \,,$$

with $u_0^{(i)}$ close to the average $\langle \Phi^{(i)} \rangle$; all of these functions are local representatives of functions on the manifold.

As a matter of fact, following this road one proves a proposition that, essentially, extend to the gyroscopic motions the results of Proposition 4.

Proposition 5:   Let $H = h + \varepsilon f$ be as in Proposition 4, with f analytic in a neighborhood of the proper rotations, too. There exist δ, c, $\varepsilon_* > 0$ such that, if $\varepsilon < \varepsilon_*$, then up to

$$|t| \leq (\text{const}) \, e^{(\varepsilon_*/\varepsilon)^{1/4}} \tag{6.8}$$

i)   any initial datum in $\overline{\mathcal{M}}_\delta$ does not escape $\overline{\mathcal{M}}_{2\delta}$;

ii) Γ, Λ stay almost constant, and $\gamma^{(i)}$ advances almost regularly:

$$|\Gamma_t - \Gamma_0|, |\Lambda_t - \Lambda_0| \leq (\text{const}) \sqrt{\varepsilon} \,, \qquad |\dot{\gamma}_t^{(i)} - \beta \Gamma_0/A_3| \leq (\text{const}) \sqrt{\varepsilon} \,;$$

iii) if β is nonresonant up to the cut-off $N = c(\varepsilon_*/\varepsilon)^{1/4}$, then the average $\langle f \rangle$ stays also almost constant,

$$|\langle f \rangle(R_t, M_t) - \langle f \rangle(R_0, M_0)| < (\text{const}) \, \varepsilon^{1/4} \,.$$

The interpretation is the same as for Proposition 4; in particular, in the resonant case, chaotic motions of M are not excluded, for no matter how small ε. The improvement of [Gu], however, applies here too, namely chaotic motions possibly exist only in low resonances, up to a cut-off $N' = \mathcal{O}(\log \varepsilon^{-1})$.

Whether such chaotic motions effectively exist or not where theoreticaly allowed, is a delicate question. Numerical computations seem to indicate that gyroscopic motions, at variance with non gyroscopic ones, are more regular than expected, and chaotic motions occur, possibly, only in very few resonances of low order. Work is in progress to further improve Proposition 5, and prove that this is indeed the situation.

7 The Stability
of the Lagrangian Equilibrium Points $L_4 - L_5$

As the last physical application of Nekhoroshev theory we shall consider the problem the stability of the Lagrangian equilibrium points $L_4 - L_5$, in the so-called spatial circular restricted three body problem.

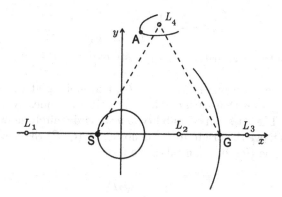

Fig. 30. *The Sun and Jupiter in the corotating system; the Lagrangian equilibrium points $L_1, \ldots, L_4$; an asteroid near L_4.*

A. The Problem

Let us consider two masses $m_1 = (1 - \mu)M$ and $m_2 = \mu M$, say the Sun and Jupiter, interacting via a Kepler potential, in circular motion around the common center of mass, at distance, respectively, μR and $(1 - \mu)R$ from it. It is convenient to introduce dimensionless quantities, such that $M = 1$, $R = 1$, $\Omega \equiv 2\pi/T = 1$, T being the common period of rotation (the gravitational constant entering Kepler potential is then also one), and to pass to the corotating frame, namely the frame with origin in the center of mass, plane xy coinciding with the plane of the motion, x axis passing through m_2 (see figure 30). Consider now a third object of negligible mass, say an asteroid, subject to the gravitational attraction of the two primary bodies, but too small to influence them (the restricted problem). It is not difficult to recognize that in such a rotating frame there are exactly five equilibrium positions for the asteroid, where the gravitational forces and the centrifugal force exactly balance. Three equilibrium points, commonly denoted L_1, L_2, L_3, are collinear to m_1 and m_2, that is stay on the x axis (their existence is very obvious). The two remaining positions, denoted L_4, L_5, are instead located on the opposite sides of the x axis, in such a way to form with m_1 and m_2 two equilateral triangles (see the figure), that is

$$L_{4,5} = (\tfrac{1}{2} - \mu, \pm\tfrac{\sqrt{3}}{2}, 0) \ .$$

Recognizing the existence of L_4 and L_5 is less immediate, but still is not difficult (elementary geometry is sufficient); L_4, L_5 are also called the "triangular" Lagrangian equilibrium points.[30]

The Hamiltonian of the asteroid in the rotating frame is easily seen to be

$$H(p_x, p_y, \ldots, z) = \frac{1}{2}(p_x^2 + p_y^2 + p_z^2) - xp_y + yp_x + V(x, y, z) \ ,$$

with

$$V(x, y, z) = -\frac{1-\mu}{\varrho_-(x, y, z)} - \frac{\mu}{\varrho_+(x, y, z)} \ ,$$

$\varrho_\pm(x, y, z)$ denoting the distance of the asteroid from the Sun $(-)$ and from Jupiter $(+)$.

By expanding H_0 around L_1, L_2, or L_3, and looking at the second order terms, one recognizes that such equilibrium points are linearly unstable, and thus unstable. The question of stability is instead definitely nontrivial for L_4 and L_5. Let us move the origin to L_4; denoting by (Q, P) the new coordinates and momenta, the Hamiltonian takes the form

$$H' = \frac{P^2}{2} - Q_1 P_2 + Q_2 P_1 + V'(Q) \ ,$$

with

$$V'(Q) = -\tfrac{1-\mu}{\varrho'_-(Q)} - \tfrac{\mu}{\varrho'_+(Q)} - \text{ linear part}$$

$$\varrho'_\pm(Q) = (Q^2 \pm Q_1 + \sqrt{3}Q_2 + 1)^{1/2} \ .$$

A little computation shows that the quadratic part of this Hamiltonian is

$$H_2 = \frac{1}{2}P^2 + P_1 Q_2 - P_2 Q_1 + \frac{1}{8}Q_1^2 - \frac{5}{8}Q_2^2 + \frac{1}{2}Q_3^2 - \frac{3\sqrt{3}}{4}(1 - 2\mu)Q_1 Q_2 \ .$$

---

[30] It is worthwhile to mention that in the more general elliptic problem (Jupiter and the Sun proceeding non uniformly on elliptic orbits) the triangular Lagrangian equilibria are replaced by elliptic orbits $L_4(t)$, $L_5(t)$ such that, at any t, Jupiter, the Sun and the asteroid form an equilateral triangle. The existence of such solutions was also discovered by Lagrange.

By diagonalizing H_2 one finds six eigenvalues $\pm i\omega_j$, $j = 1, 2, 3$, with

$$\omega_1 = \sqrt{\frac{1 + \sqrt{\Delta(\mu)}}{2}} , \qquad \omega_2 = -\sqrt{\frac{1 - \sqrt{\Delta(\mu)}}{2}} , \qquad \omega_3 = 1 ,$$

$\Delta(\mu) = 1 - 27\mu + 27\mu^2$. Correspondingly the diagonalized Hamiltonian, in the normal coordinates denoted (p, q), assumes the form

$$H''(p, q) = h_2(p, q) + f^{(3)}(p, q) , \tag{7.1}$$

with

$$h_2(p, q) = \frac{1}{2} \sum_{j=1}^{3} \omega_j (p_j^2 + q_j^2) ,$$

while $f^{(3)}$ is a series starting with terms cubic in p, q. The three frequencies are all real, and correspondingly the equilibrium point is elliptic, if $\Delta(\mu) > 0$, that is if

$$\mu < \mu_R = \frac{1}{2}\left(1 - \sqrt{\frac{23}{27}}\right) \simeq 0.038520 ;$$

μ_R is called the Routh limit. Both the value μ_{SJ} relative to the Sun–Jupiter system and the value μ_{EM} relative to the Earth–Moon system are far below μ_R, namely

$$\mu_{SJ} \simeq 0.000953 , \qquad \mu_{EM} \simeq 0.01215 .$$

Due to the presence of one negative frequency, the Lagrangian equilibrium points L_4, L_5, though elliptic, are not necessarily stable, and the question of their stability — a couple of centuries after Lagrange's work — is still open. This is probably the oldest "elementary" unsolved problem of Celestial Mechanics, perhaps of Mechanics. For the planar case (motion of the asteroid in the xy plane), the problem was positively solved during the sixties and the early seventies, within KAM theory; low dimensionality is essential, in order for the two–dimensional KAM tori provide a topological obstruction inside the three dimensional energy surface, and diffusion is forbidden. For the spatial problem, instead, the question is still open.

In recent years, some work has been done to discuss the problem of the stability of L_4, L_5 within Nekhoroshev theory, with the aim to prove that the equilibrium, though possibly not perpetually stable, is nevertheless stable for long times, namely times growing exponentially with the distance ε of the initial datum from the equilibrium point. Before entering the question, however, we must make a step back, and discuss more in general the problem of the application of Nekhoroshev methods to elliptic equilibria.

B. Nekhoroshev–Like Results for Elliptic Equiliria

Consider an analytic Hamiltonian system in a neighborhood of an equilibrium point,

$$H(p,q) = h_2(I(p,q)) + f^{(3)}(p,q) , \qquad (p,q) \in \mathbb{R}^{2n} , \qquad (7.2)$$

where

$$h_2(I) = \omega \cdot I , \qquad I_j(p,q) = \frac{p_j^2 + q_j^2}{2} ,$$

and $f^{(3)}$ is a series in p, q, starting with terms of order 3. Nekhoroshev conjectured, already in his 1977 paper, that exponential stability extends to such systems too, essentially as KAM results do. The conjectured result is thus that, if the initial datum is sufficiently close to the origin, say if

$$\varepsilon := \|I(p_0, q_0)\|^{1/2} \le \varepsilon_*$$

with suitable ε_*, then it is

$$\|I(p_t, q_t)\|^{1/2} < (\text{const}) \, \varepsilon^b \qquad \text{for} \quad |t| \le (\text{const}) \, e^{(\varepsilon_*/\varepsilon)^a} , \qquad (7.3)$$

with some $a, b > 0$. The analogy with KAM theorem suggests the following possible procedure:

i. Exclude a finite number of resonances, more precisely assume that $\nu \cdot \omega \ne 0$ for $|\nu| \le s$ with some $s \ge 4$. Then for small ε, by means of s elementary "Birkhoff steps", it is possible to put the system in "Birkhoff normal form" up to the order s, namely

$$H^{(s)}(p,q) = h^{(s)}(I(p,q)) + f^{(s+1)}(p,q) , \qquad (7.4)$$

where $f^{(s+1)}$ is a series in p, q starting at order $s + 1$, and

$$h^{(s)}(I) = h_2(I) + \sum_{k=2}^{[s/2]} h_{2k}(I) , \qquad (7.5)$$

[.] denoting the integer part; h_{2k} is a homogeneous polynomial of degree k in $I_1, \ldots, I_n$, and correspondingly $h_{2k} \circ I$ is a polynomial of degree $2k$ in p, q.

ii. Assume that $h^{(s)}$ satisfies some convenient geometric assumption, like convexity of $h^{(s)}$ as function of I, and try to apply Nekhoroshev theory to $H^{(s)}$, using $h^{(s)}$ as the integrable part.

While point (i) is easy and well established, point (ii) is far from trivial, since the action-angles variables are singular whenever an action vanishes. With reference to the figure 31, left, stability of actions is proven in the bulk, but not near the hyperplanes $I_j(p,q) = 0$, in particular not in a neighborhood of the origin. An improvement was produced in [Lo2]: the size of the excluded region there shrinks to zero at the equilibrium point, see figure 31, right, but still the stability region does not contain any open neighborhood of this point. Let us stress that, while in KAM theory the aim is "only" to work in a subset of the phase space of large measure, and so excluding a neighborhood of the

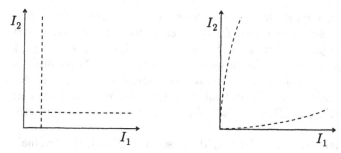

Fig. 31. *In a layer around coordinate planes $I_j = 0$, $j = 1, \ldots, n$, the ordinary proof of Nekhoroshev theorem fails* (left). *The improvement in [Lo2] reduces the layers to wedge–shaped regions* (right).

coordinate plains is fairly acceptable, instead in Nekhoroshev theory working in an open set around the equilibrium point is mandatory.

As a matter of fact, the literature concerning long time stability for elliptic equilibria took soon a different direction, namely it abandoned the original Nekhoroshev suggestion, and studied elliptic equilibria as perturbations of isochronous systems, using h_2 as the unperturbed Hamiltonian. As for the case of the linear systems that we studied in Section 2, this approach needs a strong arithmetic assumption on the frequencies, namely that ω satisfies the Diophantine condition (2.3). For isochronous systems, thanks to the fact that ω and thus the small denominators $\nu \cdot \omega$ are constant, it is rather natural to work perturbatively in the Cartesian variables p, q (essentially as Birkhoff did at a formal level), so the difficulty connected with the lack of analyticity of the action angle variables in this approach disappears. The result is an exponential estimate like (7.3) [Gi1]. Applications to the Lagrangian equilibria L_4, L_5 were also soon produced; see [GDFGS] and, for later improvements, [GS,Gi2] and references there quoted. Such results belong, in our language (Section 1), to the realm of "exponential estimates", rather than of Nekhoroshev theorem.

On the one hand, such an approach is simple and powerful, and leads to nice results of "practical stability" in connection, for example, with the triangular Lagrangian equilibria corresponding to the Sun-Jupiter masses.[31]

---

[31] In such a case, of course, it is not known whether ω is Diophantine, and thus if an arbitrarily large number of perturbative steps, leading to exponential estimates, can be performed. But ω is known sufficiently well as to exclude all resonances up to, say, $|\nu| = 30$; this allows to make 30 (computer assisted) perturbative steps, and to obtain stability times larger than the Universe lifetime, with a basin of stability sufficient to contain some of the asteroids which are known to gravitate around L_4, L_5. Perturbation theory, due to the finite precision knowledge of ω, is finite order, so in a sense it is improper to speak of exponential estimates. But clearly, the approach is successful, and "practical stability" is acheived, just because there is, behind, the general result of exponential estimates for Diophantine frequencies.

On the other hand the approach is weak, if one wishes to know about the stability of elliptic equilibria for open sets of frequencies, and in particular for the Lagrangian equilibria L_4, L_5 for generic values of $\mu \in (0, \mu_R)$. Indeed, as we remarked in Section 2A, if we take any ball in $\mathbb{R}^n$, Diophantine frequencies are there abundant in measure: but such abundancy does not trivially tranfer to submanifolds of $\mathbb{R}^n$, in particular not to the curve $\omega(\mu) \in \mathbb{R}^3$, parametrized by μ, entering the Hamiltonian of L_4, L_5; Diophantine frequencies could be there quite exceptional.

Only recently, in [FGB,Ni1,GFB] (see also [Pö2]), the original Nekhoroshev conjecture was taken again into consideration, and long time stability of elliptic equilibria was proved for open sets of frequencies. In [FGB,GFB] the proof makes use of the standard geometric construction of Nekhoroshev theorem; as a matter of fact, the difficulty related to the use of Cartesian variables in a non isochronous system is identical to the one solved in connection with gyroscopic rotations, and the method there developed turns out to work in the general problem of elliptic equilibria, too. [Ni1,Pö2] instead follow the alternative method of proof introduced in [Lo1]. The common statement, up to minor differences, is the following.

Proposition 6:   *Let H be as in (7.2), analytic in a ball $\|I(p,q)\|^{1/2} < R$ for some $R > 0$, and assume that ω does not satisfy any resonance relation up to $|\nu| = s$, with $s \geq 4$. Further assume that h_4, as defined in (7.5), provides quasi–convexity. There exist positive constants ε_*, T, B, a, b such that if $\varepsilon < \varepsilon_*$, where $\varepsilon = \|I(p(0), q(0))\|^{1/2}$, then up to*

$$|t| \leq T\, e^{(\varepsilon_*/\varepsilon)^a} \tag{7.6}$$

it is

$$\|I(p(t), q(t))\|^{1/2} < B(\varepsilon/\varepsilon_*)^b . \tag{7.7}$$

In [FGB] it is $a = b = 1/n$, as well as $a = 1/(2n)$, $b = 1/2$; in [GFB,Ni1] it is instead $b = 1$, $a = (s-3)/(4n)$.

The weakness of Proposition 6, in view of its application to the triangular Lagrangian equilibria, is the assumption of quasi–convexity: as we shall see, such an assumption is never satisfied by the Hamiltonian of L_4, L_5. Nevertheless, as we shall discuss in the next paragraphs, the method of proof used in [FGB,GFB] allows to weaken in an essential way the convexity assumption, so as to suitably extend the result of stability to the Lagrangian equilibria, too.

C. Nekhoroshev Stability of L_4 and L_5 – Part I

The construction of the normal form for the Hamiltonian of L_4, L_5, and the analysis of its geometric properties, are conceptually simple but technically complicated operations, which require some computer assistence; the analysis reported below was performed with the aid of *Mathematica*.

First of all, to construct the normal form of order $s = 4$, one must exclude all resonances of $\omega(\mu)$ up to order 4. In principle there are four of them, namely $\nu = (0, 2, 1)$, $(1, 2, 0)$, $(0, 3, 1)$, $(1, 3, 0)$, for μ in the interval $(0, \mu_R)$: but the first and the third resonance turn out to be not present among the Fourier components of the perturbation, so practically, to construct the normal form of order 4, only two values of μ must be excluded, namely

$$\mu_{(1,2,0)} \simeq 0.0242939 , \qquad \mu_{(1,3,0)} \simeq 0.0135160 .$$

Let us write $h_4(I) = \frac{1}{2} A(\mu) I \cdot I$, and let $B(\mu)$ denote the restriction of $A(\mu)$ to the plane $\Pi(\mu)$ orthogonal to $\omega(\mu)$. Computer assisted analysis shows instead that the two eigenvalues of $B(\mu)$ have opposite sign, for any $\mu \in (0, \mu_R)$, so $h^{(4)} = h_2 + h_4$ never satisfies the quasi–convexity assumption entering the above Proposition 6.

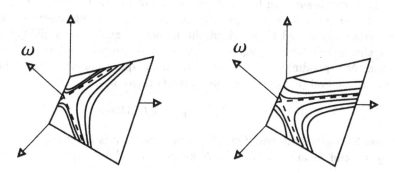

Fig. 32. *Illustrating the notion of directional quasi–convexity.*

The question, fortunately, is more subtle. The lack of quasi convexity shows that the level curves of $h^{(4)}$, in the plane $\Pi(\mu)$, have the hyperbolic structure of figure 24, right, and we know that the asymptots, in such a situation, provide potential escape directions. But the actions, in the problem at hand (as well as for any elliptic equilibrium) are necessarily nonnegative: so, in order for escape along an asymptot to be possible, the asymptot itself must point in the first octant, that is it must have all components of the same sign, see figure 32, right. If instead the asymptot points towards the walls of the first octant, see figure 32, left, then motions along it, if any, are bounded. In particular, if a pair of Cartesian coordinates $(p_j(t), q_j(t))$ goes through the origin at some t^*, so that $I(t)$ reaches the coordinate plane $I_j = 0$ at t^*, later on $I(t)$ is necessarily "bounced back"; see figure 33. Formally, one can introduce — for this as well as for any problem of elliptic equilibria, in any dimension — the notion of *directional quasi–convexity* [BFG2], and say that a function $h^{(4)} = h_2 + h_4$, with $h_2(I) = \omega \cdot I$ and $h_4(I) = \frac{1}{2} AI \cdot I$, $I = 1, \ldots, n$

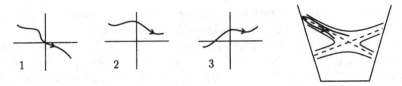

Fig. 33. *Oscillator No. 1 passes through the origin. Correspondingly $I(t)$ touches the coordinate plane $I_1 = 0$, and is bounched back.*

is directionally quasi–convex, if h_2 and h_4 never vanish simultaneously for $I_1, \ldots, I_n \geq 0$, $I \neq 0$. As shown in [BFG2], *one of the proofs of Proposition 6*, namely the one in [FGB] *allows to replace the quasi–convexity assumption by the weaker assumption of directional quasi convexity, with the same result,* namely the estimates (7.6) and (7.7), with either $a = b = 1/n$ or $a = 1/(2n)$, $b = 1/2$.

The obvious question then poses, whether the assumption of directional quasi–convexity is satisfied by the Hamiltonian of L_4, L_5 for $\mu \in (0, \mu_R)$. To answere, one must look at the sign of the components of the eigenvectors of the matrix $B(\mu)$ introduced above. A careful numerical analysis, see [BFG2] for details, shows that, for both eigenvectors, the three components have different sign, and correspondingly the system is directional quasi–convex, for all values of μ in the interval $(0, \mu_R)$, except in an interval (μ_1, μ_2),

$$\mu_1 \simeq 0.0109137 \, , \qquad \mu_2 \simeq 0.0163768 \, ;$$

see figure 34, dashed interval. Out of this interval, that is for either $\mu < \mu_1$ or $\mu > \mu_2$, L_4 and L_5 are proven to be Nekhoroshev stable.

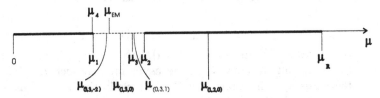

Fig. 34. *The μ axis, between 0 and μ_R. The hypothesis of directional quasi–convexity is satisfied only on the solid line. The different exceptional values of μ, where for different reasons Nekhoroshev stability is not proved, are reported. The value μ_{EM} of the Earth–Moon system is also reported.*

To investigate the long time stability of the equilibrium inside the interval (μ_1, μ_2), the elementary method of confinement illustrated in Section 5, based on quasi–convexity and conservation of energy, is not sufficient, and one must resort to the not easy notion of steepness. The next paragraph is devoted to a short illustration of this not much known property.

D. About Steepness

Steepness is a somehow technical notion, whose definition requires care. Consider any integrable Hamiltonian $h(I)$, $I \in \mathcal{B} \subset \mathbb{R}^n$.

Definition: Let Π be any linear subspace of $\mathbb{R}^n$; h is said to be Π-*steep in the point* $I \in \mathcal{B}$, with steepness constants $\alpha, m, \delta > 0$, if for any $u \in \Pi$, $\|u\| \leq \delta$, it is

$$\sup_{0 \leq \eta \leq 1} \|\omega_\Pi(I + \eta u)\| \geq m\|u\|^\alpha ,$$

where ω_Π denotes the orthogonal projection of ω on Π.

In the essence: ω_Π may vanish in I (this happens if I is on a resonance, and Π is its plane of fast drift), but then, moving far from I inside Π, ω_Π grows at least as a power of the distance from I. Steepness is now readly defined:

Definition: The Hamiltonian h is said to be *steep in* $\mathcal{B}$, with steepness constants α_j, m_j, δ_j, $j = 1, \ldots, n-1$, if it is Π-steep in any point $I \in \mathcal{B}$, for any subspace Π of $\mathbb{R}^n$ of dimension r between 1 and $n-1$, with steepness constants α_r, m_r, δ_r.

In Nekhoroshev theorem (Proposition 2) the assumption of quasi–convexity can be replaced by the weaker assumption of steepness. The exponential estimates, however, worsen, and in particular the exponents a and b entering (5.3) get smaller. It turns out that a, b depend only on $\alpha_1, \ldots, \alpha_{n-1}$, so these are the most important steepness constants to which pay attention. Smaller values of $\alpha_1, \ldots, \alpha_n$ provide better (i.e. larger) exponents a, b. A very recent result [Ni2] improving [Nek1,Nek2], valid for steep h with nonsingular Hessian, is $a = b = 1/(2n\Pi_j\alpha_j)$.

The following statements are easy to prove, an provide useful exercises to get familiar with the notion of steepness; we there use the compact notations $h'u = \sum_i \frac{\partial h}{\partial I_i} u_i = \omega \cdot u$, $h''uu = \sum_{ij} \frac{\partial^2 h}{\partial I_i \partial I_j} u_i u_j$, $h'''uuu = \sum_{ijk} \frac{\partial^3 h}{\partial I_i \partial I_j \partial I_k} u_i u_j u_k$.

i. Let h be quasi–convex, i.e. assume that for any $I \in \mathcal{B}$

$$h'(I)u = 0 , \qquad h''(I)uu = 0 \qquad \Longrightarrow \qquad u = 0 ,$$

for any $I \in \mathcal{B}$. Then h is steep, with $\alpha_1 = \ldots = \alpha_n = 1$ (the best possible values).

ii. The Hamiltonian $h = \frac{1}{2}(I_1^2 - I_2)^2 + I_3^2$ is steep on all lines, but not on the planes $I_3 = (\text{const})$. Conversely, $h = I_1^2 - I_2^2 + I_3$ is steep on all planes, but not on the lines parallel to $(1, \pm 1, 0)$.

iii. The Hamiltonian

$$h = \frac{1}{2}(I_1^2 - I_2^2) + \frac{1}{3}I_1^3 + I_3$$

is steep, with $\alpha_1 = 2$, $\alpha_2 = 1$.

iv. Let the 3-jet of h be non degenerate, i.e. assume that everywhere in B

$$h'(I)u = 0 \,, \qquad h''(I)uu = 0 \,, \qquad h'''(I)uuu = 0 \qquad \Longrightarrow \qquad u = 0 \,.$$

Then h is steeep, and for $n = 3$ it is $\alpha_1 = 2$, $\alpha_2 = 1$.

Non degeneracy of the 3–jet of h is a natural generalization of quasi–convexity. The generalization, however, is not trivial (the proof is easy only for $n = 3$), and moreover it does not procede further, namely the non degeneracy of the 4–jet does not imply steepness. A counterexample is

$$h = \frac{1}{2}(I_1^2 - I_2)^2 + \sum_{j=3}^{n} I_j^2 \,.$$

For such a system, in fact, it is not difficult to find a perturbation, for example $f = \cos\varphi_1 + 2I_1 \cos\varphi_2$, such that $h + \varepsilon f$ admits unbounded motions with speed ε.

Remark: For steep but non quasi–convex Hamiltonians, the energy conservation does not provide confinement of the actions. Indeed:

v. The Hamiltonian

$$h = \frac{1}{2}(I_1^2 - I_2^2 + I_3^2) + \frac{1}{3}I_1^3$$

is steep, with $\alpha_1 = 2$, $\alpha_2 = 1$, but in the plane Π through $I^o = (0, 0, I_3^o)$, orthogonal to $\omega(I^o) = (0, 0, I_3^o)$, the level lines $h = (\text{const})$ are not bounded.

The only known mechanism of confinement, for Hamiltonians steep but not quasi–convex, is the Nekhoroshev "trapping", mentioned in Section 3. Here we can understand better the idea of trapping, which is technically complicated but conceptualy simple: for any initial datum $I(0)$ inside Z_Λ (but far from resonances other than in Λ, so as to avoid "overlapping"), the motion, we know, takes place up to a negligible error on the plane of fast drift Π_Λ. But for a steep system, any motion on Π_Λ cannot proceed far from the initial datum, without a growth of $\omega_{\Pi_\Lambda} = \omega \cdot u/\|u\|$, for some $u \in \Pi_\lambda$. Since the resonant vectors $\nu_1, \ldots, \nu_r$ are a basis in Π_Λ, at least one of the small denominators $\omega \cdot \nu_j$ necessarily grows, and correspondingly the point $I(t)$ exits from Z_Λ towards a less resonant region, where a stronger normal form can be used.

The 3–jet non degeneracy provides a very useful sufficient condition for steepness, easy to test in practice (testing directly steepness is harder). Such a property was successfully used in [MG,GM], for a steep but non quasi–convex Hamiltonian describing the motion of an asteroid in the main belt. As we shall see in the next final paragraph, the same property turns out to be useful to study the long time stability of the triangular Lagrangian equilibria, in the interval (μ_1, μ_2) where directional quasi–convexity is absent.

E. Nekhoroshev Stability of L_4 and L_5 – Part II

For the general case of an elliptic equilibrium with Hamiltonian (7.4), it is easy to see that the condition of non degeneracy of the 3–jet of $h^{(s)}$ is satisfied iff $s \geq 6$ and

$$\omega \cdot I = 0 , \quad h_4(I) = 0 , \quad h_6(I) = 0 \quad \Longrightarrow \quad I = 0 . \qquad (7.8)$$

As a matter of fact, by rearranging the proof of Proposition 6 contained in [GFB], the assumption of quasi–convexity of $h^{(s)}$ can be weakened to the non degeneracy of the 3–jet of $h^{(s)}$, though stability times worsen and the minimal s gets larger. Precisely:

Proposition 7: *Consider the Hamiltonian (7.4), with $h^{(s)}$ as in (7.5), $s \geq 8$. Assume that (7.8) is satisfied, and moreover that the restriction of the quadratic form h_4 to the plane orthogonal to ω is nonsingular. Then the exponential estimates (7.6), (7.7) hold, with $a = \min(\frac{s-7}{20}, \frac{s+1}{36})$ and $b = 1$.*

To apply such a proposition to L_4 and L_5, first of all one must check that the normal form $H^{(s)}$ can be constructed (at least) up to the order $s = 8$. To this purpose, for each $j = 3, \ldots, 8$ one must exclude all values of μ, such that $\nu \cdot \omega(\mu) = 0$ for some ν actually present in $f_{j+1}^{(j+1)}$; these are indeed the terms of the perturbation to be "killed" at step $j - 2$, to construct $H^{(j+1)}$. Only values of μ in the interval (μ_1, μ_2) need to be considered. As a result, see [BFG2] for details, it turns out that the eight-order normal form can be constructed everywhere in (μ_1, μ_2), except for three points, namely the already met $\mu_{(1,3,0)}$, and the new points

$$\mu_{(0,3,1)} \simeq 0.0148525 , \qquad \mu_{(3,3,-2)} \simeq 0.0115649 .$$

As a second step, for all values of μ for which the normal form of order eight can be constructed, it is necessary to check if the steepness assumption used in Proposition 7 is satisfied. Accurate numerical computations, see [BFG2] for details, show that the non singularity assumption on $h^{(4)}$ is always satisfied in (μ_1, μ_2), while the non degeneracy of the 3–jet of $h^{(6)}$ fails to be satisfied in just one point of the interval, namely

$$\mu_3 \simeq 0.0147808 .$$

So Proposition 7 applies, and long time stability occurs, for all $\mu \in (\mu_1, \mu_2)$ but the four exceptional values $\mu_{(0,3,1)}$, $\mu_{(3,3,-2)}$, $\mu_{(1,3,0)}$ and μ_3.

The overall conclusion is that *the Lagrangian equilibrium points L_4, L_5 are Nekhoroshev stable for any μ in the interval $(0, \mu_R)$, with the exception of five "bad" points, namely the four above inside (μ_1, μ_2), and $\mu_{(1,2,0)}$.* The situation is summarized in figure 34.

Let us stress, however, that the stability properties of L_4, L_5 are not expected to be uniform in $(0, \mu_R)$: on the contrary, the theoretical expectation is that the stability times worsen in the interval (μ_1, μ_2), where the assumption of directional quasi–convexity is violated, and of course further worsen if the exceptional points where the theory fails are approached. As is remarkable, the value μ_{EM} relative to the Earth–Moon problem lies inside the interval of weaker stability (μ_1, μ_2), and moreover, see figure 34, it is rather close to $\mu_{(3,3,-2)}$. As is known, no bodies have been ever observed to gravitate around the triangular Lagrangian equilibria of the Earth–Moon system. Of course, there can be several reasons for such an absence, like the (rather strong) influence of the Sun [GJMS], or the ellipticity of the underlying two body problem. The worse stability of the ideal circular three body problem, however, could also contribute.

Whether the difference in the geometric properties of the system, namely quasi–convexity or weaker steepness properties, does effectively result in observable differences of the stability properties, is a very general question, which goes far beyond L_4 and L_5, or elliptic equilibria, and concerns the whole Nekhoroshev theory. Nekhoroshev, in his 1977 paper, explicitly conjectured that different steepness properties should lead to numerically observable differences in the stability times. Such a study, as is known, is not easy, since it based, in the essence, on the possibility of observing numerically, for small perturbations, the Arnol'd diffusion — a quite difficult task, as is well known — and of putting in evidence possible differences in its speed. It is hard to say whether such an investigation can be effectively carried on. But certainly, the Hamiltonian of L_4, L_5 provides, at least, a promising candidate for such a study, since by just varying a natural parameter in the system, the steepness properties change significantly, and occasionally also disappear.

References

[A]   H. Andoyer, *Cours de Méchanique Celeste* (Gautier-Villars, Paris 1923).

[B]   G. Benettin, *Nekhoroshev-like Results for Hamiltonian Dynamical Systems*, lectures given at the Noto School Non-Linear Evolution and Chaotic Phenomena, G. Gallavotti and P.W Zweifel Editors (Plenum Press, New York, 1988).

[BCaF]   G. Benettin, A. Carati and F. Fassò, *On the conservation of adiabatic invariants for a system of coupled rotators.* Physica D **104**, 253–268 (1997).

[BCS]   G. Benettin, A. Carati and P. Sempio, *On the Landau–Teller approximation for the energy exchanges with fast degrees of freedom.* Journ. Stat. Phys. **73**, 175–192 (1993).

[BCG]   G. Benettin, A. Carati e G. Gallavotti, *A rigorous implementation of the Landau–Teller approximation for adiabatic invariants.* Nonlinearity **10**, 479-505 (1997).

[BChF1]   G. Benettin, A.M. Cherubini and F. Fassò, *A "changing chart" symplectic algorithm for rigid bodies and other Hamiltonian systems on manifolds.* SIAM Journ. on Sc. Computing **23**, 1189–1203 (2001).

[BChF2] G. Benettin, A.M.Cherubini e F. Fassò, *Regular and Chaotic motions of the fast rotating rigid body: a numerical study*. Discr. Cont. Dyn. Sys. **4**, 521–540 (2002).

[BF1]   G. Benettin and F. Fassò, *From Hamiltonian perturbation theory to symplectic integrators, an back*. Appl. Num. Math. 29, 73-87 (1999).

[BF2]   G. Benettin e F. Fassò, *Fast rotations of the symmetric rigid body: a general study by Hamiltonian perturbation theory. Part I*. Nonlinearity **9**, 137–186 (1996).

[BFG1]   G. Benettin, F. Fassò and M. Guzzo, *Fast rotations of the symmetric rigid body: a study by Hamiltonian perturbation theory. Part II, Gyroscopic rotations*. Nonlinearity **10**, 1695–1717 (1997).

[BFG2]   G. Benettin, F. Fassò and M. Guzzo, *Nekhoroshev–stability of L4 and L5 in the spatial restricted three-body problem*. Regular and Chaotic Dynamics 3, 56-72 (1998).

[BGa]   G. Benettin and G. Gallavotti, *Stability of Motions near Resonances in Quasi Integrable Hamiltonian Systems*. Journ. Stat. Phys. **44**, 293 (1986).

[BGi]   G. Benettin and A. Giorgilli, *On the Hamiltonian interpolation of near to the identity symplectic mappings, with application to symplectic integration algorithms*. Journ. Stat. Phys. **73**, 1117–1144 (1994).

[BGG1]   G. Benettin, L. Galgani e A. Giorgilli, *Realization of Holonomic Constraints and Freezing of High Frequency Degrees of Freedom, in the Light of Classical Perturbation Theory. Part I*. Comm. Math. Phys. **113**, 87-103 (1987).

[BGG2]   G. Benettin, L. Galgani and A. Giorgilli, *Realization of Holonomic Constraints and Freezing of High–Frequency Degrees of Freedom in the Light of Classical Perturbation Theory. Part II*. Comm. Math. Phys. **121**, 557-601 (1989).

[BGG3]   G. Benettin, L .Galgani e A. Giorgilli, *A Proof of Nekhoroshev Theorem for Nearly-Integrable Hamiltonian Systems*. Celestial Mechanics **37**, 1-25 (1985).

[BHS]   G. Benettin, P. Hjorth and P. Sempio, *Exponentially long equilibrium times in a one dimensional collisional model of a classical gas*. Journ. Stat. Phys. 94, 871-892 (1999).

[Bo1]   L. Boltzmann, *On certain questions of the theory of gases*. Nature 51, 413 (1895).

[Bo2]   L. Boltzmann, *Vorlesungen über Gastheorie*, Vol II, Section 45 (Barth, Leipzig 1898). English translation: *Lectures on gas theory* (University of Cal. Press, 1966).

[BS]   G. Benettin and P. Sempio, *Adiabatic invariants and trapping of point charge in a strong non–uniform magnetic field*. Nonlinearity **7**, 281–303 (1994).

[D]   A. Deprit, *Free rotation of a rigid body studied in phase plane*. Am. J. Phys. **55**, 424 (1967).

[DGJS]   A. Delshalms, V. Gelfreich, A. Jorba and T. M. Seara, *Exponentially small splitting of separatrices under fast quasiperiodic forcing*. Comm. Math. Phys. **189**, 35–71 (1997).

[E]   L.H. Eliasson, *Absolutely convergent series expansions for quasi–periodic motions*. Math. Phys. Electronic J. **2**, paper 4, 33 pp. (1996).

[F1]   F. Fassò, *Lie series method for vector fields and Hamiltonian perturbation theory*, J. Appl. Math. Phys. (ZAMP) **41**, 843–864 (1990).

[F2]   F. Fassò, *The Euler–Poinsot top: a non-commutatively integrable system without global action–angle coordinates*. J. Appl. Math. Phys. **47**, 953-976 (1996).

[F3]   F. Fassò, *Hamiltonian perturbation theory on a manifold*. Cel. Mech. and Dyn. Astr. **62**, 43–69 (1995).

[FGB]   F. Fassò, M. Guzzo e G. Benettin, *Nekhoroshev-stability of elliptic equilibria of Hamiltonian systems*. Comm. Math. Phys. **197**, 347–360 (1998).

[Ga1]   G. Gallavotti, *Quasi–Integrable Mechanical Systems*, in *Critical phenomena, Random Systems, Gauge Theories*, K. Osterwalder and R. Stora editors, *Les Houches*, Session XLIII, 1984 (North–Holland, Amsterdam 1986).

[Ga2]   G. Gallavotti, *Twistless KAM tori, quasi flat homoclinic intersections, and other cancellations in the perturbation series of certain completely integrable hamiltonian systems. A review.* Reviews Math. Phys. **6**, 343–411 (1994).

[GDFGS]   A. Giorgilli, A. Delshams, E. Fontich, L. Galgani e C. Simó, *Effective Stability for a Hamiltonian System near an Elliptic Equilibrium Point, with an Application to the Restricted three Body Problem.* J. Diff. Eq. **77**, 167-198 (1989).

[GFB]   M. Guzzo, F. Fassò e G. Benettin, *On the stability of elliptic equilibria.* Math. Phys. Electronic J. **4**, paper 1, 16 pp. (1998).

[GG]   A. Giorgilli and G. Galgani, *Rigorous estimates for the series expansions of Hamiltonian perturbation theory.* Celestial Mech. **37** 95–112 (1985).

[Gi1]   A. Giorgilli, *Rigorous results on the power expansions for the integrals of a Hamiltonian system near an elliptic equilibrium point.* Ann. Inst. Henri Poincaré - Physique Thèorique **48**, 423–439 (1988).

[Gi2]   A. Giorgilli, *On the problem of stability for near to integrable Hamiltonian systems.* Proceedings of the International Congress of Mathematicians, Vol. III (Berlin, 1998).

[GJMS]   G. Gomez, A. Jorba, J. Masdemont and C. Simo, *A quasiperiodic solution as a substitute of L4 in the Earth-Moon system.* In: *Predictability, stability, and chaos in N-body dynamical systems* (Cortina d'Ampezzo, 1990), 433–438, NATO Adv. Sci. Inst. Ser. B Phys., 272 (Plenum, New York, 1991).

[GM]   M. Guzzo e A. Morbidelli, *Construction of a Nekhoroshev like result for the asteroid belt dynamical system.* Cel. Mech. & Dyn. Astr. **66**, 255-292 (1997).

[GS]   A. Giorgilli and C.H. Skokos, *On the stability of the Trojan asteroids*, Astronomy and Astrophysics **317**, 254-261 (1997).

[Gu]   M. Guzzo, *Nekhoroshev stability of quasi–integrable degenerate Hamiltonian Systems.* Regular and Chaotic Dynamics 4, 78-102 (1999).

[J1]   J.H. Jeans, *On the vibrations set up in molecules by collisions.* Phil. Mag. **6**, 279 (1903).

[J2]   J.H. Jeans, *On the partition of energy between matter and Aether.* Phil. Mag. **10**, 91 (1905).

[J3]   J.H. Jeans, *The dynamical theory of gases*, second edition, Chapter XIV. Cambridge Univ. Press (Cambridge, 1916).

[Li]   J.E. Littlewood, Proc. London Math. Soc. **9**, 343 (1959); **9**, 525 (1959).

[LN]   P. Lochak e A.I. Neishtadt, *Estimates of stability time for nearly integrable systems with a quasiconvex Hamiltonian.* Chaos 2, 495–499 (1992).

[Lo1]   P. Lochak, *Canonical perturbation theory via simultaneous approximation.* Russ. Math. Surv. **47**, 57-133 (1992).

[Lo2] P. Lochak, *Stability of Hamiltonian systems over exponentially long times: the near linear case*. In H. Dumas, K. Meyer, D. Schmidt (eds), *Hamiltonian Dynamical Systems - History, Theory, and Applications*, The IMA Volumes in Mathematics and its Applications **63**, 221-229 (Springer, New York, 1995).

[LT] L. Landau and E. Teller, *On the theory of sound dispersion*. Physik. Z. Sowjetunion **10**, 34 (1936). Also in *Collected Papers of L. D. Landau*, edited by D. Ter Haar, page 147 (Pergamon Press, Oxford 1965).

[MG] A. Morbidelli e M. Guzzo, *The Nekhoroshev theorem and the Asteroid Belt dynamical system*. Cel. Mech. & Dyn. Astr. **65**, 107-136 (1997).

[NL] A.I. Neishtadt and M.L. Lidov, *The method of canonical transformations in problems of the rotation of celestial bodies and Cassini laws (Russian)*. In *Determination of the motion of spacecraft (Russian)*, pag. 74–106 (Izdat. "Nauka", Moscow, 1975).

[Nei] A.I. Neishtadt, *On the accuracy of conservation of the adiabatic invariant*, Prikl. Mat. Mekh. **45**:1, 80-87 (1981) [J. Appl. Math. Mech. **45**:1, 58-63 (1982)]

[Nek1] N.N. Nekhoroshev, *Behaviour of Hamiltonian systems close to integrability*. Funct. Anal. Appl. **5**, 338-339 (1971) [Funk. An. Ego Prilozheniya, **5**, 82-83 (1971)].

[Nek2] N.N. Nekhoroshev, *An exponential estimate of the time of stability of nearly integrable Hamiltonian systems*. Usp. Mat. Nauk **32**:6, 5-66 (1977) [Russ. Math. Surv. **32**:6, 1-65 (1977)].

[Ni1] L. Niederman, *Nonlinear stability around an elliptic equilibrium point in an Hamiltonian system*. Nonlinearity **11** 1465–1479 (1998).

[Ni2] L. Niederman, *Exponential stability for small perturbations of steep integrable dynamical systems*. Erg. Theory Dyn. Sys. **2**, 593-608 (2004).

[OH] T.M. O'Neil, P.G. Hjorth, *Collisional dynamics of a strongly magnetized pure electron plasma*. Physics of Fluids **28**, 3241, (1985).

[OHBFM] T.M. O'Neil, P.G. Hjorth, B. Beck, J. Fajans, and J. Malmberg, in *Collisional relaxation of a strongly magnetized pure electron plasma (theory and experiment)*. In *Strongly Coupled Plasma Physics* (North-Holland, Amsterdam 1990).

[Po1] H. Poincaré, *Les Méthodes Nouvelles de la Méchanique Céleste*, Vol. 1 (Gautier–Villars, Paris, 1892).

[Pö1] J. Pöschel, *Nekhoroshev estimates for quasi–convex Hamiltonian Systems*, Math. Z. **213**, 187–216 (1993).

[Pö2] J. Pöschel, *On Nekhoroshev's estimate at an elliptic equilibrium*. Internat. Math. Res. Notices 1999, no. 4, 203–215.

[Ra] D. Rapp, *Complete classical Theory of Vibrational Energy exchange*. Journ. Chem. Phys. **32**, 735–737 (1960).

[Ru] R. Rutgers, Ann. Phys. **16**, 350 (1933).

[S] C. Simò, *Averaging under fast quasiperiodic forcing*. In *Hamiltonian mechanics, integrability and chaotic behavior*, J. Seimenis editor, Nato ASI Series B 331 (Plenum Press, New York 1994).

[SM] C. Siegel and J. Moser, *Lectures on Celestial Mechanics* (Springer, Berlin, 1971).

The Adiabatic Invariant Theory and Applications

Jacques Henrard

Departement de Mathematique FUNDP 8,
Rempart de la Vierge, B-5000 Namur, Belgium
Jacques.Henrard@fundp.ac.be

1 Integrable Systems

1.1 Hamilton-Jacobi Equation

We shall summarize in the section a few results of the theory of Hamiltonian system.

Canonical Transformations

By definition a canonical transformation from the phase space of n *variables* $(q_1, \cdots, q_n)$ and n *momenta* $(p_1, \cdots, p_n)$ to the phase space of n variables $(\beta_1, \cdots, \beta_n)$ and n momenta $(\alpha_1, \cdots, \alpha_n)$ is a (possibly time dependent) transformation such it transforms any Hamiltonian system into an Hamiltonian system; i.e. for any function $H(q, p)$ there exists a function $K(\beta, \alpha)$ such that the system of differential equations

$$\dot{q}_i = \frac{\partial H}{\partial p_i} \quad ; \quad \dot{p}_i = -\frac{\partial H}{\partial q_i} \quad 1 \leq i \leq n \,,$$

is transformed into the system of differential equations,

$$\dot{\beta}_i = \frac{\partial H}{\partial \alpha_i} \quad ; \quad \dot{\alpha}_i = -\frac{\partial H}{\partial \beta_i} \quad 1 \leq i \leq n \,,$$

A necessary and sufficient condition for a transformation to be canonical is that its Jacobian matrix

$$M = \frac{\partial(\beta_1, \cdots, \beta_n, \alpha_1, \cdots, \alpha_n)}{\partial(q_1, \cdots, q_n, p_1, \cdots, p_n)} \,,$$

verify the condition

$$M\Re M = \mu\Re \quad \text{with} \quad \Re = \begin{pmatrix} 0_n & I_n \\ -I_n & 0_n \end{pmatrix},$$

where 0_n is the $(n \times n)$ null matrix, and I_n is the $(n \times n)$ identity matrix. When a transformation is canonical there exists a *remainder function* $R(\beta, \alpha, t)$ such that

$$\begin{pmatrix} \partial\beta/\partial t \\ \partial\alpha/\partial t \end{pmatrix} = \begin{pmatrix} \partial R/\partial\alpha \\ -\partial R/\partial\beta \end{pmatrix}.$$

The "new" Hamiltonian K is equal to $\mu H' + R$, where H' is the function H expressed in the "new" variables (β, α). A canonical transformation for which the *multiplier* μ is unity is a *symplectic transformation*.

A constructive method to generate symplectic transformation is the following:

For any twice differentiable function $S(q, \alpha)$ such that the Hessian $(\partial^2 S/\partial q \partial\alpha)$ is regular, the transformation from the phase space (q, p) to the phase space (β, α) implicitly defined by

$$p_i = \frac{\partial S}{\partial q_i} \quad ; \quad \beta_i = \frac{\partial S}{\partial \alpha_i} \quad 1 \leq i \leq n,$$

is a symplectic transformation.

Note that this is not the only way to construct symplectic transformations and that not all symplectic transformations can be generated in this way.

Hamilton-Jacobi Equation

A function $S(q, \alpha)$ is a complete solution of the *Hamilton-Jacoobi equation* corresponding to an Hamiltonian function $H(q, p)$ if the functions $(\partial S/\partial\alpha_i)$ are independent and if there exists a function $K(\alpha)$ such that

$$H(q_1, \cdots, q_n, \frac{\partial S}{\partial q_1}, \cdots, \frac{\partial S}{\partial q_n}) = K(\alpha_1, \cdots, \alpha_n).$$

When we know a complete solution of Hamilton-Jacobi equation the Hamiltonian system derived from H may be considered as solved. Indeed in the "new" phase space (β, α) the system is trivial. We have

$$\dot{\alpha}_i = -\frac{\partial K}{\partial \beta_i} \quad \longrightarrow \alpha_i = \alpha_i(0),$$
$$\dot{\beta}_i = \frac{\partial K}{\partial \alpha_i} = n_i(\alpha) \longrightarrow \beta_i = n_i t + \beta_i(0).$$

Of course, except in exceptional case the problem of finding a complete solution of Hamilton-Jacobi equation is at least as difficult as the problem of solving the original system of ordinary differential equations. A few of these "exceptional" cases are reviewed in the next section.

1.2 Integrables Systems

Traditionnaly one calls *integrable* an Hamiltonian system the solution of which can be reduced to quadrature. Other authors prefer to consider *integrable* an Hamiltonian system which can be transformed (by a symplectic transformation) into one depending only on the momenta. None of these definitions is really satisfactory as the only way of knowing whether a system can be reduced to quadrature or transformed in a special form is to effectively reduce or transform it. Hence one generally put forward *methods* for reducing (or transforming) some classes of systems and in some sense consider as integrable those systems which fall in one of the classes. Three main classes are usually considered:

Liouville Theorem

Consider an Hamiltonian system $\mathcal{H}(q_1, \cdots, q_n, p_1, \cdots, p_n)$, of n degrees of freedom, for which are known n independant first integrals $(F_i(q, p), 1 \leq i \leq n)$ in involution (i.e. such that $(F_i; F_j) = 0$, where $(.;.)$ is the Poisson bracket).

Locally, it is always possible to solve for the momenta the set of equations $(F_i(q, p) = \alpha_i)$

$$p_i = P_i(q_1, \cdots, q_n, \alpha_1, \cdots, \alpha_n) \qquad (1 \leq i \leq n) . \qquad (1)$$

If need be one can exchange some momenta for some variables by symplectic transformations of the type $(q'_k = p_k, p'_k = -q_k)$.

The n functions $p_i - P_i(q, \alpha)$ are also in involution (this is called the *Jacobi lemma*, see for instance Hagihara, 1970). Indeed from the identities

$$F_i(q, P(q, \alpha)) = \alpha_i \quad , 1 \leq i \leq n ,$$

we deduce, by differentiation with respect to the q_k

$$\frac{\partial F_i}{\partial q_k} = -\sum_{m=1}^{n} \frac{\partial F_i}{\partial p_m} \frac{\partial P_m}{\partial q_k} = \sum_{m=1}^{n} \frac{\partial F_i}{\partial p_m} \frac{\partial(p_m - P_m)}{\partial q_k} .$$

We have also (trivially) the identities

$$\frac{\partial F_i}{\partial p_k} = \sum_{m=1}^{n} \frac{\partial F_i}{\partial p_m} \frac{\partial(p_m - P_m)}{\partial p_k} .$$

and thus

$$\sum_{k=1}^{n} \frac{\partial F_i}{\partial q_k} \frac{\partial F_j}{\partial p_k} = \sum_{k=1}^{n} \sum_{m=1}^{n} \frac{\partial F_i}{\partial p_m} \frac{\partial(p_m - P_m)}{\partial p_k} \sum_{\ell=1}^{n} \frac{\partial F_j}{\partial p_\ell} \frac{\partial(p_\ell - P_\ell)}{\partial p_k}$$

$$= \sum_{m=1}^{n} \frac{\partial F_i}{\partial p_m} \sum_{\ell=1}^{n} \frac{\partial F_j}{\partial p_\ell} \sum_{k=1}^{n} \frac{\partial(p_m - P_m)}{\partial p_k} \frac{\partial(p_\ell - P_\ell)}{\partial p_k} ,$$

The Poisson brackets (F_i, F_j) are equal to

$$(F_i; F_j) = \sum_{m=1}^{n} \frac{\partial F_i}{\partial p_m} \sum_{\ell=1}^{n} \frac{\partial F_j}{\partial p_\ell} (p_m - P_m; p_\ell - P_\ell) \ .$$

As we have assumed that the Jacobian matrix $(\partial F_i/\partial p_m)$ is regular, the $(F_i; F_j)$ cannot vanish unless the $(p_m - P_m; p_\ell - P_\ell)$ vanish as well.

From this we conclude that for all m and ℓ

$$(p_m - P_m; p_\ell - P_\ell) = (p_m; p_\ell) + (P_m; P_\ell) + (p_m; P_\ell) + (P_m; p_\ell)$$
$$= \frac{\partial P_\ell}{\partial q_m} - \frac{\partial P_m}{\partial q_\ell} = 0 \ .$$

The vector field (P_m) is thus a gradient and there is a function $S(q, \alpha)$ such that

$$p_m = \frac{\partial S}{\partial q_m}(q_1, \cdots, q_n, \alpha_1, \cdots, \alpha_n) \ . \tag{2}$$

This function is a complete solution of the Hamilton-Jacobi equation and generates a symplectic transformation from (q, p) to (β, α). The transformed Hamiltonian $K(\beta, \alpha)$ is a function of the α alone as $\dot{\alpha}_i = (\partial K/\partial \beta_i) = 0$. The system is trivial in the new coordinates, the α are constant and the β are linear functions of the time.

In the most interesting case where the n-dimensional invariant manifolds $\{F_i = \alpha_i, 1 \leq i \leq n\}$ are compact and connected, they are n-tori and the variables β or linear combinations of them are angular variables (see for instance Dubrovin et al., 1985). Hence the general solution of the system amount to the definition of *angles-actions canonical variables*. We shall come back later on this notion.

Liouville theorem is probably the most general theorem about integrable systems and it gives us nice pieces of information about the geometry of the solutions, but it is not very constructive. The two other classes of integrable systems we are about to describe are less general but we can (in principle) recognize right away if a particular Hamiltonian belongs to them.

Stäckel Systems

The first class of integrable Hamiltonian systems we shall consider has been described in (Stäckel, 1905) and has received his name, although, as usual, there might be some precursors. It is described in most advanced textbooks and we give here briefly a somewhat generalized version of it.

Consider an Hamiltonian system $\mathcal{H}(q_1, \cdots, q_n, p_1, \cdots, p_n)$ of the form

$$\mathcal{H} = \sum_{i=1}^{n} a_i(q_1, \cdots, q_n) H_i(q_i, p_i) \ , \tag{3}$$

where the H_i depends only upon a single degree of freedom and the functions a_i are such that there exist functions $b_i(q_i, \alpha_1, \cdots, \alpha_n)$ with

$$\sum_{i=1}^{n} a_i(q_1, \cdots, q_n) b_i(q_i, \alpha_1, \cdots, \alpha_n) = K(\alpha_1, \cdots, \alpha_n), \qquad (4)$$

and such that the Jacobian $(\partial b_i / \partial \alpha_j)$ is regular.

Such an Hamiltonian system is integrable by *separation of variables*. Indeed the Hamilton-Jacobi equation

$$\sum_{i=1}^{n} a_i(q) H_i \left(q_i, \frac{\partial S}{\partial q_i} \right) = K(\alpha_1, \cdots, \alpha_n) = \sum_{i=1}^{n} a_i(q) b_i(q_i, \alpha_1, \cdots, \alpha_n).$$

can also be written

$$\sum_{i=1}^{n} a_i(q) \left[H_i(q_i, \frac{\partial S}{\partial q_i}) - b_i(q_i, \alpha_1, \cdots, \alpha_n) \right] = 0,$$

a complete solution of which can be obtained by separation of variables

$$S(q, \alpha) = \sum_{i=1}^{n} S_i(q_i, \alpha_1, \cdots, \alpha_n), \qquad (5)$$

with S_i solution of

$$H_i(q_i, \frac{\partial S_i}{\partial q_i}) = b_i(q_i, \alpha_1, \cdots, \alpha_n). \qquad (6)$$

Russian Dolls Systems

The second class of integrable Hamiltonian systems we shall consider is not as widely known. We have seen it described in (Landau and Lifchitz, 1960) and in (Arnold, 1985) and the name we give to it is not a reflection on the nationality of these authors but on the way the Hamiltonian function presents itself.

Let us consider an Hamiltonian function $\mathcal{H} = H_n$ where the function H_n is obtained from the recursive formula

$$H_0 = 0 \qquad ; \qquad H_i = H_i(q_i, p_i, H_{i-1}) \quad , \quad 1 \le i \le n. \qquad (7)$$

A complete solution of the Hamilton-Jacobi equation can also be obtained also by separation of variables

$$S(q, \alpha) = \sum_{i=1}^{n} S_i(q_i, \alpha_i, \cdots, \alpha_n), \qquad (8)$$

with S_i solution of

$$H_i\left(q_i, \frac{\partial S_i}{\partial q_i}, K_{i-1}(\alpha_{i-1}, \cdots, \alpha_n)\right) = K_i(\alpha_i, \cdots, \alpha_n). \tag{9}$$

where the K_i are, at this stage, arbitrary and can be taken for instance as $K_i = \alpha_i$. It is only when we shall introduce the concepts of action-angle variables (in the next section) that a pertinent choice can be made.

The intersection of the two classes of integrable systems is not empty (we shall see later on that, for instance, the Hamiltonian of the two-body problem is in this intersection) but none of them contains the other.

1.3 Action-Angle Variables

We want to discuss here a practical method of defining angle-action variables for Russian dolls systems. We shall consider specifically one and two degrees of freedom systems. The generalization to n degrees of freedom is not difficult. The usefulness of such a formalism appears only when these simple systems are viewed as first approximations of more complicated systems. Then the canonical formalism prepares them for the application of a perturbation theory.

A typical case is the case where the external parameters of the system change slowly with the time. A first approximation is obtained by freezing the parameters and perturbation theory shows that the action of the frozen system is the "adiabatic invariant". We shall discuss thist in the next chapter.

Angle-action variables cannot be defined smoothly accross saddle-connections of one-degree of freedom systems. But transition accross such saddle connections (such as for instance transition of a pendulum with slowly varying length - from circulation to libration) are very significant features. We shall consider this in chapter 3.

One-Degree of Freedom

Let us consider a one-degree of freedom dynamical system described by the Hamiltonian function

$$H(q, p) \tag{10}$$

which we assume to be an analytical function of the variable q and its conjugate momentum p, defined for (q, p) belonging to an open domain D of a two-dimensional manifold. The value of the Hamiltonian function (10) being constant along the solution curves of the dynamical system, these solutions curves lie along the level curves of the Hamiltonian function. The simplest case is when the level curves are closed and do not contain critical points (points such that the gradient ∇H of the Hamiltonian function is zero). The solutions are then periodic in the time.

We shall assume that, in the domain D, only this simplest case occurs. By this assumption we exclude, from the domain D, the saddle connections where one level curve of the Hamiltonian function contains one or more critical points and orbits asymptotic to these critical points. We shall comment on the saddle connections in chapter 3. We exclude also the cases where the level curves and the orbits extend to infinity. These orbits are usually not very interesting candidates for a perturbation theory.

In summary, we assume that D is

1. an open, bounded invariant set,
2. does not contain critical points.

The extension to a domain containing a single stable equilibrium point is not difficult but necessitates some special discussions that we prefer to avoid here.

In such a domain D , the general solution of the dynamical system described by the Hamiltonian (10) can be written

$$q = Q(t,h)$$
$$p = P(t,h) \tag{11}$$

where the functions P, Q are periodic in the time t of period $T(h)$. The parameter h is the value of the Hamiltonian function. In writing the general solution (11) we have assumed that an initial point (corresponding to $t = 0$) has been chosen on each solution curve by taking $q_0 = Q(0,h)$ and $p_0 = P(0,h)$ on a curve defined by an analytical function

$$F(q_0, p_0) = 0 . \tag{12}$$

This curve should of course intercept transversaly all the solutions in the domain D .

Our aim, in this section, is to write the general solution (11) under the form of a canonical transformation:

$$q = Q^\star(\psi, J)$$
$$p = P^\star(\psi, J) \tag{13}$$

from an angular variable ψ (increasing by 2π along each closed solution curve) and an action J , its conjugate momentum, which will obviously take the role of h in labelling each solution curve. This will be done by defining ψ and J as functions of t and h .

An obvious choice is to define ψ as a normalized time

$$\psi = \frac{2\pi}{T(h)} t \tag{14}$$

and to find the function $h(J)$ which makes

$$Q^\star(\psi, J) = Q(\frac{T(h(J))}{2\pi} \psi, h(J))$$

$$P^\star(\psi, J) = P(\frac{T(h(J))}{2\pi} \psi, h(J))$$

a canonical transformation. We have to check

$$(Q^\star; P^\star) = \frac{\partial Q^\star}{\partial \psi} \frac{\partial P^\star}{\partial J} - \frac{\partial Q^\star}{\partial J} \frac{\partial P^\star}{\partial \psi}$$

$$= \frac{T}{2\pi} \frac{\partial h}{\partial J} \left\{ \frac{\partial Q}{\partial t} \frac{\partial P}{\partial h} - \frac{\partial Q}{\partial h} \frac{\partial P}{\partial t} \right\} = 1 \qquad (15)$$

When we substitute to $\frac{\partial Q}{\partial t}$ and $\frac{\partial P}{\partial t}$ the right-hand members of the Hamiltonian differential equations, the condition (15) becomes

$$(Q^\star; P^\star) = \frac{T}{2\pi} \frac{\partial h}{\partial J} \left\{ \frac{\partial H}{\partial p} \frac{\partial P}{\partial h} + \frac{\partial H}{\partial q} \frac{\partial Q}{\partial h} \right\} = 1 . \qquad (16)$$

But from the identity

$$H(Q(t,h), P(t,h)) = h \qquad (17)$$

it is easy to conclude that the expression in brackets in (16) is equal to one and thus that the unknown function $h(J)$ is defined implicitly as the solution of

$$\frac{\partial J}{\partial h} = \frac{T(h)}{2\pi} \qquad (18)$$

Equation (18) is also of course a definition of the action variable J . This definition can be written under a form from which its geometrical meaning is made more apparent.

The following identity is not difficult to check

$$\frac{\partial}{\partial J} \left\{ \frac{\partial Q^\star}{\partial \psi} P^\star - \frac{\partial P^\star}{\partial \psi} Q^\star \right\} = 2(Q^\star; P^\star) + \frac{\partial}{\partial \psi} \left\{ \frac{\partial Q^\star}{\partial J} P^\star - \frac{\partial P^\star}{\partial J} Q^\star \right\}$$

By integrating both members with respect to ψ , we find:

$$\frac{\partial}{\partial J} \int_0^{2\pi} \left\{ \frac{\partial Q^\star}{\partial \psi} P^\star - \frac{\partial P^\star}{\partial \psi} Q^\star \right\} d\psi = 4\pi + \left[\frac{\partial Q^\star}{\partial J} P^\star - \frac{\partial P^\star}{\partial J} Q^\star \right]_0^{2\pi} \qquad (19)$$

The last term in (19) disappears as the functions $P^\star, Q^\star$ are 2π-periodic in ψ . Hence we find that, up to an arbitrary additive constant, the action J is equal to:

$$J = \frac{1}{4\pi} \int_0^{2\pi} \left\{ \frac{\partial Q^\star}{\partial \psi} P^\star - \frac{\partial P^\star}{\partial \psi} Q^\star \right\} d\psi \qquad (20)$$

or equivalently to

$$J = \frac{1}{4\pi} \int_0^T \left\{ \frac{\partial Q}{\partial t} P - \frac{\partial P}{\partial t} Q \right\} dt$$

or

$$J = \frac{1}{4\pi} \oint pdq - qdp \qquad (21)$$

where the path integral (21) is taken along the closed solution curve.

The last expression makes it obvious that $2\pi J$ can be usually defined geometrically as the area enclosed by the solution curve. We say usually because in some instances, the closed solution curve does not enclose a finite area (for instance when the closed solution curve goes around a cylinder). In these cases, the expression (21) is still well-defined and related to an area, but should receive another geometrical interpretation. Notice also that the area we are talking about is an oriented area. The direction of motion along the solution curve defines the sign of J.

In most textbooks the canonical transformation to action-angle variables is not defined in the same way but rather by means of the mixed generating function and the Hamiltonian-Jacobi equation. This other definition is equivalent and indeed may seem simpler. We did not follow the traditional presentation because the implicit character of the mixed generating function hides most of the topological difficulties of the problem. Let us sketch anyway this usual presentation.

Let us assume that the canonical transformation (13) is defined implicitly by the mixed generating function $S(q, J)$:

$$p = \frac{\partial S}{\partial Q} \quad , \quad \psi = \frac{\partial S}{\partial J} \tag{22}$$

and let us assume that it is such that the Hamiltonian function $H(q, p)$ is transformed into a function $K(J)$ of J alone. The corresponding Hamilton-Jacobi equation is:

$$H(q, \frac{\partial S}{\partial q}) = K(J) \tag{23}$$

and its solution is given by

$$S(q, J) = \int_{q_0}^{q} \mathcal{P}(q', K(J)) \, dq' \tag{24}$$

where the function $\overset{.}{\mathcal{P}}(q, h)$ is defined implicitly by the identity

$$H(q, \mathcal{P}(q, h)) = h .$$

Notice that the implicit function $\mathcal{P}$ may not be unique and that the integral defining S is actually a path-integral. For instance in the case of the pendulum

$$H = \frac{1}{2}p^2 - b\cos q$$

there is an ambiguity in the definition of the function $\mathcal{P}$

$$\mathcal{P} = \pm\sqrt{2h + 2b\cos q}$$

which must be solved in connection with the definition of the path integral (24). $\mathcal{P}$ is positive when q is increasing and $\mathcal{P}$ is negative when q is decreasing along the solution. Such difficulties do not arise with the explicit definition we have chosen. Setting aside those difficulties, we observe that from the definition of the canonical transformation:

$$\psi = \frac{\partial S}{\partial J} = \frac{\partial K}{\partial J} \int_{q_0}^{q} \frac{\partial P}{\partial h} \, dq \, ,$$

if we assume that q_0 does not depend upon h. If we cannot, or do not wish, to make this assumption, the computation becomes much more involved.

If we want the variable ψ to be an angular variable, increasing by 2π after a complete circuit along the periodic orbit, we should have

$$2\pi = \frac{\partial K}{\partial J} \frac{\partial}{\partial h} \oint P(q, h) \, dq$$

and thus, up to an additive constant,

$$J(h) = \frac{1}{2\pi} \oint P(q, h) \, dq$$

which is equivalent to (21).

Two Degree of Freedom Separable Systems

A n-degree of freedom separable system is in some sense a juxtaposition of n one-degree of freedom systems, with minimal interaction between them. It would then seems enough to develop the one-dimensional case as we just did. Nevertheless there are a few particular points worth mentionning. Let us then investigate with more details the case of a two-degree of freedom system. The extension to n-degree of freedom is straightforward although the notations may become clumsy.

Let us consider a Russian doll system with two degrees of freedom

$$H(q_1, p_1, L(q_2, p_2)) \, . \tag{25}$$

The differential equations corresponding to the second degree of freedom

$$\dot{q}_2 = \frac{\partial H}{\partial L} \frac{\partial L}{\partial p_2} \quad , \quad \dot{p}_2 = -\frac{\partial H}{\partial L} \frac{\partial L}{\partial q_2}$$

can be viewed as a one-degree of freedom system

$$\frac{dq_2}{d\tau} = \frac{\partial L}{\partial p_2} \quad , \quad \frac{dp_2}{d\tau} = -\frac{\partial L}{\partial q_2} \tag{26}$$

in the "pseudo-time"

$$\tau = \int_0^t \left(\frac{\partial H}{\partial L}\right) dt \, . \tag{27}$$

Notice that the "pseudo-time" τ does depend upon the first degree of freedom, but except for this, the system (26) is separated from this first degree of freedom.

If we assume that the solutions of (26) are periodic in τ of period $T_2(L)$ in a domain of the phase space (q_2, p_2), we can introduce in this domain action-angle variables

$$\varphi_2 = \tfrac{2\pi}{T_2} \tau$$
$$J_2 = \oint p_2 dq_2 - q_2 dp_2 \tag{28}$$

as we have done in the previous section. The transformation from (φ_2, J_2) to (q_2, p_2) given by

$$q_2 = Q_2^\star(\varphi_2, J_2)$$
$$p_2 = P_2^\star(\varphi_2, J_2) \tag{29}$$

is a one-degree of freedom canonical transformation, which completed by the identity transformation for the first degree of freedom, transforms the Hamiltonian (25) into

$$M(q_1, p_1, J_2) \tag{30}$$

where J_2 is a constant. If we consider the Hamiltonian (30) as a one-degree of freedom Hamiltonian in (q_1, p_1) depending upon a parameter J_2, and if the solutions of the system described by (30) are periodic of period $T_1(M)$ in a domain of the phase space (q_1, p_1), it is natural to introduce the action-angle variables

$$\psi_1 = \tfrac{2\pi}{T_1} t$$
$$J_1 = \oint p_1 dq_1 - q_1 dp_1 \tag{31}$$

by means of the one-degree of freedom canonical transformation, depending upon the parameter J_2:

$$q_1 = Q_1^\star(\psi_1, J_1, J_2)$$
$$p_1 = P_1^\star(\psi_1, J_1, J_2) \tag{32}$$

The question is now: can we make out of the two one-degree of freedom canonical transformations (29) and (32), one two-degree of freedom canonical transformation ?

To answer this question, we shall need, as we shall see, to distinguish in the scaled "pseudo-time" φ_2 a mean value, which will be used as the angular variable ψ_2 of the action-angle pair, and a periodic correction $\varrho(\psi_1, J_1, J_2)$ which will take into account the periodic variations of the "pseudo-time" with the motion of the first degree of freedom.

Let us first juxtapose the transformations (29) and (32) but, while doing so, let us give us some freedom by allowing us the possibility of correcting the definition of the angle variable ψ_2 in terms of φ_2. We shall see later on that this correction is the one we just mentioned.

$$q_1 = Q_1^\star(\psi_1, J_1, J_2)$$
$$p_1 = P_1^\star(\psi_1, J_2, J_2)$$
$$q_2 = Q_2^\star(\psi_2 + \varrho, J_2)$$
$$p_3 = P_2^\star(\psi_2 + \varrho, J_2) \tag{33}$$

The "correction" ϱ is assumed to be a yet unknown function of (ψ_1, J_1, J_2) .

It is a matter of a little algebra to verify that the Poisson bracket conditions of canonicity:

$$(Q_i^\star; P_j^\star) = \delta_{ij} \quad , \quad (Q_i^\star; Q_j^\star) = (P_i^\star; P_j^\star) = 0$$

amounts to the following partial differential equations for the unknown function ϱ:

$$\frac{\partial \varrho}{\partial \psi_1} = \frac{\partial Q_1^\star}{\partial J_2} \frac{\partial P_1^\star}{\partial \psi_1} - \frac{\partial Q_1^\star}{\partial \psi_1} \frac{\partial P_1^\star}{\partial J_2}$$

$$\frac{\partial \varrho}{\partial J_1} = \frac{\partial Q_1^\star}{\partial J_2} \frac{\partial P_1^\star}{\partial J_1} - \frac{\partial Q_1^\star}{\partial J_1} \frac{\partial P_1^\star}{\partial J_2} \tag{34}$$

The Froebenius condition of integrability of this set of partial differential equations reduce after some algebra to the condition

$$\frac{\partial}{\partial J_2} \left[\frac{\partial Q_1^\star}{\partial \psi_1} \frac{\partial P_1^\star}{\partial J_1} - \frac{\partial Q_1^\star}{\partial J_1} \frac{\partial P_1^\star}{\partial \psi_1} \right] = 0$$

which is obviously verified in view of the fact that the transformation (32) is a one-degree of freedom canonical transformation. Hence the partial differential equations (34) can be integrated and yield

$$\varrho = \int_0^{\psi_1} \left[\frac{\partial Q_1^\star}{\partial J_2} \frac{\partial P_1^\star}{\partial \psi_1} - \frac{\partial Q_1^\star}{\partial \psi_1} \frac{\partial P_1^\star}{\partial J_2} \right] d\psi_1 + \int^{J_1} G(J_1, J_2) \, dJ_1 \tag{35}$$

where the function $G(J_1, J_2)$ is defined as

$$G(J_1, J_2) = \left[\frac{\partial Q_1^\star}{\partial J_2} \frac{\partial P_1^\star}{\partial J_1} - \frac{\partial Q_1^\star}{\partial J_1} \frac{\partial P_1^\star}{\partial J_2} \right]_{\psi_1 = 0}$$

We have mentioned that the correction $\varrho(\psi_1, J_1, J_2)$ which we have just evaluated, can be viewed as a description of the relationship between the "pseudo-time" τ (see (27)) and the time t . Indeed we find easily that

$$\frac{d\varphi_2}{dt} = \frac{2\pi}{T_2} \frac{d\tau}{dt} = \frac{dM}{dJ_2}$$

On the other hand, the time derivative of the angular variable ψ_2 is given by

$$\frac{d\psi_2}{dt} = \frac{\partial K}{\partial J_2}$$

where K is the Hamiltonian function expressed in the action variables

$$K(J_1, J_2) = M(Q_1^\star(\psi_1, J_1, J_2), P_1^\star(\psi_1, J_1, J_2), J_2) \tag{36}$$

Differentiating the identity (36) with respect to J_2 we find

$$\frac{d\varrho}{dt} = \frac{d\varphi_2}{dt} - \frac{d\psi_2}{dt} = -\frac{\partial M}{\partial q_1}\frac{\partial Q_1^\star}{\partial J_2} - \frac{\partial M}{\partial p_1}\frac{\partial P_1^\star}{\partial J_2}$$

which, by using the differential equations in q_1 and p_1 becomes

$$\frac{d\varrho}{dt} = \frac{\partial Q_1^\star}{\partial J_2}\frac{\partial P_1^\star}{\partial t} - \frac{\partial Q_1^\star}{\partial t}\frac{\partial P_1^\star}{\partial J_2} \qquad (37)$$

Considering the linear relationship between the time and ψ_1 , (37) reproduces the time derivative of (35). The second integral in (35) which gives the value of ϱ at $\psi_1 = 0$, represents a "canonical synchronization" of the two time variables φ_2 and ψ_2 .

From the fact that $\varrho(\psi_1, J_1, J_2)$ is, up to a scale factor, the difference between the "pseudo-time" variable φ_2 and the uniform time variable ψ_2 , we can hope that actually ψ_2 reproduces the mean value of the "pseudo-time" and ϱ the periodic corrections. This is indeed the case. To check it we recall that J_1 is defined as

$$J_1 = \frac{1}{4\pi}\int_0^{2\pi}\left\{P_1^\star\frac{\partial Q_1^\star}{\partial\psi_1} - Q_1^\star\frac{\partial P_1^\star}{\partial\psi_1}\right\}\,d\psi_1$$

Differentiating the identity with respect to J_2 gives, after an integration by part,

$$0 = \varrho(2\pi, J_1, J_2) - \varrho(0, J_1, J_2) - \frac{1}{2}\left[P_1^\star\frac{\partial Q_1^\star}{\partial J_2} - Q_1^\star\frac{\partial P_1^\star}{\partial J_2}\right]_0^{2\pi}$$

Due to the periodicity of $Q_1^\star, P_1^\star$ with respect to ψ_1 the last term disappears and we conclude that ϱ is indeed 2π-periodic with respect to ψ_1 .

2 Classical Adiabatic Theory

The Adiabatic Invariant

Let us consider an Hamiltonian function which depends upon a parameter λ

$$H(q, p, \lambda) \qquad (38)$$

and let us consider that this parameter λ varies slowly with the time. By this we mean not only that $d\lambda/dt$ is small but that higher order derivatives of λ are smaller yet, i.e. that there exists a small quantity ε such that

$$\frac{1}{n!}\left|\frac{d^n\lambda}{dt^n}\right| \le \varepsilon^n \qquad (39)$$

Our results will be valid for ε "sufficiently small", i.e. they will be asymptotic results. To simplify the notation we shall assume actually that

$$\lambda = \varepsilon t . \qquad (40)$$

This can be done without loss of generality. The assumption (39) or (40) may seem to be strong but it is essential. It is not always quoted in full and is sometime hidden in the naive picture (pleasantly recalled by Arnold, 1978) that the "devil" pulling the strings (i.e. making λ a function of the time) is not only slow but ignores what the dynamical system does. Well, actually, he may know it but condition (39) makes him powerless to adjust to the dynamical system.

For a small to moderate length of time, the trajectory of the dynamical system described by (38) will not differ much from the trajectory of the "frozen system" $H(q, p, \lambda_0)$ where λ has been "frozen" to its constant initial value $\lambda_0 = \lambda(0)$. Later on, for a small interval of time around the value $t^\star$, the trajectories will again be close to the trajectories of the system $H(q, p, \lambda^\star)$ frozen at a different value $\lambda^\star = \lambda(t^\star)$. For a small interval of time around any given time $t^\star$, we can approximate the trajectory by its "guiding trajectory" which is defined as the trajectory of the system frozen at this given time, with initial condition $(q(t^\star), p(t^\star))$. The problem addressed by the adiabatic invariant theory is to describe the evolution with time of the guiding trajectory: How do we find at time $t^\star$, the guiding trajectory of the trajectory starting at q_0, p_0 at time $t = 0$.

To address this question we shall make use of course of the angle-action variables introduced in the previous chapter. But the transformation to angle-action variable now depends upon the parameter λ and thus upon the time

$$\begin{aligned} q &= Q^\star(\psi, J, \lambda) \\ p &= P^\star(\psi, J, \lambda) \end{aligned} \qquad (41)$$

We extend the phase space to (λ, q, Λ, p), where λ is a scaled time variable and Λ its conjugate momentum, and replace the time dependent Hamiltonian function $H(q, p, \varepsilon t)$ by a two-degree of freedom autonomous Hamiltonian $H(q, p, \lambda) + \varepsilon \Lambda$.

The one-degree of freedom canonical transformation (41) is extended to a two-degree of freedom canonical transformation by

$$\begin{aligned} \lambda^\star &= \lambda' \\ \Lambda &= \Lambda' + R(\psi, J, \lambda') \end{aligned} \qquad (42)$$

where the remainder function R is given by the time derivative of the mixed generating function (24)

$$R = -\frac{\partial S}{\partial \lambda}$$

or, if we want to avoid using this mixed generating function, by the expression

$$R = \int_0^\psi \left(\frac{\partial Q^\star}{\partial \psi} \frac{\partial P^\star}{\partial \lambda} - \frac{\partial Q^\star}{\partial \lambda} \frac{\partial P^\star}{\partial \psi} \right) d\psi + \int^J \left(\frac{\partial q_0}{\partial J} \frac{\partial p_0}{\partial J} - \frac{\partial q_0}{\partial J} \frac{\partial p_0}{\partial J} \right) dJ \qquad (43)$$

which can be deduced from the symplectic condition. In any case we do not need here to know the exact form of the remainder function R except for the fact that it is a periodic function of ψ.

The new Hamiltonian of the dynamical system is now

$$K' = K(J, \lambda') + \varepsilon \left\{ \Lambda' + R(\psi, J, \lambda') \right\} \tag{44}$$

and it is a straightforward application of the classical perturbation theory to generate a canonical transformation close to the identity

$$(\psi, \lambda', J, \Lambda') \longrightarrow (\emptyset\psi, \lambda', \emptyset J, \emptyset\Lambda') \tag{45}$$

such that the new Hamiltonian function

$$\emptyset K = K(\emptyset J, \lambda') + \varepsilon \left\{ \emptyset\Lambda' + \emptyset R(\emptyset J, \lambda', \varepsilon) \right\} + \varepsilon^{n+1} K_r(\emptyset\psi, \emptyset J, \lambda', \varepsilon) \tag{46}$$

does not depend upon the angular variable ψ up to terms of order ε^n for a given integer n.

To see this we just have to check that the vector space $\mathcal{F}$ of analytical function of (ψ, J, λ), periodic of period 2π in ψ is the direct sum of the vector space $\mathcal{F}_1$ of analytical function of (ψ, J, λ) with zero mean value in ψ and of $\mathcal{F}_2$ the set of analytical function of (J, λ). Furthermore, $\mathcal{F}_1$ belongs to the image of $\mathcal{F}$ by the operator

$$(K; \cdot) = - \left(\frac{\partial K}{\partial J} \right) \frac{\partial}{\partial \psi}$$

if $\frac{\partial K}{\partial J}$ is different from zero. Notice that the function $\frac{\partial K}{\partial J} = \frac{2\pi}{T}$ will enter the denominator at each step of the averaging procedure and thus that we have to make sure that it is bounded away from zero uniformly in ε in order to insure that the unaveraged remainder $\varepsilon^n K_r$ can be made as small as needed for small values of ε. Hence the domain $D(\lambda)$ on which we have defined the angle-action variables and now the averaged angle-action variables $(\emptyset\psi, \emptyset J)$ should not contain a saddle connection in its closure.

The differential equation for the averaged action $\emptyset J$ is

$$\left| \frac{d\emptyset J}{dt} \right| = \varepsilon^{n+1} \left| \frac{\partial K_r}{\partial \psi} \right| = C_1 \varepsilon^{n+1} \tag{47}$$

where C_1 is the supremum of $\left| \frac{\partial K_r}{\partial \psi} \right|$ in the domain $D(\lambda)$.

It can be used in a straightforward manner to evaluate the time-variation of $\emptyset J$:

$$|\emptyset J(t) - \emptyset J(0)| \leq C_1 \varepsilon^{n+1} t \tag{48}$$

as long as the trajectory remains in the domain $\emptyset D(\lambda)$, where $\emptyset D(\lambda)$ is the image of $D(\lambda)$ by the averaging transformation. It can be reduced to $0 \leq \psi \leq 2\pi$ and $\emptyset J_{\min}(\lambda) \leq \emptyset J \leq \emptyset J_{\max}(\lambda)$. Of course the constant C_1 in (47) depends upon the order n and may get very large for large n.

As we can monitor the variation of $\emptyset J$ by (48) itself, the estimate (48) is valid as long as one of the limit $\emptyset J_{\min}(\lambda)$ or $\emptyset J_{\max}(\lambda)$ does not approach $\emptyset J(0)$ or as long as $|t| \leq \varepsilon^{-n}$. Hence the estimate is valid for a very long time ($|t| \leq \varepsilon^{-n}$) unless the trajectory is forced out of the domain $D(J)$ of definition of the action-angle variable by approaching, for instance, a saddle-connection.

The averaged action $\emptyset J$ is not immediately accessible, and its geometrical meaning is somewhat blurred by the averaging procedure defining it. The non-averaged action J which differs from $\emptyset J$ by terms of the order of ε verify a weaker but perhaps more useful inequality:

$$|J(t) - J(0)| \leq C_2 \varepsilon , \quad \text{for } |t| \leq \varepsilon^{-n} \tag{49}$$

unless of course the trajectory is forced out of the domain $D(\lambda)$ before this time. This is why the action is called an adiabatic invariant and how it answers the question we raised at the beginning of this section: At time t^* the guiding trajectory of the trajectory starting at q_0, p_0 at time $t = 0$ is this guiding trajectory which admits the same action (labelled by the same value J) than the starting guiding trajectory.

The non-averaged momentum J , the classical action-variable, can be expressed as a function of the averaged variable $(\bar{\psi}, \bar{J})$ by means of the perturbation series. It leads to

$$J = \bar{J} + \varepsilon J_n(\bar{\psi}, \bar{J}, \lambda, \varepsilon) \tag{50}$$

where J_n is an analytical function periodic of period 2π in $\bar{\psi}$. The first order contribution of J_n is easy to compute and will be useful later on. We have

$$J = \bar{J} - \varepsilon \left(\frac{\partial K}{\partial J} \right)^{-1} \{ R(\bar{\psi}, \bar{J}, \lambda) - < R(\bar{\psi}, \bar{J}, \lambda) > \} + \mathcal{O}(\varepsilon^2) , \tag{51}$$

where $< \cdot >$ stands for the averaged value over $\bar{\psi}$. Inverting (51) we obtain:

$$\bar{J} = J + \varepsilon \left(\frac{\partial K}{\partial J} \right)^{-1} \{ R(\psi, J, \lambda) - < R(\psi, J, \lambda) > \} + \mathcal{O}(\varepsilon^2) . \tag{52}$$

Applications

The Modulated Harmonic Oscillator

As a first example let us consider the modulated harmonic oscillator, the Hamiltonian of which is

$$\mathcal{H}(q, p) = \frac{1}{2} \left(p^2 + \omega(\lambda) q^2 \right) , \tag{53}$$

with $\lambda = \varepsilon t$. The general solution is

$$q = \frac{\sqrt{2h}}{\omega} \sin(\omega t) ,$$
$$p = \sqrt{2h} \cos(\omega t .$$

We have choosen the line of initial conditions as $q = 0$. The period is $2\pi/\omega$ for all orbits. From formula (18) or from formula (21) we find

$$J = \frac{h}{\omega} . \tag{54}$$

Indeed one of the first mention of the principle of adiabatic invariance is a remark made by Einstein at one of the Solvay conference that changing slowly the frequency of the oscillator will keep the action constant but change the energy accordingly. This was an important remark in view of the fact that in his mind the oscillator was a simplified model of an atom submitted to a varying magnetic field. The action should be quantified and thus could not "change slowly".

The Two Body Problem

The central force problem to which the two body problem can be reduced, is described in spherical coordinates by the Hamiltonian,

$$\mathcal{H}(q,p) = \frac{1}{2m} \left[p_r^2 + \frac{1}{r^2} \left(p_\vartheta^2 + \frac{p_\varphi^2}{\cos^2 \vartheta} \right) \right] + \frac{m}{r} , \tag{55}$$

This Hamiltonian is both a Stäckel Hamiltonian and a "Russian doll" Hamiltonian. It is thus integrable and it is well known that, in terms of the traditional elliptic elements, the actions are

$$L = \sqrt{ma} , \quad G = \sqrt{ma(1 - e^2)} , \quad H = \sqrt{ma(1 - e^2)} \cos I , \tag{56}$$

where a is the semi major axis, e the eccentricity, and I the inclination of the orbit.

Let us consider a slow variation of the mass m of the attracting center. As the actions are kept constant, it is an immediate conclusion that the shape of the orbit (given by the parameters e and I) stays constant but that the size of the orbit (the semi-major axis) varies as the inverse of the mass.

The Pendulum

Various physical problems of interest can be modelized by a pendulum with slowly varying parameters.

The most obvious one is, of course, the pendulum itself with variable length $\lambda(t)$:

$$H = \frac{1}{2}I^2 - b(t)\cos\varphi \quad \text{with} \quad b = gL^3 . \tag{57}$$

Notice that we should not use the usual normalization $y = p_\varphi/L^2$ which, from the Hamiltonian

$$H' = \frac{1}{2}p_\varphi^2 / L^2 - gL\cos\varphi$$

leads to the Hamiltonian

$$H'' = \frac{1}{2}y^2 - \frac{g}{L}\cos\varphi .$$

Indeed, when λ is a function of time, the usual normalization is no longer canonical. Instead, we have used a change of time scale $\tau = t/\lambda^2$.

More generally, many resonance problems with variable restoring torque can be modelized by (57).

On top of the (slow) variation of the restoring torque $b(t)$ of the pendulum, one can take into account a (small) outside torque $(-\dot{c})$ by considering the differential equation

$$\ddot{\varphi} = -b\sin\varphi - \dot{c} . \tag{58}$$

Defining the momentum $I = \dot{\varphi} + c$, one is led to the Hamiltonian function

$$H = \frac{1}{2}(I - c)^2 - b\cos\varphi . \tag{59}$$

In plasma physics, one considers particles moving in a wave field with slowly varying amplitude and phase velocity leading to the equation (see, for instance, Cary et al., 1986)

$$\ddot{\varphi} = -b(t)\sin(\varphi - d(t))$$

The equation for the angular variables $\psi = \varphi - d$ is similar to (58) with $\dot{c}$ replaced by $\dot{d}$. Hence we are led to (59) with c replaced by d.

Menyuk (1985) prefers to consider a two modes system

$$H = \frac{1}{2}I^2 - \alpha\cos(\varphi - \varepsilon t) - \beta\cos(\varphi + \varepsilon t)$$

which can be put under the form (59) if we take

$$\begin{cases} b\sin d = (\alpha - \beta)\sin\varepsilon t , \\ b\cos d = (\alpha + \beta)\cos\varepsilon t . \end{cases} \tag{60}$$

The equation for the synchroneous motor:

$$\ddot{\varphi} = -b_0 \sin \varphi + a\dot{\varphi} \tag{61}$$

with a small dissipative term $(a\dot{\varphi})$ has been studied by Andronov *et al.* (1966) and Urabe (1954, 1955). Burns (1978) applied their results to the rotation of Mercury. This problem can also be modelized by the Hamiltonian (57). If we define the "momentum" I by

$$I = \dot{\varphi}e^{-at} , \tag{62}$$

and the new time variable τ by:

$$a\tau = e^{at} , \tag{63}$$

we are led to the differential equations:

$$\frac{d\varphi}{d\tau} = I \quad , \quad \frac{dI}{d\tau} = -e^{-2at}b_0 \sin \varphi = -(a\tau)^{-2}b_0 \sin \varphi , \tag{64}$$

which corresponds to the Hamiltonian (55) with $b = b_0e^{-2at} = (a\tau)^{-2}b_0$.

It may seem strange that a dissipative problem like (61) is mapped onto an Hamiltonian problem like (55). This apparent paradox is explained when one considers that (62) is time dependent and thus that a conservation of area in the phase space (φ, I) corresponds to an exponential decrease in area in the phase space $(\varphi, \dot{\varphi})$.

From this brief review, it is obvious that the slowly varying pendulum can modelize a large variety of interesting phenomena which all can be described by the Hamiltonian function (59). We shall slightly modify its expression to have $h = 0$ on the stable equilibrium and study the Hamiltonian function:

$$h = \frac{1}{2}(I - c)^2 + 2b \sin^2 \frac{\varphi}{2} \tag{65}$$

where b and c are slow functions of the time.

The action-angle variables (ψ, J) of the frozen system (65) are well-known. They are related to the variable (φ, I) by means of

In case of libration	In case of circulation
$\alpha = h/2b < 1$	$\beta^{-1} = h/2b > 1$
$\sin \varphi/2 = \sqrt{\alpha} \sin \ell$	$\sin \varphi/2 = \sin \vartheta$
$S = 4\sqrt{b}\{(\alpha - 1)\mathbf{F}(\ell, \alpha) + \mathbf{E}(\ell, \alpha)\} + c\varphi$	$S = 4\sqrt{b/\beta}\mathbf{E}(\vartheta, \beta)\cdot \text{sgn}\,(I - c) + c\varphi$
$\psi = \mathbf{F}(\ell, \alpha)\pi/2\mathbf{K}(\alpha)$	$\psi = \mathbf{F}(\vartheta, \beta)(\pi/\mathbf{K}(\beta))\cdot \text{sgn}\,(I - c)$
$J = 8\sqrt{b}\{(\alpha - 1)\mathbf{K}(\alpha) + \mathbf{E}(\alpha)\}/\pi$	$J = \frac{4}{\pi}\sqrt{b/\beta}\mathbf{E}(\beta) + c\,\text{sgn}\,(I - c)$
$\partial J/\partial h = 2\sqrt{b}\mathbf{K}(\alpha)/\pi$	$\partial J/\partial h = \sqrt{\beta/b}\mathbf{K}(\beta)/\pi$

The functions $\mathbf{F}(\ell,\alpha)$, $\mathbf{E}(\ell,\alpha)$, $\cdots$ are the usual elliptic integrals (see Abramowitz and Stegun, 1965, for the notations) and $\mathbf{Z}(\ell,\alpha)$ which appears later is the Jacobi's zeta function.

What is a little less known, although it can be found under various forms, more or less explicit in Best (1968), Timofeev (1978), Menyuk (1985), are the formulae for the slowly varying pendulum. One finds that the remainder function of the canonical transformation going from (φ, I) to (ψ, J) is

in case of Libration:

$$\varepsilon R = \dot{c}\varphi + \frac{2\dot{b}}{\sqrt{b}}\mathbf{Z}(\ell,\alpha) \, ,$$

in case of Circulation:

$$\varepsilon R = \frac{\dot{c}}{\mathbf{K}(\beta)}\{2\mathbf{K}(\beta)\vartheta - \pi\mathbf{F}(\vartheta,\beta)\} + \frac{2\dot{b}}{b}\sqrt{b/\beta}\mathbf{Z}(\vartheta,\beta) \, .$$

In both cases, the mean value of the remainder function vanishes

$$< R >= \frac{1}{2\pi}\int_0^{2\pi} R \, d\psi = 0 \, .$$

From this, it is easy to compute the first order correction to the adiabatic invariant. From (I.72), we obtain

in case of Libration:

$$\bar{J} = J + \frac{2}{\pi}\mathbf{K}(\alpha)\{\frac{2\dot{b}}{b}\mathbf{Z}(\ell,\alpha) + \frac{\dot{c}}{\sqrt{b}}\varphi\} + \mathcal{O}(\frac{\varepsilon^2\log^2(\alpha-1)}{\alpha-1}) \, ,$$

in case of Circulation:

$$\bar{J} = J + \frac{1}{\pi}\mathbf{K}(\beta)\left\{\frac{2\dot{b}}{b}\mathbf{Z}(\vartheta,\beta) + 2\dot{c}\vartheta\sqrt{\beta/b}\right\} - \dot{c}\mathbf{F}(\vartheta,\beta)\sqrt{\beta/b}$$

$$+ \mathcal{O}(\frac{\varepsilon^2\log^2(\beta-1)}{\beta-1})$$

The Magnetic Bottle

If the adiabatic invariance received prominence because of its role in the early formulation of quantum mechanics, its importance in classical mechanics became first of significance for applications in connection with the magnetic momentum of gyration of a charged particle in a strong magnetic field. This was shown to be an invariant by Alfven (1950) in his investigation of cosmical rays. Very soon afterwards, its usefulness in the theoretical design of devices for controlling hot plasmas (Stellarators, Tokamaks, Mirror Machines, $\cdots$)

was recognized (see, for instance, Kruskal, 1952; see also Freidberg, 1982 for a recent review).

We shall try in this section to suggest why the adiabatic invariance is so important in this context, without, of course, giving a full account of its technical applications. This would require by itself a complete review paper which we are not competent to write.

The motion of a particule of mass m and electric charge e in an electromagnetic field is controled by the Hamiltonian function:

$$H = \frac{1}{2m}\|\mathbf{p} - \frac{e}{c}\mathbf{A}(\mathbf{x})\|^2 + e\varphi(\mathbf{x}) \tag{66}$$

where φ and $\mathbf{A}$ are respectively the electric potential and the magnetic vector potential of the field:

$$\mathbf{E} = -\text{grad } \varphi \ ,$$

$$\mathbf{B} = \text{rot } \mathbf{A} \ .$$

The vector $\mathbf{x}$ is the position vector of the particle and the vector $\mathbf{p}$ its momentum related to its velocity $\mathbf{V}$ by

$$\mathbf{p} = m\mathbf{V} + \frac{e}{c}\mathbf{A} \ . \tag{67}$$

Let us assume that the vector-potential and the magnetic field are given by

$$\mathbf{A} = B_0(1 + b(x_3))x_1\mathbf{e}_2 \ , \tag{68}$$

$$\mathbf{B} = B_0(1 + b)\mathbf{e}_3 - B_0 b' x_1 \mathbf{e}_1 \ , \tag{69}$$

where (x_1, x_2, x_3) are the cartesian coordinates of $\mathbf{x}$ in an orthonormal basis $(\mathbf{e}_1, \mathbf{e}_2, \mathbf{e}_3)$ and b' is the first derivative of b with respect to x_3.

This magnetic field describes a two-dimensional "magnetic bottle" (with two throats). The magnetic field is an almost constant field in the direction of $\mathbf{e}_3$ but slightly (if b' is small) modulated. The magnetic lines are given by

$$x_1 = \frac{x_1(0)}{1 + b(x_3)} \quad , \quad x_2 = x_2(0) \tag{70}$$

and their shape is illustrated in Figure 24 for $b = \beta^2 x_3^2$.

It would have been more realistic to consider a magnetic field with cylindrical symmetry described for instance by:

$$\mathbf{A} = \frac{B_0}{2}(1 + b)[x_1\mathbf{e}_2 - x_2\mathbf{e}_1] \ ,$$

$$\mathbf{B} = B_0(1 + b)\mathbf{e}_3 - \frac{B_0 b'}{2}[x_1\mathbf{e}_1 + x_2\mathbf{e}_2]$$

or a toroidal stellarator (Kovrizhnykh, 1984) but the geometry we have adopted will simplify the calculations without changing essentially the analysis.

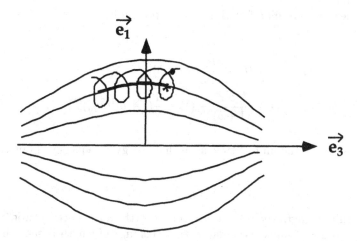

Fig. 1. The magnetic lines in the plane (e_1, e_3). The motion of the particle is approximately a circle centered at the gyrocenter c. The gyrocenter itself moves slowly along the magnetic line bouncing back and forth in the "bottle".

Assuming at first no electric field, the Hamiltonian reads

$$H = \frac{1}{2m}\{p_1^2 + p_3^2 + [p_2 - \frac{eB_0}{c}(1+b)x_1]^2\} . \tag{71}$$

We introduce now the "guiding center" coordinates by means of the following canonical transformation

$$
\begin{aligned}
x_1 &= \tfrac{1}{1+b}Y_c + \tfrac{1}{(1+b)^{1/2}}y_g & p_1 &= \tfrac{eB_0}{c}(1+b)^{1/2}Y_g \\
x_2 &= y_c + \tfrac{1}{(1+b)^{1/2}}Y_g & p_2 &= \tfrac{eB_0}{c}Y_c \\
x_3 &= y_3 & p_3 &= \tfrac{eB_0}{c}\{Y_3 + \tfrac{b'}{2(1+b)}Y_g y_g + \tfrac{b'}{(1+b)^{3/2}}Y_c Y_g\} .
\end{aligned}
\tag{72}
$$

The quantities (Y_g, Y_c, Y_3) are the momenta respectively conjugated to the variables (y_g, y_c, y_3). Geometrically speaking, $(Y_c/(1 + b), y_c, y_3)$ are the coordinates of a point: the guiding center (or gyrocenter). Remark that the curves along which Y_c and y_c are constant are precisely the magnetic lines defined in (70). On the other hand, the quantities (y_g, Y_g) can be viewed as the coordinates (scaled by a factor $(1 + b)^{1/2}$) of the moving particle in a frame centered at the guiding center.

This geometrical interpretation of the canonical transformation (72) may seem peculiar in the fact that both the variables (y_g, y_c) and their momenta

(Y_g, Y_c) are interpreted in terms of position (respectively of the guiding center and of the particle). This is not that unusual; after all, the possibility of treating variables and momenta on the same foot is one of the advantages of Hamiltonian mechanics.

The new Hamiltonian function of the problem is:

$$K = \frac{c}{eB_0} H = \frac{eB_0}{2mc} \{(1+b)[y_g^2 + Y_g^2]$$
$$+ [Y_3 + \frac{b'Y_g}{(1+b)^{3/2}}(Y_c + \frac{1}{2}(1+b)^{1/2}y_g)]^2\} . \tag{73}$$

Let us choose the unit of time such that the gyrofrequency is unity:

$$\frac{eB_0}{mc} = 1$$

and the unit of length such that the gyroradius (the norm of the vector (y_g, Y_g)) is of the order of unity. We assume that this unit of length is such that the scale on which the magnetic field changes significantly is large (say of the order of $1/\varepsilon^2$). With this assumption in mind, we introduce a scaling of the third dimension together with polar coordinates for the gyro-coordinates

$$y_g = \sqrt{2G} \sin g , \; Y_g = \sqrt{2G} \cos g ,$$
$$y_c = y , \qquad Y_c = Y , \tag{74}$$
$$y_3 = \frac{1}{\varepsilon} z , \qquad Y_3 = \varepsilon Z ,$$

which brings the Hamiltonian (73) under the form

$$K = (1+c)G + \frac{\varepsilon^2}{2}[Z + \frac{\varepsilon c'}{(1+c)^{3/2}}(Y + \frac{1}{2}\sqrt{2G(1+c)} \sin g)\sqrt{2G} \cos g]^2 \tag{75}$$

where c is a scaled version of the function b

$$b(y_3) = c(\varepsilon^2 y_3) = c(\varepsilon z) . \tag{76}$$

The function $1 + c(\cdot)$ and its derivatives are assumed to be of the order of unity in the domain of interest.

If we "freeze" the third coordinate by considering the function c as a constant, the Hamiltonian function (75) is actually a one-degree of freedom Hamiltonian expressed in its action-angle variables (g, G).

What makes the problem somewhat different from the other problems we have investigated in the previous section is that the (hopefully slow) dependence upon the time is not direct but the result of its (slow) dependence upon a second-degree of freedom (z, Z). To investigate the motion of this second degree of freedom, we need some knowledge about the motion of the first one.

Hence the problem deviates from the narrow frame we have considered up to now and should be considered in the general frame of perturbation theory. In this case it is not difficult to show that we can define a canonical transformation from (g, G, z, Z) to $(\bar{g}, \bar{G}, \bar{z}, \bar{Z})$ such that, in the new (averaged) variables, the transformed Hamiltonian $\bar{K}$ depends upon $\bar{g}$ only through terms of the order of ε^{N+1}:

$$\bar{K} = (1+c)\bar{G} + \frac{\varepsilon^2}{2}\bar{Z}^2 + \frac{\varepsilon^4}{2}\frac{c'^2\bar{G}}{(1+c)^3}[\bar{Y}^2 + \frac{\bar{G}}{8}(1+c)] + \prime(\varepsilon^6) . \tag{77}$$

A first approximation of $\bar{K}$, the one which is explicitly written in (77) is, of course, the averaged value of K with respect to g.

We can now consider $\bar{G}$ as a constant. (It is an adiabatic invariant, its time derivative being of the order of ε^{N+1}) and analyse (77) as a one-degree of freedom Hamiltonian in $(\bar{z}, \bar{Z})$. Let us restrict ourselves to a simple case where the function c is given by

$$c(x) = \frac{d}{2}x^2 . \tag{78}$$

Then the leading terms of (77) reproduce the harmonic oscillator

$$\bar{K} = \frac{\varepsilon^2}{2}[\bar{Z}^2 + (d^2\bar{G})\bar{z}^2] + 0(\varepsilon^4) , \tag{79}$$

the frequency of which is a function of $\bar{G}$, the (averaged) orbital magnetic momentum of the particle.

Hence, at least in a first approximation, the guiding center of the particle (coordinates: $Y/(1+b), y, z/\varepsilon$) bounces back and forth along a magnetic line (Y and y constant) between two "mirror points": $z = \pm z_M$ with

$$z_M = \frac{\bar{Z}(0)}{d}\frac{1}{\sqrt{G}} . \tag{80}$$

Confinement of the plasma inside the magnetic bottle depends crucially upon the fact that z_M does not increase beyond a given bound on a very long time scale. Two things may happen: $\bar{Z}(0)$ may change due, for instance, to collisions between particles inside the plasma or $\bar{G}$ may change due also to collisions or to a default in the adiabatic invariance.

As we have just recalled, the invariance of $\bar{G}$ is only asymptotic. In the framework of the model just discussed for the magnetic bottle, Chirikov (1979) estimates the changes in $\bar{G}$ over a bounce period as proportional to

$$\Delta\bar{G} \sim \frac{1}{\varepsilon}\exp\{-\frac{2}{3\varepsilon}\} , \tag{81}$$

a quantity exponentially small with ε.

On the other hand, the model just discussed is, of course, only approximative. Fluctuations in the magnetic field or electric field may complicate the topology of the "frozen system" corresponding to (75) with $c = $ constant. We have found this system to be just the harmonic oscillator with (g, G) as action variables. But fluctuations in the fields may introduce a separatrix in the phase space of the "frozen" system. The adiabatic invariance of the averaged $\bar{G}$ may then be in default at each crossing of the separatrix. We shall investigate this case later when we have described the tools to deal with it.

3 Neo-adiabatic Theory

3.1 Introduction

By virtue of his own success, the classical adiabatic invariant theory is often led to a trap. Indeed it is able to describe slow but finite deformation of the guiding trajectory (trajectory of the frozen system to which the real trajectory stays close). But simple dynamical systems such as the pendulum possess saddle connections and during its deformation the guiding trajectory may very well bump on a critical curve where the theory is no longer valid.

As far as we know, Timofeev (1978) was the first to give a precise (and correct) estimate of the change of the adiabatic invariant in the particular case of a pendulum, the restoring torque of which varies linearly with time. Such a result could be gathered also from the estimates of Yoder (1973-1979) but Yoder was interested in capture probability and not so much in change in the adiabatic invariant.

More recently a very throughout analysis of "separatix crossing" led Cary et al. (1986) (see also Escande, 1985) and independently Neishtadt (1986) to very general estimates of the change in the invariant and of its distribution with respect to the initial phase. The basic ideas for such an analysis can also be found in Hannay (1986).

Estimates of the change in the invariant are not only useful in order to follow precisely the guiding trajectory but mostly because of the fact that it can produce chaotic motion (Menyuk, 1985). Changes in the invariant are very sensitive to the initial phase and so is the "final" (after transition) phase. If the system is forced to go periodically through a transition this is bound to produce the very unstable and unpredictable kind of motion known as "chaotic motion". From the distribution of the changes, estimates of the "diffusion time" or the Lyapunov characteristic number of the motion could be derived.

Celestial Mechanicians were not so worried about changes in the invariant or chaotic motion but rather about probability of capture. Indeed in most instances and specifically in the case of the pendulum, when the guiding trajectory comes close to the critical curve (let us say coming from positive rotation), it can end up in two possible states, either libration or negative circulation. If the pendulum is a model of a resonance, this means a capture (or a non-capture) into resonance and Celestial Mechanics has many of these resonances (either Orbit-Orbit or Spin-Orbit) to explain.

As a matter of fact this problem of "capture into resonance" was investigated even before its connection with the adiabatic invariant was perceived (Goldreich, 1965, 1966). Formulae based upon a pendulum model were proposed for the probability of capture in the Spin-Orbit case (Goldreich and Peale, 1966) and the Orbit-Orbit case (Yoder, 1973-1979). Yoder and independently Neishtadt (1975) were apparently the first to make the connection between this problem and the adiabatic invariant theory. Henrard (1982) proposed a formula to compute the probability of capture for general Hamiltonian systems (with one degree of freedom and slowly varying).

This formula (see 126) is simple and almost intuitive. It is interesting to notice that it was stated without proof for the nonlinear oscillator by Dobrott and Green (1971) under the name of "Kruskal Theorem". A similar formula applies for a class of dissipative systems and is stated by Arnold (1964).

3.2 Neighborhood of an Homoclinic Orbit

We assume that the one-degree of freedom dynamical system described by the Hamiltonian function

$$H(x, \lambda) = h \tag{82}$$

possesses in its domain D of definition one and only one non-degenerate unstable equilibrium $x^\star(\lambda)$, limit point of two homoclinic trajectories $\Gamma_1(\lambda)$ and $\Gamma_2(\lambda)$.

The global topology of the two homoclinic curves $\Gamma_1(\lambda)$ and $\Gamma_2(\lambda)$ may be of various types as shown in Figure 2.

All these dynamical systems are equivalent on an open neighborhood of the critical curve and we shall use the bow-tie model which is easier to draw to illustrate our analysis.

Notice that the angle-action variables introduced in the first chapter cannot be defined on the full domain D as it contains a critical curve on which they are singular.

But we can define three subdomains on which they are well-defined. The domain D_1 (resp. D_2) is the open set of D touching Γ_1 (resp. Γ_2) and D_3 is the open set of D touching both curves (see Figure 3). Most of our analysis will be devoted to the estimation of limits when the periodic trajectories defined in one of these domains approach its boundary Γ_1 , Γ_2 or $\Gamma_3 = \Gamma_1 \cup \Gamma_2$.

In order to simplify the subsequent analysis, and without loss of generality, we shall make three assumptions.

First, and this is trivial, we shall assume that $h = 0$ corresponds to the critical curve formed by $x^\star(\lambda)$, $\Gamma_1(\lambda)$ and $\Gamma_2(\lambda)$. This can always be achieved by subtracting $H(x^\star(\lambda), \lambda)$ from the Hamiltonian. In the same spirit, we shall assume that the value of h is positive in the domain D_3 and negative in D_1 and D_2. This can always be achieved by changing, if need be, the sign of one of

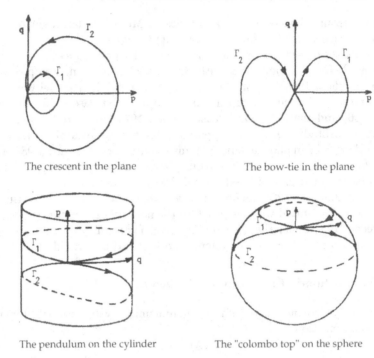

Fig. 2. Different types of global topology of the Homoclinic orbits.

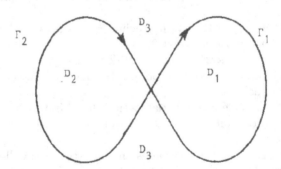

Fig. 3. The three subdomains defined by the homoclinic orbits Γ_1 and Γ_2 .

the canonical coordinates q or p in order to change the sign of the Hamiltonian function.

Let us remark that this assumption imposes the direction of the time arrow on the orbits (Figure 3 has been drawn accordingly) and subsequently the sign of the action-variables J_i ($1 \leq i \leq 3$) in each domain D_i. The sign will be positive if the orbits are travelled clockwise and negative if they are travelled counter-clockwise.

We shall assume also that $x^\star(\lambda) \equiv 0$ and that the time scale $\omega(\lambda)$ defined in (85) is actually independent of λ and equal to its value $\omega(\tau)$ for a fixed τ (the pseudo-crossing time) to be defined later. These two conditions can be achieved at the price of slight modifications of the parametrization of the system and does not affect the generality of the analysis.

As mentioned earlier, an important part of our analysis will consist in defining and estimating quantities (actually functions of the parameter λ) which describe the dynamical system in a small neighborhood of the homoclinic orbit. At the lowest order, these quantities are the critical values of the action-variables (defined below), the time scale at the unstable equilibrium $\omega(\lambda)$ (defined in (85)), the "steepness" parameters $h_i^\star$ (defined in (95)) and the "out-of-symmetry" parameters g_i (defined in (98)) introduced by Cary et al. (1986).

Let us start by defining the critical values of the action-variables $J_i^\star(\lambda)$ ($1 \le i \le 3$) as the limits of the action-variable in the domain D_i when the periodic curves tend towards the homoclinic curves. They are

$$J_i^\star(\lambda) = \frac{1}{4\pi} \oint_{\Gamma_i} p\,dq - q\,dp\,, \quad 1 \le i \le 2\,.$$

$$J_3^\star(\lambda) = J_1^\star(\lambda) + J_2^\star(\lambda)\,,$$

The integrals are of course finite as they are the area (divided by 2π) of the domain D_i ($1 \le i \le 2$):

$$J_i^\star(\lambda) = \frac{1}{4\pi} \oint_{\Gamma_i} p\,dq - q\,dp\,, \quad 1 \le i \le 2\,. \tag{83}$$

3.3 Close to the Equilibrium

It is well-known that, in the vicinity of an equilibrium, one can "normalize" an Hamiltonian system (Birkhoff, 1927). This normalization is in general only asymptotic but the formal power series can be shown in some cases to be convergent (e.g. Siegel and Moser, 1971) and thus the normalization to be analytical. This is the case for a one-degree of freedom system such as the one we are analysing.

Hence there exists a disk of radius δ around the unstable equilibrium $x = 0$ of the system (82) in which is defined an analytical canonical transformation from the phase space $x = (q, p)$ to the phase space $z = (z_1, z_2)$:

$$x = X_N(z, \lambda) \tag{84}$$

which transforms the Hamiltonian function $H(x, \lambda)$ into the normalized Hamiltonian

$$h = H_N(Z, \lambda) = \omega(\lambda)Z + \mathcal{O}(Z^2) \tag{85}$$

where Z is the product of the two coordinates

$$Z = z_1 z_2 . \tag{86}$$

The function $\omega(\lambda)$ is one of the eigen-values (the other one is $-\omega(\lambda)$) of the matrix of the linearized system. It is bounded away from zero as we have assumed that the equilibrium $x = 0$ is non-degenerate and it can always be chosen as positive, if need be by exchanging z_1 and z_2. Furthermore, as we have mentioned in the previous section, it can be made independent of λ by a change of the time variable.

We shall also consider the inverse of the function (85):

$$z_1 z_2 = Z(h, \lambda) = \frac{h}{\omega} + \mathcal{O}(h^2) . \tag{87}$$

In the plane (z_1, z_2) the trajectories are given by the branches of the hyperbola $z_1 \cdot z_2 = Z(h, \lambda)$ as shown in Figure 4. In the domain D_3 the two branches belong to the same trajectory while in the domain D_1 and D_2 the two branches belong to different orbits (one in D_1 and the other one in D_2).

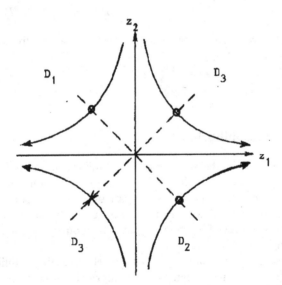

Fig. 4. Trajectories in normalized coordinates (z_1, z_2) showing the apices (∘) and the anti-apex (×).

In each of the three open domains D_i, we can define angle-action variables (ψ_i, J_i). For this we have to choose a curve of "initial conditions" (see (I.9)). We shall choose $z_1 = z_2 = \sqrt{Z}$ for D_3 and $z_1 = -z_2 = \pm\sqrt{|Z|}$ for D_1 and D_2. This initial point along a trajectory will be called its "apex". The return point $z_1 = z_2 = -\sqrt{Z}$ along a trajectory in D_3 will be called the "anti-apex". Apex and anti-apex are called "vertex" by Cary et al. (1986).

The normalizing transformation (84) is not uniquely defined although the normalized Hamiltonian (85) is uniquely defined. This makes the definition of the apices coordinate-dependent. We shall come back on this later.

The transformation from the normalizing coordinates (z_1, z_2) to the angle-action variables (ψ_i, J_i) of each domain D_i are easy to define. The generating functions $S'(z_1, J_i, \lambda)$ is (see (24)):

$$S'_i(z_1, J_i, \lambda) = \int_{\pm\sqrt{|Z_i|}}^{z_1} \frac{Z_i}{z_1} dz_1 + \frac{1}{2}Z_i = \pm\frac{1}{2}Z_i \log \frac{z_1^2 e}{|Z_i|} \tag{88}$$

where Z_i is a yet unknown function of J_i and λ. Its definition depends upon the global properties of the trajectory and it cannot be determined by the analysis of this section which is purely local being confined to the disk of radius δ around the origin. We shall determine this function or rather its inverse $J_i = \mathcal{J}_i(Z, \lambda)$ in the next section.

Note that a "$\pm$" sign is inserted in (88) and in what follows, to indicate that the sign of the function should be adjusted (in an obvious way) in accordance with the quadrangle of the plane (z_1, z_2) to which the domain D_i belongs.

When we consider that $\lambda = \varepsilon t$, the normalizing transformation (84) and the transformation to action-angle variables are time-dependent. The remainder function to be added to H_N in order to produce the "new Hamiltonian" of the dynamical system is the sum of the remainder function of the normalizing transformation $R_N(z, \lambda)$ and the remainder function of the transformation to action-angle variables, $R'_i(\psi_i, J_i, \lambda)$.

The equilibrium $x = 0$ being sent on $z = 0$, the normalizing transformation has no independent term and the remainder function R_N has no linear term

$$R_N(z, \lambda) = \mathcal{O}(\|z\|^2) . \tag{89}$$

On the other hand, we have for the second remainder function:

$$R'_i(\psi_i, J_i, \lambda) = \frac{\partial S'}{\partial \lambda} = \pm\frac{1}{2}\left(\frac{\partial Z_i}{\partial \lambda}\right) \log \frac{z_1^2}{|Z_i|} = \left(\frac{\partial Z_i}{\partial \lambda}\right)\left(\frac{\partial Z_i}{\partial J_i}\right)^{-1} \psi_i .$$

Summing the two contributions and defining the function $J_i = \mathcal{J}_i(Z, \lambda)$ as the inverse of the yet unknown function mentioned earlier, we have

$$R_i(\psi_i, J_i, \lambda) = -\left(\frac{\partial \mathcal{J}_i}{\partial \lambda}\right) \psi_i + R_N(z, \lambda) . \tag{90}$$

3.4 Along the Homoclinic Orbit

In this section we shall evaluate the unknown functions $\mathcal{J}_i(Z, \lambda)$ we just mentioned and the first order correction to the adiabatic invariant expressed by (94) or (96). These evaluations will make it necessary to introduce the steepness parameters h_i^* (see (95)) and the out-of-symmetry parameters g_i (see (98)) mentioned earlier.

Let us remember that $2\pi J_i$ is the area enclosed by the closed curve $H(x, \lambda) = h = H_N(Z, \lambda)$. It can be evaluated as the difference between the area $2\pi J_i^*(\lambda)$ enclosed by the critical curve and an area that can be divided into two parts A_1 and A_2 as shown in Figure 5 (which is drawn for the domain D_2).

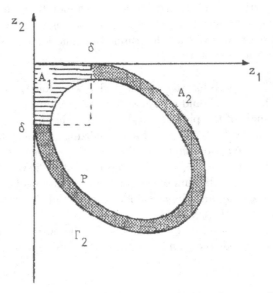

Fig. 5. Evaluation of the area enclosed by the curve P.

The area A_1 is equal to

$$A_1 = \int_{|Z/\delta|}^{\delta} \frac{|Z|}{z_1} dz_1 + \delta\left(\frac{|Z|}{\delta}\right) = |Z| \log \frac{\delta^2 e}{|Z|} . \tag{91}$$

The area A_2 is an analytical function of h (and thus of Z) vanishing with h (and thus with Z). Collecting those results and remembering the sign convention we made at the beginning of the section, we obtain

$$\mathcal{J}_i(Z, \lambda) = J_i^*(\lambda) + \frac{Z}{2\pi} \log \frac{\Phi_i(Z, \lambda)}{|Z|} \qquad (1 \leq i \leq 2) \tag{92}$$

where the functions $\Phi_i(Z, \lambda) = \delta^2 e \exp(A_2/|Z|)$ are analytical functions. These two functions are invariants of the dynamical system and, together with the function $Z(h, \lambda)$, they characterize it completely. These are the functions we introduced in the previous section. The functional dependences of J_i with respect to h:

$$J_i(h, \lambda) = \mathcal{J}_i(Z(h, \lambda), \lambda) \qquad (1 \leq i \leq 2) \tag{93}$$

will also be most useful. Their approximations close to the homoclinic orbits are given by

$$J_i(h, \lambda) = J_i^\star(\lambda) + \frac{h}{2\pi\omega} \log \frac{eh_i^\star}{|h|} + \mathcal{O}(h^2 \log |h^{-1}|), \tag{94}$$

The parameters

$$h_i^\star(\lambda) = \frac{\omega(\lambda)}{e} \Phi_i(0, \lambda) \qquad (1 \leq i \leq 2) \tag{95}$$

are the "steepness parameters" mentionned earlier. They measure the rates at which J_i approach $J_i^\star$ when h goes to zero. As such they will enter in many of our estimates.

Formula (92) is valid for the two domains D_1 and D_2. In order to evaluate the area enclosed by a trajectory in the domain D_3, we have to add twice the area A_1 plus the two areas of the type A_2 corresponding to each lobe along Γ_1 and Γ_2. We find

$$\mathcal{J}_3(Z, \lambda) = J_3^\star(\lambda) + \frac{Z}{\pi} \log \frac{\Phi_3(Z, \lambda)}{|Z|}$$

with

$$\Phi_3(Z, \lambda) = [\Phi_1(Z, \lambda) \, \Phi_2(Z, \lambda)]^{1/2} \quad , \quad J_3^\star(\lambda) = J_1^\star(\lambda) + J_2^\star(\lambda) .$$

Hence J_3 is approximated by

$$J_3(h, \lambda) = J_3^\star(\lambda) + \frac{h}{\pi\omega} \log \frac{eh_3^\star}{|h|} + \mathcal{O}(h^2 \log |h^{-1}|), \tag{96}$$

with

$$h_3^\star(\lambda) = [h_1^\star \, h_2^\star]^{1/2} \tag{97}$$

We turn now to the evaluation of the first order corrections to the adiabatic invariants for small (but not too small) values of h. From (52), we have

$$\bar{J}_i = J_i + \varepsilon \left(\frac{\partial J_i}{\partial h} \right) \{ R(\psi_i, J_i, \lambda) - < R(\psi_i, J_i, \lambda) > \} + \mathcal{O}(\varepsilon^2 h^{-1} \log^2 |h^{-1}|) .$$

In estimating the error term, we made use of (52) but also of (94) in order to estimate the derivatives of h with respect to J_i.

We shall evaluate the adiabatic invariant $\bar{J}_i$ at the apex ($\psi_i = 0$). From (90) we have that

$$R_i(0, J_i, \lambda) = R_N(\pm\sqrt{|Z|}, \pm\sqrt{|Z|}) = \mathcal{O}(|Z|) = \mathcal{O}(h) .$$

It remains to evaluate the mean value of the remainder functions. After some computation (see (Henrard 1993) for details) we find

$$< R_i > = \left(\frac{\partial J_i}{\partial h}\right)^{-1} \{-g_i(\lambda) + \mathcal{O}(h \log|h^{-1}|)\} \quad 1 \le i \le 2 ,$$

$$< R_3 > = \left(\frac{\partial J_3}{\partial h}\right)^{-1} \{-g_3(\lambda) + \pi\Delta_{12} + \mathcal{O}(h \log|h^{-1}|)\} ,$$

with

$$\Delta_{12} = \frac{\partial J_1}{\partial \lambda} \frac{\partial J_2}{\partial h} - \frac{\partial J_2}{\partial \lambda} \frac{\partial J_1}{\partial h}$$

and

$$g_3(\lambda) = g_1(\lambda) + g_2(\lambda) . \tag{98}$$

The functions $g_i(\lambda)$, which are important because they measure the first order corrections to the adiabatic invariants (see below), vanish when the functions R_i ($1 \le i \le 2$) are odd in ψ. This is the case when the dynamical system possesses the right type of symmetry and when the apices are chosen accordingly. This is why we have called these functions the "out-of-symmetry" parameters. Most of the simple dynamical systems have the right type of symmetry and the corresponding functions $g_i(\lambda)$ vanish. For more general systems, the functions can be evaluated numerically, for instance, by means of the numerical integration of the variational equations.

Gathering these results, we find that the adiabatic invariants in each of the three domains D_i are given by

$$\bar{J}_i = J_i + \varepsilon g_i + \mathcal{O}(\varepsilon h \log|h^{-1}|, \varepsilon^2 h^{-1} \log^2|h^{-1}|) \quad 1 \le i \le 2 , \tag{99}$$

$$\bar{J}_3 = J_3 + \varepsilon\{g_3 - \pi\Delta_{12}\} + \mathcal{O}(\varepsilon h \log|h^{-1}|, \varepsilon^2 h^{-1} \log^2|h^{-1}|) \tag{100}$$

where the J_i ($1 \le i \le 2$) are evaluated at the apices.

3.5 Traverse from Apex to Apex

We shall now be concerned with solutions of the non-autonomous system described by the Hamiltonian function:

$$H(x, \varepsilon t) = h(t) . \tag{101}$$

As we have seen in Section 3.3, this system is equivalent in a disk of radius δ around the origin, to the system described by

$$H'(z, \varepsilon t) = H_N(Z, \varepsilon t) + \varepsilon R_N(z_1, z_2, \varepsilon t) \tag{102}$$

in the normalizing coordinates (z_1, z_2).

We shall be concerned more specifically with a "traverse" from apex to apex (or from apex to anti-apex) close to one of the homoclinic orbits Γ_i.

Let us assume that at time t_0, a trajectory of (101) is at an apex (or anti-apex) with $h = h_0$, $\lambda = \lambda_0$, $z_1^2 = z_2^2 = \zeta_0^2 = |Z(h_0, \lambda_0)|$, and that the following apex (or anti-apex) corresponds to $t = t_1$, $h = h_1$, $\lambda = \lambda_1$, $z_1^2 = z_2^2 = \zeta_1^2 = |Z(h_1, \lambda_1)|$.

We plan to evaluate the difference in "energy" and in time between those two consecutive apices:

$$\Delta h = h_1 - h_0 \quad , \quad \Delta \lambda = \lambda_1 - \lambda_0 = \varepsilon \, \Delta T = \varepsilon \, (t_1 - t_0) \, . \qquad (103)$$

In order to obtain these estimates, we compare the solution of the non-autonomous system (101) (or (102)) which passes through an apex at time λ_j/ε with the energy h_j:

$$x(t, h_j, \lambda_j) \quad \text{or} \quad z(t, h_j, \lambda_j) \quad (1 \leq j \leq 2) \, . \qquad (104)$$

with the solution of the autonomous system described by $H(x, \lambda_j)$ or $H_N(Z, \lambda_j)$ which we denote

$$x^*(t, h_j, \lambda_j) \quad \text{or} \quad z^*(t, h_j, \lambda_j) = (\zeta_j \exp\{\Omega_j t\} \, , \, \zeta_j \exp\{-\Omega_j t\}) \qquad (105)$$

where $\Omega_j = \Omega(\zeta_j^2, \lambda_j)$, the function Ω being the derivative $\partial H_N / \partial Z$.

The comparison is quite delicate if one wishes to reach very small values of h_0 (of the order of $\exp\{-1/\varepsilon\}$) which implies very long periods of time (of the order of $1/\varepsilon$).

The main step (developed in detail in Henrard 1993) is to compare, in the disk of radius δ around the origin, the solution $z(t, h_j, \lambda_j)$ of the non-autonomous system with the solution

$$u^* = (\zeta_j \exp\{\mu_j(t)\}, \zeta_j \exp\{-\mu_j(t)\}) \quad , \quad \mu_j = \int_{t_j}^{t} \Omega(\zeta_j^2, \varepsilon t) \, dt \, , \qquad (106)$$

of the intermediary system described by $H_N(Z, \varepsilon t)$.

We find the estimate

$$\|z - u^*\| \leq c_6 \varepsilon \quad \text{for} \quad c_7 \exp\{-\frac{1}{c_1 \varepsilon}\} \leq h_j \leq c_5 \qquad (107)$$

where c_1, c_5, c_6, c_7 are constants independent of ε.

It is for the comparison of u^* and z^* that the assumption we have made that ω is independent of λ is useful. Indeed this assumption makes the estimate, in the disk of radius δ around the origin:

$$|\mu_j - \Omega_j t| \leq c_8 \varepsilon h_j \log |h_j^{-1}| \qquad (108)$$

sharper than the corresponding estimate ($|\mu_j - \Omega_j t| \leq c_8 \varepsilon \log |h_j^{-1}|$) to which one would be led if ω, the leading term in Ω, were indeed a function of time. The estimate (108) leads to a total estimate

$$\|z - z^\star\| \leq c_9 \varepsilon \qquad (109)$$

in the disk of radius δ around the unstable equilibrium.

The value of ΔT, the time spent from apex (h_0, λ_0) to the next one (h_1, λ_1) is then estimated as follows. Let

$$\Delta T = T_0^\varepsilon + T_1^\varepsilon + T_\delta^\varepsilon \qquad (110)$$

where $T_0^\varepsilon(h_0, \lambda_0)$ and $T_1^\varepsilon(h_1, \lambda_1)$ are the values of the time spent in the disk of radius δ in the neighborhood of the two apices and T_δ^ε the value of the time spent outside this disk. The superscript ε is there to recall that we are considering the non-autonomous system with $\lambda = \varepsilon t$.

From lengthty computations (see Henrard 1993), we get an estimate for ΔT as a mean value of the periods of two trajectories of the autonomous system, the initial conditions of which correspond to the value of h and λ at the apices

$$\Delta T = \frac{1}{2}\{T(h_0, \lambda_0) + T(h_1, \lambda_1)\} + \mathcal{O}(\varepsilon \log h_m^{-1})$$

$$= \pi\{(\frac{\partial J}{\partial h}(h_0, \lambda_0) + (\frac{\partial J}{\partial h})(h_1, \lambda_1)\} + \mathcal{O}(\varepsilon \log h_m^{-1}), \qquad (111)$$

where h_m is the minimum value of h_0 and h_1. We now proceed by estimating Δh:

$$\Delta h = h_1 - h_0 = \varepsilon \int_{t_0}^{t_1} \frac{\partial H}{\partial \lambda}(x, \varepsilon t)\, dt . \qquad (112)$$

The integral can be split into two parts: One starting from t_0 on an interval of $T(h_0, \lambda_0)/2$ and the other one on an interval $T(h_1, \lambda_1)/2$ ending at t_1. Each of these integrals is then compared with the corresponding integrals with $x^\star(t, h_i, \lambda_i)$ substituted to x and λ_i substituted to εt. We obtain eventually (see (Henrard, 1993) for details)

$$\Delta h = \varepsilon \int_0^{T(h_j, \lambda_j)} \frac{\partial H}{\partial \lambda}(x_j^\star, \lambda_j)\, dt + \mathcal{O}(\varepsilon^2 \log h_m^{-1}) . \qquad (113)$$

where the subscript j may be taken indifferently as 0 or 1.

It remains to compute the integral in the right-hand member of (113).

From (43) we compute:

$$R(2\pi) - R(0) = \left(\frac{\partial K}{\partial J}\right)^{-1} \int_0^{2\pi} \left[\frac{\partial H}{\partial p}\frac{\partial P^*}{\partial \lambda} + \frac{\partial H}{\partial q}\frac{\partial Q^*}{\partial \lambda}\right] d\psi$$

$$= \left(\frac{\partial K}{\partial J}\right)^{-1} \int_0^{2\pi} \left[\frac{d}{d\lambda}H(Q^*, P^*, \lambda) - \frac{\partial H}{\partial \lambda}\right] d\psi$$

$$= \left(\frac{\partial K}{\partial J}\right)^{-1} \int_0^{2\pi} \left[\frac{\partial K}{\partial \lambda} - \frac{\partial H}{\partial \lambda}\right] d\psi,$$

because $H(Q^*, P^*, \lambda) = K(J, \lambda)$. As the remainder function is periodic, the above integral is zero. We conclude that

$$\int_0^\infty \frac{\partial H}{\partial \lambda}(x_j^*, \lambda_j)\, dt = \left(\frac{\partial K}{\partial J}\right)^{-1} \int_0^{2\pi} \frac{\partial K}{\partial \lambda}\, d\psi = 2\pi \left(\frac{\partial K}{\partial J}\right)^{-1} \frac{\partial K}{\partial \lambda}.$$

Eventually we obtain

$$\Delta h = -2\pi\varepsilon \left(\frac{\partial J}{\partial \lambda}\right)(h_j, \lambda_j) + \mathcal{O}(\varepsilon^2 \log |h_m^{-1}|). \tag{114}$$

The last equality is obtained by differentiating $K(J(h, \lambda), \lambda) = h$ with respect to λ.

The approximations (111) and (114) define mappings from (h_0, λ_0) to (h_1, λ_1), from apex to apex in each of the domains D_i. These mappings reproduce (approximately) the behaviour of the non-autonomous dynamical system in the vicinity of the homoclinic orbit. They are Poincaré's mappings with the apices defining the surfaces of section.

In what follows we shall use only an approximation of this mapping which is easier to handle. It is obtained by substituting the approximations (94) for the functions J_i

$$\Delta\lambda_i = \frac{\varepsilon}{2\omega}\left\{\log\frac{h_i^*}{|h_0|} + \log\frac{h_i^*}{|h_1|}\right\} + \mathcal{O}(\varepsilon^2 \log|h_m^{-1}|, \varepsilon h_M \log h_M^{-1});$$

$$\Delta h_i = -2\pi\varepsilon\left(\frac{\partial J_i^*}{\partial \lambda}\right) + \mathcal{O}(\varepsilon^2 \log|h_m^{-1}|, \varepsilon h_M \log h_M^{-1}). \tag{115}$$

The subscripts (i) in Δh_i, $\Delta\lambda_i$ have been inserted to recall that the mapping is different in each of the domains D_i. The functions $\omega(\lambda)$, $h_i^*(\lambda)$ and $J_i^*(\lambda)$ are evaluated at $\lambda = \lambda_0$. We recall also that h_m (resp. h_M) stands for the minimum (resp. maximum) of the absolute values of h_0 and h_1.

Formulae (115) are not meaningful if $\varepsilon \log |h_m^{-1}|$ is not small. We thus make the assumption

$$h_m \geq \varepsilon\eta \gg \exp\{-\varepsilon^{-1}\}. \tag{116}$$

Later, we shall be led to the choice

$$\eta = \frac{1}{\varepsilon} \exp\{-\varepsilon^{-1/3}\} \tag{117}$$

in order to minimize the error terms on the final results.

3.6 Probability of Capture

We are now in a position where we can analyse the transition from one domain to another one. We shall investigate in this section the basic question: where does the trajectory go when, from inside the domain D_i (which is shrinking), it is pushed towards the critical curve ? Does it stay indefinitely close to the critical curve ? Does it end up eventually well inside one of the other domains D_j where the adiabatic invariant can again inform us about its ultimate fate, and which one of the other domains ?

We shall show that, except for a set of initial conditions, the measure of which is exponentially small with ε , the trajectory does end up in one of the other two domains after a time such that the parameter λ has not changed significantly.

In some cases we shall be able to say which one of the other domains is visited. In other cases, it depends very sensitively upon the initial conditions. So sensitively that the accuracy on the initial conditions needed to decide which one it is, is not physically meaningful and, as a consequence, we shall resort to a probabilistic argument.

Let us first investigate the case where the trajectory is initially in domain D_3 and approaches the critical curve close enough so that the formula (115) becomes meaningful. As we are approaching the critical curve and not going away from it, Δh_3 , the increment of h (see (59)), is negative and, at each turn, from apex to apex, the value of h decreases by an amount proportional to ε (we assume of course that the $\partial J_i^\star / \partial \lambda$ are bounded away from zero). Eventually, h takes on a value h_0 such that

$$0 < h_0 \le -\Delta h_3 . \tag{118}$$

This is the last time the trajectory goes through the apex in domain D_3. We shall call it the main apex. As we use the approximation (115), we have to exclude from our consideration, initial conditions such that h_0 comes closer to one of its limiting values (0 and $-\Delta h_3$) than $\varepsilon\eta$ (see 116).

This is part of the set of initial conditions we were mentioning earlier and for which our analysis fails. The corresponding trajectories could stay for a very long time, possibly forever, close to the "unstable equilibrium". Note that the "unstable equilibrium" is an equilibrium of the "frozen" system with λ constant. In the system we are analysing, with $\lambda = \varepsilon t$, the equilibrium may be replaced by a very complicated invariant set.

Let us assume now that the two domains D_i ($1 \leq i \leq 2$) increase in size. It means that Δh_1 and Δh_2 (see (115)) are also negative and that $\Delta h_3 = \Delta h_1 + \Delta h_2$ is larger in absolute value than either of them. If h_0 happens to be in the interval

$$\varepsilon \eta \leq h_0 \leq -\Delta h_1 - \varepsilon \eta \,, \tag{119}$$

the first traverse along Γ_1 after that will bring the trajectory inside the domain D_1 with a negative value of h. From there-on, the trajectory will loose energy at the rate of Δh_1 for each turn in D_1 and will end up well inside this domain.

On the other hand, if h_0 is in the interval

$$-\Delta h_1 + \varepsilon \eta < h_0 < -\Delta h_3 - \varepsilon \eta \,, \tag{120}$$

the trajectory will arrive at the anti-apex in domain D_3 with a value of the energy equal to $h'_0 = h_0 + \Delta h_1$, with

$$\varepsilon \eta < h'_0 < -\Delta h_2 - \varepsilon \eta \,. \tag{121}$$

The traverse along Γ_2 after this will bring the trajectory inside D_2 and from there-on it will go deeper and deeper in D_2.

If we do not know the exact value of h_0 but assume that the distribution of possible values is uniform on the interval of definition (118) (we shall come back on this assumption later), the probability of the trajectory ending up in D_i is proportional to the length of the interval (119) or (121). As a consequence, we have

$$P_i = \frac{\Delta h_i}{\Delta h_3} = \frac{\partial J_i^\star}{\partial \lambda} \Big/ \frac{\partial J_3^\star}{\partial \lambda} + \mathcal{O}(\varepsilon \log(\varepsilon \eta)^{-1}) \tag{122}$$

where P_i is the probability of the trajectory ending up in domain D_i. With the assumption (118), the error term is $\varepsilon^{2/3}$.

If, on the other hand, the two domains D_i ($1 \leq i \leq 2$) do not increase in size but only one of them does, say D_1 , the trajectory will certainly end up in that domain. Indeed only Δh_1 is negative and the trajectory can only leave D_3 along Γ_1 and enters then D_1. Once it has entered it, it will remain in it, decreasing its energy by Δh_1 at each traverse.

Let us investigate now the case where the trajectory is initially in one of the two domains D_i ($1 \leq i \leq 2$). Let us choose D_2 to simplify the notations.

The value of Δh_2 is then positive (as we are approaching the critical curve) and we shall eventually enter the domain D_3 (except possibly for an exponentially small set of initial conditions). At the first apex in Domain D_3, which we shall call the main apex, the energy is h_0 with

$$\varepsilon \eta < h_0 < \Delta h_2 - \varepsilon \eta \tag{123}$$

as we have crossed $h = 0$ in the last traverse along Γ_2 just before this apex.

Again we have to consider two cases according to the sign of Δh_1. If it is positive, the energy will increase at each successive traverse and the trajectory will end up in D_3.

If Δh_1 is negative and if h_0 happens to fall in the interval

$$\varepsilon\eta \leq h_0 \leq -\Delta h_1 - \varepsilon\eta \,, \tag{124}$$

the trajectory will enter the domain D_1 on its first traverse along Γ_1 and will remain there loosing energy at each successive traverse in D_1.

If h_0 does not belong to the interval (124), it means that it belongs to

$$-\Delta h_1 + \varepsilon\eta \leq h_0 \leq \Delta h_2 - \varepsilon\eta \tag{125}$$

and that $-\Delta h_1 < \Delta h_2$ or that $\Delta h_3 = \Delta h_2 + \Delta h_1 > 0$. Hence the trajectory does not enter D_1 on its first traverse along Γ_1 and increases its energy by Δh_3 on the total trip from apex to apex. This will be true for the successive trips from apex to apex until formula (115) is no longer valid and we are deep enough in domain D_3.

Again if we do not know the exact value of h_0 but assign a uniform distribution of probability on its value in the domain of definition (123), the probability P_i of the trajectory ending up in D_i ($i = 1$ or 3) is proportional to the length of the intervals (124) or (125):

$$P_1 = -\frac{\partial J_1^\star}{\partial\lambda} \bigg/ \frac{\partial J_2^\star}{\partial\lambda} + \mathcal{O}(\varepsilon\log(\varepsilon\eta)^{-1}) \,,$$

$$P_3 = \frac{\partial J_3^\star}{\partial\lambda} \bigg/ \frac{\partial J_2^\star}{\partial\lambda} + \mathcal{O}(\varepsilon\log(\varepsilon\eta)^{-1}) \,.$$

The various cases we have analysed may be summarized in a unique formula. We may consider a jump from domain D_i to domain D_j ($1 \leq i, j \leq 3$) if the trajectories are leaving D_i, i.e.

$$\text{leaving } D_i: \qquad \text{sgn}(h_i) \cdot \left(\frac{\partial J_i^\star}{\partial\lambda}\right) > 0 \,.$$

In that case, the probability of the jump from D_i to D_j is given by:

$$P_r(i,j) = -\text{sgn}(h_i h_j)\frac{\partial J_j^\star}{\partial\lambda} \bigg/ \frac{\partial J_i^\star}{\partial\lambda} + \mathcal{O}(\varepsilon\log(\varepsilon\eta)^{-1}) \,, \tag{126}$$

where $\text{sgn}(h_i)$ is the sign of h in the domain D_i. Written in this way, Formulae (71) and (72) are independent of the assumption on the sign of h made in Section 3.2.

Of course, formula (126) should be understood with the following convention. If the right-hand member is negative, the probability is actually zero and if the right-hand member is larger than one, the probability is actually one.

We shall call the function $P_r(i,j)$ the probability function. It is equal to the probability of transition when its value lies between zero and one.

We ought to come back now on the assumption that h_0, the value of the Hamiltonian at the main apex, is a random variable uniformly distributed on its interval of definition (see (118) or (123)).

When the probabilistic argument is introduced simply by our lack of knowledge about the precise initial conditions (or for that matter the precise modelization of the dynamical system) of a unique "test particle" as it happens in most problems of capture into resonance in Celestial Mechanics, then the assumption is as good as another one. On the other hand, if we are thinking in terms of distribution of many test particles in a dynamical system as it is natural in problems involving charged particles in a plasma, then it becomes important to relate the distribution on the values of h_0 (at the main apex) with the distribution of initial conditions far from the transition. Neishtadt (1975) found that it is a simple consequence of Liouville's Theorem.

We shall paraphrase Neishtadt's argument by using Poincaré-Cartan Integral Invariant.

Let us take two small sets of points P_i ($1 \leq i \leq 2$) in the extended phase space (q, p, t). We take them at the main apex, centered respectively around a value $h_0(i)$ of h_0:

$$P_i : (q, p, t) \text{ such that } \begin{cases} z_1 = z_2(\text{apex}) \, , \\ h_0 \in [h_0(i) - \delta h, h_0(i) + \delta h] \, , \\ t \in [t_0 - \delta t, t_0 + \delta t] \} \, . \end{cases} \qquad (127)$$

The values of the Integral Invariant for these sets of points are then

$$\int \int_{P_i} dq \, dp - dH \, dt = - \int \int_{P_i} dH \, dt = -4\delta h \cdot \delta t \, . \qquad (128)$$

Let us define Q_i ($1 \leq i \leq 2$) as the sets of points in phase space translated from P_i along the trajectories back to a time $t = \tau$ when they are far away from the transition. As the integrals in (74) remain invariant, we have

$$\int \int_{Q_i} dq \, dp - dH \, dt = \int \int_{Q_i} dq \, dp = -4\delta h \cdot \delta t \, .$$

The areas of the two sets of initial conditions Q_i are then equal. Hence if the distribution of test particles in the phase-space far from transition is uniform, so is the distribution of values of h_0 for test particles crossing the apex per unit of time.

We have assumed in the argument above a uniform distribution of test particles in the full phase-space far from transition because it is the simplest assumption. Actually the set of points Q_i can be shown to be very narrow strips along the guiding trajectories far from transition (see Escande, 1985), and thus it is enough to assume that the distribution of test particles is uniform in ψ.

3.7 Change in the Invariant

The results of Section 3.5 concerning the changes in h and λ in one traverse must be combined to obtain the total changes in h and λ (and from there in the adiabatic invariant) for a trajectory leaving one domain D_i ($1 \leq i \leq 3$) and entering another one D_j ($1 \leq j \neq i \leq 3$).

Let us start a trajectory at an apex A_N corresponding to N complete traverses (apex to apex) along the curve Γ_i in the domain D_i before reaching the main apex A_0 (the one just before the "crossing" of the separatrix). The value of h and λ at each apex A_k ($0 \leq k \leq N$) in between will be denoted h_k and λ_k.

At each apex A_k , the value of the adiabatic invariant is given by $\bar{J}_i(h_k, \lambda_k)$ where the function $\bar{J}_i(h_k, \lambda_k)$ can be deduced recursively from (59).

Far from the critical curve, the value of $\bar{J}_i$ should remain constant from apex to apex but, close to the critical curve, it is no longer true and it is precisely these differences that we wish to evaluate.

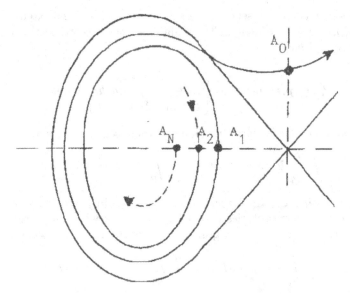

Fig. 6. First half of the trajectory from A_N to A_0.

From (59), we know that from apex to apex, the difference $\Delta h = h_{k+1} - h_k$ remains more or less constant. But this is not the case for the difference $\Delta \lambda = \lambda_{k+1} - \lambda_k$ which depends sensitively upon the value of h_k.

It is thus the successive values of λ_k and their dependence upon the "final" state (h_0, λ_0) at the main apex that will be the key to the variation of the adiabatic invariant. Put otherwise the rate of change of h per traverse remains constant but the time spent in a traverse is very sensitive to initial conditions. From this it follows that the guiding trajectory (the trajectory of the autonomous system defined by $J_i(h, \lambda)$) and the true trajectory lose synchronization when we approach the critival curve as the true trajectory may spend a variable amount of time close to the unstable equilibrium.

It is this default of synchronization that we can evaluate by comparing the "true time of transit":

$$\Lambda_i = \lambda_0 - \lambda_N \tag{129}$$

with the "pseudo time of transit":

$$\Lambda_i^\star = \tau_i - \lambda_N \tag{130}$$

where τ_i is the value of λ where transition from D_i to D_j would take place if the adiabatic invariant were conserved. The "pseudo crossing time" τ_i is thus defined by

$$J_i^\star(\tau_i) = \bar{J}_i(\lambda_N, h_N) \,. \tag{131}$$

The loss of synchronization is the difference $\Lambda_i - \Lambda_i^\star$ and it can be evaluated (see Henrard 1993) as a function of the value h_0 of the Hamiltonian at the main apex and of the pseudo crossing time τ_i. Of course, the same is true for the second half of the trajectory, between the "main apex" A_0 and the apex (or anti-apex) B_M, where again we are far enough from the critical curve for the action J_j to be considered as constant. A detailed analysis shows that the error is minimized if we take

$$N = M \sim \log(\varepsilon\eta)^{-1} \sim \varepsilon^{-1/3} \,. \tag{132}$$

Because $h_N \sim N\Delta h \sim N\varepsilon \sim \varepsilon^{2/3}$, we are, for this value of h_N , deep enough in the domain D_2 for the adiabatic invariant to be preserved.

The loss of synchronization between the real trajectory and the guiding trajectory is instrumental in computing the change in the adiabatic invariant during a transition. Indeed, from the definition of the pseudo crossing time, we have, for a transition from domain D_i to domain D_j $(1 \leq i \neq j \leq 3)$

$$\begin{aligned}
\Delta\bar{J} &= \bar{J}_j(h_M, \lambda_M) - \bar{J}_i(h_N, \lambda_N) \\
&= J_j^\star(\tau_j) - J_i^\star(\tau_i) \\
&= J_j^\star(\tau_i) - J_i^\star(\tau_i) + (\frac{\partial J_j^\star}{\partial \lambda})(\tau_j - \tau_i) + \mathcal{O}(\varepsilon^{4/3}\log^2\varepsilon^{-1}) \,.
\end{aligned} \tag{133}$$

The first difference in the right-hand member of (133) is simply the jump resulting from the definition of the action variable as an area. It would exist even if the action J were a perfect invariant during transition. The third term involves the loss of synchronization on both sides of the crossing of the critical curve. The error term comes from the neglected terms of the order of $(\tau_i - \tau_j)^2$.

From the evaluation of the loss of synchronization in the domains D_i and D_j, we find

$$\Delta \bar{J} = \Delta_1(i,j) + \Delta_2(i,j) + \mathcal{O}(\varepsilon^{4/3} \log^2 \varepsilon^{-1}),$$

$$\Delta_1(i,j) = J_j^\star - J_i^\star + \varepsilon \left(\frac{\partial J_j^\star}{\partial \lambda}\right) \left\{ \left(\frac{\partial J_j^\star}{\partial \lambda}\right)^{-1} g_j - \left(\frac{\partial J_i^\star}{\partial \lambda}\right)^{-1} g_i \right\} \quad (134)$$

$$\Delta_2(i,j) = \frac{\varepsilon}{\omega} \left(\frac{\partial J_j^\star}{\partial \lambda}\right) G_{ij}(z).$$

The first terms Δ_1 depends only upon the pseudo-crossing-time τ_i and not upon the value of h_0 at the main apex. Due to its symmetry, its contribution to the change in the adiabatic invariant is not cumulative but cancels out when we consider periodic jumps back and forth between the two domains.

It can be shown also that while the quantities g_i and g_j do depend upon the choice of the particular normalizing transformation used in defining the apices (see section 3.4), the combination of them which appears in (135) is actually independent of this choice.

The second term Δ_2 contains the meaningful part of the adiabatic invariant change. The analytical expression of the function G_{ij} depends upon whether one of the domains involved in the jump is the "double" domain D_3 or not. We have

$$\begin{aligned}
G_{k3} = G_{3k} &= \frac{1}{2}(1 - 2z)(1 - 2\alpha) \log \varepsilon^{-1} \\
&+ \frac{1}{2}(1 - 2z) \left[\log \frac{h_k^\star \varepsilon}{b_k} - 2\alpha \log \frac{h_3^\star \varepsilon}{b_3}\right] \\
&+ \log \left\{ \frac{\Gamma(\alpha - \alpha z)\Gamma(1 - \alpha z)\Gamma(z)}{(2\pi)^{3/2}} \right\}
\end{aligned} \quad (135)$$

where

$$\alpha = \frac{b_k}{b_3} \geq 0 \quad , \quad \eta \leq z = \frac{b_k - h_0}{b_k} \leq \min(1, \alpha^{-1}) - \eta,$$

and when neither (i) nor (j) is equal to 3:

$$\begin{aligned}
G_{ij} &= z(1 + \alpha) \log \varepsilon^{-1} \\
&+ z \left[\log \frac{h_i^\star \varepsilon}{b_i} + \alpha \log \frac{h_j^\star \varepsilon}{b_j}\right] \\
&+ \log \left\{ \frac{\Gamma(1 - z)\Gamma(1 - \alpha z)}{2\pi z \sqrt{\alpha}} \right\}
\end{aligned} \quad (136)$$

where

$$\alpha = \frac{b_i}{b_j} \geq 0 \quad , \quad \eta \leq z = \frac{h_0}{b_i} \leq \min(1, \alpha^{-1}) - \eta.$$

Notice that, in (136), the function G_{ij} is symmetric. It is invariant for the permutation $(\alpha, z) \rightarrow (\alpha^{-1}, \alpha z)$ resulting from the exchange of the indices (i) and (j).

Formulae (135),(135) and (136) summarize the effect of the separatrix crossing upon the value of the adiabatic invariant. They are equivalent to the formulae obtained by Cary et al. (1986) except for the error terms. We have displayed them somewhat differently in order to isolate in Δ_2 the terms depending upon the value of h_0 at the principal apex.

Also, in displaying the functions G_{ij} ($1 \le i \ne j \le 3$), we have isolated on the first lines the leading terms in $\log \varepsilon^{-1}$. The other terms are of the order of unity except for a very small range of values of z near the limit of definition where they can reach at most the order of $\varepsilon^{-1/3}$.

As we have seen in Section 3.6, the value of h_0 at the main apex can be considered as a random variable the distribution of which is uniform on its interval of definition. Hence Δ_2 is also a random variable, the distribution of which is characterized mainly by its mean value and its second moment:

$$< \Delta_2 > = \frac{1}{z_{\max}} \int_0^{z_{\max}} \Delta_2 \, dz \quad , \quad \sigma^2(\Delta_2) = \frac{1}{z_{\max}} \int_0^{z_{\max}} [\Delta_2 - < \Delta_2 >]^2 \, dz \ .$$

For the same reasons of symmetry than in the case of Δ_1 , the mean value of Δ_2 does not contribute to changes in the adiabatic invariant that can be cumulative. Here again, if a test particle jumps from domain D_i to domain D_j , and then back to D_i , the contributions of the mean value of Δ_2 for each jump cancel each other.

The real key to the diffusive change in the adiabatic invariant is then the second moment which can be called the diffusion parameter. If we consider only the leading term (in $\log \varepsilon^{-1}$) in its expression, we find

$$\sigma_{ij}(\Delta_2) = \frac{b_j}{\max\{b_i, b_j\}} \left| \frac{\partial J_1^\star}{\partial \lambda} - \frac{\partial J_2^\star}{\partial \lambda} \right| \frac{\varepsilon \log \varepsilon^{-1}}{2\omega\sqrt{3}} \tag{137}$$

for a jump from domain D_i to domain D_j. We recall that the quantities b_m are given by $b_m = 2\pi\varepsilon \left| (\partial J_m^\star / \partial \lambda) \right|$

The leading term (137) in the diffusion parameter disappears in a special but important case, the symmetric case when

$$\frac{\partial J_1^\star}{\partial \lambda} = \frac{\partial J_2^\star}{\partial \lambda} \ . \tag{138}$$

In that case, there can be no transition between domains D_1 and D_2. According to the sign of $h_3(\partial J_3^\star / \partial \lambda)$, we can have a transition from both D_1 and D_2 to D_3 or a transition from D_3 to either D_1 or D_2 with equal probability.

In order to compute the diffusion parameter in the symmetric case, we ought to go back to the complete formula (135). Fortunately, this formula can be much simplified as we have $\alpha = \frac{1}{2}$. We find:

$$\sigma_{ij}(\Delta_2) = \left|\frac{\partial J_j^\star}{\partial \lambda}\right| \left[1 + \frac{1}{\pi^2}\log^2\frac{h_i^\star h_j^\star}{h_3^\star h_3^\star}\right]^{1/2} \frac{\pi\varepsilon}{2\omega\sqrt{3}} . \tag{139}$$

When the geometric symmetry (138) is accompanied by a time symmetry such that

$$h_1^\star = h_2^\star \tag{140}$$

(which implies that $h_3^\star = h_1^\star = h_2^\star$), the second term of the square root in (101) disappears and we obtain:

$$\sigma_{ij}(\Delta_2) = \left|\frac{\partial J_j^\star}{\partial \lambda}\right| \frac{\pi\varepsilon}{2\omega\sqrt{3}} . \tag{141}$$

This last formula is the one given by Timofeev (1978) in the case of the pendulum with varying amplitude and by Cary et al. (1986) in the general symmetric case.

3.8 Applications

The Magnetic Bottle

As we mentionned in the second chapter, the model discussed there is, of course, only approximative. Fluctuations in the magnetic field or electric field may complicate the topology of the "frozen system" (corresponding to (75) with $c = 0$) by introduce a separatrix in the phase space. The adiabatic invariance of the averaged $\bar{G}$ may then be in default at each crossing of the separatrix.

This effect has been investigated for instance by Dobrott and Greene (1971) in the case of the stellator in which a weak but short periodic poloidal magnetic field is superimposed on top of the main toroidal field (see also Kovrizhnykh, 1984) or by Aamodt (1971-1972) who considers short-wavelength fluctuations in the electric field due to collective modes in the plasma itself.

We shall discuss briefly this last application. Let us assume that superimposed on the magnetic field (69), there is a short-wavelength electric field in the direction perpendicular to the magnetic field and slightly modulated in the direction of the magnetic field:

$$\varphi = \frac{m}{e}F(\varepsilon^2 x_3)\cos(kx_1) . \tag{142}$$

We introduce the "guiding center" coordinates as in (50) and a scaling of the third dimension:

$$y_3 = \frac{1}{\varepsilon}z \quad , \quad Y_3 = \varepsilon Z \tag{143}$$

to obtain

$$K = \frac{1}{2}(1+c)(Y_g^2 + y_g^2) + F(\varepsilon z)\cos[\frac{kY_c}{1+c} + \frac{ky_g}{(1+c)^{1/2}}] + \mathcal{O}(\varepsilon^2) . \quad (144)$$

As it can be seen in Figure 7, the motion (y_g, Y_g) can be severely distorted by the electric field corresponding to φ. This does not preclude the application of the adiabatic invariant theory and the definition of "mirror points". Simply, the adiabatic invariant is no longer the (averaged) magnetic momentum $\bar{G}$ but a more complicated function and the mirror points are no longer given by (80).

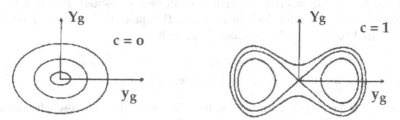

Fig. 7. Motion of the particle around its gyrocenter for the Hamiltonian (63) with $F = 2$, $k = 1$, $Y_c = 0$ and two particular values of c.

Of course the mirror points may be much different for a trapped orbit (inside the loops in Figure 7 than for un untrapped one (outside the loops). Also, we have to consider that the periodic jumps from one domain of the phase space of (y_g, Y_g) to another one generate a slow diffusion in the adiabatic invariant which may be much more important than the one estimated by Chirikov (see 81).

Resonance Sweeping in the Solar System

The orbital and spin parameters of many natural satellites in the Solar System have been significantly affected by tidal dissipation and passage through resonances. It is possible to understand the slow dynamical evolution of these parameters in terms of a few "simple models" and the use of the adiabatic invariant. Of course these simplified models do not always give an accurate quantitative answer to the problems at hand: too many physical parameters are poorly known and the mathematical approximations are sometime very crude. But they can at least be used in order to define likely scenarii of evolution (or dismiss impossible or improbable scenarii) which can then, if need be, improved either by refining the analytical model or by using numerical simulations (which are often quite costly, since we are dealing with very slow evolutions)

Let us take as an example the passage through a second order resonance of the planar planetary restricted three-body problem. The three bodies may be (Sun + Jupiter + Asteroid) or (Saturn + Mimas + particle in the ring) or (Uranus + Miranda + Umbriel).

The Hamiltonian of the restricted problem can be written:

$$\mathcal{H} = -\frac{(1-\mu)^2}{L^2} - \mu \left\{ \frac{1}{|\mathbf{r} - \mathbf{r}'|} - \frac{\mathbf{r}|\mathbf{r}'}{r'^3} \right\} , \tag{145}$$

where $(1 - \mu)$ and μ are the reduced masses of the primary and the secondary, $L = \sqrt{(1-\mu)a}$ the first action variable of the two-body problem, a the semi-major axis of the test particle, $\mathbf{r}$ and $\mathbf{r}'$ the position vector of the test particle and of the secondary with respect to the primary. We are considering here that the Hamiltonian fonction is expressed implicitely in terms of the usual Delaunay's modified elements where the quantities L, P are momenta conjugated to the angular variables λ, p, with

$$\begin{array}{ll} \lambda = \text{mean longitude of particle} \quad , L = \sqrt{(1-\mu)a} \\ p = -\text{longitude of its pericenter} , P = L\left(1 - \sqrt{1-e^2}\right) \end{array} \tag{146}$$

where e is the eccentricity of the particle. The Hamiltonian is also a function of the time through its dependence upon the longitude of the secondary $\lambda' = n't$. In case of a 3/1 internal resonance between the unperturbed mean motion of the particle $(n = \sqrt{(1-\mu)a^3})$ we have

$$3n' - n \approx 0 . \tag{147}$$

and it is usefull to introduce the Poincaré's resonance variables

$$\begin{array}{ll} \sigma = (3\lambda' - \lambda + 2p)/2 \quad , S = P , \\ \nu = -(3\lambda' - \lambda + 2p')/2 , N = 2L + P - 2\sqrt{(1-\mu)a^*} , \end{array} \tag{148}$$

where a^* is the "exact resonance" value: $a^* = a'[(1-\mu)/9]^{1/3}$. After averaging the Hamiltonian over the fast remaining angular variable λ', the Hamiltonian, expanded in powers of $\sqrt{S} \approx e$ and e' reads

$$\begin{aligned} \mathcal{H} = A(N - S)^2 &+ BS + CS\cos 2\sigma + De'^2 \cos 2\nu \\ &+ e'\sqrt{S}[E\cos(\sigma + \nu) + F\cos(\sigma - \nu)] \\ &+ \cdots . \end{aligned} \tag{149}$$

The coefficient A is of the order of unity, the coefficients C, D, E, F of the order of μ (i.e $\approx 10^{-3}$ in the Sun-Jupiter problem and $\approx 10^{-5}$ in the Planet-Satellite problems. The coefficient B is also of the order of μ in the Sun-Jupiter problem, but in the Planet-Satellite problems it should be corrected in order to take into account the oblateness of the planet by a term of the order of the dynamical oblateness J_2 which is of the order of 10^{-3} when the planet is Uranus and 5 times larger when the planet is Saturn.

When B is not much larger than the trigonometric terms the unperturbed frequencies of these terms are "small" for the same values of the momenta (i.e. when $N - S$ is small), and we have a problem of overlapping resonances which is not easy to handle. In this case, in order to simplify the analysis, we shall assume that the eccentricity of the secondary vanishes ($e' = 0$), so that only the first trigonometric term subsists and the momentum N becomes a constant.

The level curves of this one-degree of freedom system

$$\mathcal{H} = A(N - S)^2 + BS + CS \cos 2\sigma . \tag{150}$$

are shown in figure (8) for typical values of the parameter N

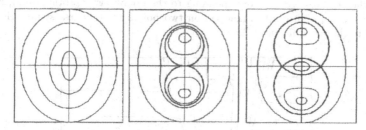

Fig. 8. Level curves of the one degree of freedom Hamiltonian for three typical values of the parameter N. The two "crescent" regions correspond to the resonance (the resonant angle σ librates), the inner region correspond to orbits with a semi-major axis larger than the resonant value and the outer region to orbits with a semi-major axis smaller than the resonant value.

In order to vizualize more easily this three-dimensional problem (N, s, σ), we introduce a kind of "surface of section", a (a, e) diagram, by indexing each orbit by the value of the semi-major axie and of the eccentricity corresponding to its intersection with the half-line $\sigma = \pi$. The orbits in the top crescent are indexed by two points in the diagram; the orbits in the lower crescent are not indexed, but this is not a problem because the orbit with $(\sigma(t), \nu(t))$ and the orbit with $(\sigma(t) + \pi, \nu(t) + \pi)$ correspond to the same orbit in the physical space. There is a one-to-one correspondence between non-resonant orbits and the points in the (a, e) diagram. (see figure 9)

Let us plot in the (a, e) diagram the curves of constant value of the adiabatic invariant, the action of the one degree of freedom Hamiltonian (150) (see figure 10). They are instrumental in describing the evolution of the system when the "parameter" N varies slowly.

The parameter N may vary from several causes according to the problem at hand: small dissipative forces like drag by a primordial gazeous nebula, migration of planets due to the ejection of asteroids in the Oort cloud, the effect of the tides raised on the planet by a satellite. Let us give a woed of explanation concerning the latter. A planet is not a rigid body and each satellite brings on a bulge on the planet. If the planet were perfectly elastic this bulge would be oriented exactly along the line planet-satellite. But a physical

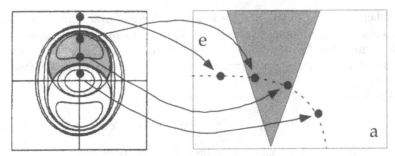

Fig. 9. Mapping between the orbits of the Hamiltonian and the (a,e) diagram. Inside the "critical curve" (corresponding to the doubly-asymptotic orbits), in the resonance zone, each orbit is mapped on two points more or less symmetric with respect to the vertical central line.

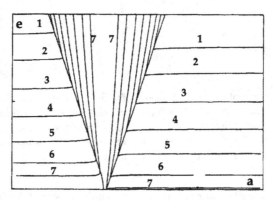

Fig. 10. The curves of constant value of the adiabatic invariant

body like a planet is usually not perfectly elastic and the bulge shows a little delay with respect to the passage of the satellite. This produce a tiny non-symmetric force accelerating the satellite (when the period of rotation of the planet is smaller than the orbital period of the satellite), or decelerating it (when the reverse is true). This tranfer energy (and angular momentum) from the rotation of the planet to the orbital motion of the satellite. The effect is proportionnal to the sixth power of the inverse of the distance planet-satellite and proportionnal to the mass of the satellite. Let us assume for the sake of simplicity that the effect is mainly felt by the larger satellite (the secondary of the restricted problem). Then the value of a' changes slowly with the time and thus the value of a^* and of N. We are in the right conditions to apply the adiabatic invariant theory.

In the case where N decreases slowly, these curves are travelled from right to left. When the representative point reach the critical curve, we have to consider whether the orbit will be captured by the resonance or "jump" over it. In this case, according to formula (126) it will be a jump and the representative

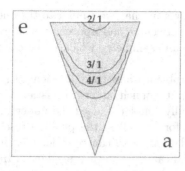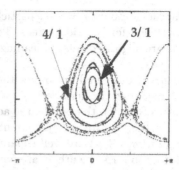

Fig. 11. Secondary resonances inside the primary resonance from (Malhotra, 1994). Location in the (A, e) diagram and a surface of section for a particular value of the energy.

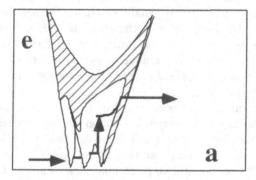

Fig. 12. Schematic scenario for the temporary capture of Miranda by the 3:1 complex of resonance with Umbriel. After a capture in the "strongest" primary resonance (the 2σ one), a secondary resonance brought it back to the border of the resonance and let it escape. the shaded area corresponds to chaotic motions.

point will resume its march on the left of the V-shaped resonance zone on the curve with the same label (with a higher eccentricity). This is a possible mechanism for exciting the eccentricity of small bodies.

In the case where N increases slowly, the curves are travelled from left to right. Comming from an orbit with semi-major axis smaller than the resonance value, the test particle sees this critical value approaching it. When the representative point in the (a, e) diagram reaches the critical curve, we have to read from formula (126) the probability of capture into resonance. This time there is indeed a non-zero probability of capture; the smaller the eccentricity, the higher the probability. The exact scaling of the probability function (Probability versus eccentricity) depends on the parameters of the problem, mainly on the value of the mass ratio μ. After capture of the orbit, we see that the semi-major axis remains more or less constant but that it is the eccentricity which increases. Physically the secondary transfer energy and angular momentum to the test particle by a mechanism similar to the one we have sketched for the tidal effect. The pericenter and apocenter of the test particle are slightly displaced leading to an asymmetry which is the cause of the transfer.

We have considered up to now the problem where the coefficient B is not much larger than the mass ratio μ. When it is much larger (for instance if the primary is Saturn), the problem is actually simpler. Indeed the unperturbed frequency (i.e. the frequency computed for $\mu = 0$) of the possible resonant angles $(2\sigma, 2\nu, \sigma + \nu)$ are well separated so that we can consider that when one is close to zero, the others are not and can thus be "averaged out". Hence instead of one resonance, we have to investigate three of them; but each of them can be analyzed separately and described by the Hamiltonian (149) where only one trigonometric term (either the one in 2σ or in 2ν or in $\sigma + \nu$ is kept. The corresponding problem is again "one-degree-of-freedom" and actually very similar to (150). We shall not pursue further this case.

An interesting borderline case is the case where B is larger than μ but not that much larger (this is the case when the primary is Uranus). In that case the resonances are disjoint for small eccentricities but interfere with each other for larger values and provoke secondary resonances inside the primary resonances (see figure 11).

If the representative point is captured in a primary resonance and evolve inside it by increasing its eccentricity, it will encounter secondary resonances and may be captured by one of them. This can lead it back to the border of the primary resonance which at this higher value of the eccentricity is rather chaotic. The representative point may then escape to the right side of the complex of resonances. This seems to have been the fate of Miranda and Umbriel a pair of satellites of Uranus which are not just outside the complex of resonance with an unusual high value of the eccentricity for Miranda (see Figure 12).

4 Crossing of a Chaotic Layer

4.1 Introduction

In many applications the one-degree of freedom model we have used is actually an approximation of a system with more degrees of freedom, obtained for instance by averaging over other frequencies. In this case one must expect that the separatrix of the model is actually, in the real problem, a stochastic layer. One may wonder if, in this case, the above mentioned estimate for the probability of capture is still valid.

One could object to the application of the above mentioned theory to such a case. It is possible that as soon as the chaotic layer is large enough that it cannot be crossed in a few revolutions of the guiding trajectory, the mechanism of capture is qualitatively different and thus the predictions of the above mentioned theory have no relevance.

In this chapter, following (Henrard and Henrard, 1991 and Henrard and Morbidelli, 1992) we shall give indications that the situation is not as desesperate as that. Roughly speaking we shall show that there are reasons to believe that in the presence of a stochastic layer the probability of capture in the growing domains (see the previous chapter) is still proportional to their growing rates (see equation 172). The main difference will be that the "capture" will no longer be instantaneous but will happen on a time scale inversely proportional to the area of the stochastic layer (see equation 171). As a result the change in the adiabatic invariant upon crossing the chaotic layer will have a random component of the order of the area of the stochastic layer (see equation 173).

4.2 The Frozen System

Let us consider the one-and-a-half degree-of-freedom Hamiltonian system depending upon a real parameter λ and defined by the Hamiltonian function:

$$H(q, p, t; \lambda) \,, \tag{151}$$

T-periodic in the time t and defined on $V \times T^1 \times I$, where V is an oriented manifold parametrized by the canonical variables (q, p) and I is an open interval of the real line.

The Poincaré section of the system will be taken at $t \equiv 0$ (modulo T) and the Poincaré map is the return map on the Poincaré section: $(q(0), p(0)) \longrightarrow (q(T), p(T))$. The Poincaré map is area-preserving. Indeed if C_2 is the image of a closed curve C_1, we have by considering the Poincaré linear integral invariant [1]:

$$\int_{C_1} p \, dq = \int_{C_2} p \, dq \,. \tag{152}$$

We shall assume that the dynamical system defined by the Poincaré map is a typical representative of a "close to integrable" and "close to a resonance" system. By this we mean the following. The Poincaré section shows a finite number of simply connected domains D_i where the Poincaré map *seems* to be regular and one connected and bounded domain D_S where the Poincaré map *seems* to be ergodic.

Generically we can expect that the Hamiltonian system we started with is not integrable and that if some invariant tori are present, they do not form open domains of regular behaviour. But typically (see for instance Hénon and Heile, 1964]), when the system is not too far away from an integrable one but close to a resonance, we can expect to see in the Poincaré section macroscopic regions which are almost completely filled by regular closed curves (trace of invariant tori upon the Poincaré section) and a macroscopic region (around the stable and unstable manifolds of the unstable periodic orbit generated by the resonance) which looks completely chaotic. We know of course that generically the "regular" regions contain almost everywhere thin layers of stochastic behaviour and that the stochastic region contains an infinite number of small "island". The point is that the layers and the islands can be very small and that we can hope to reach meaningful approximate answers about the system by ignoring them.

In each regular domain D_i of the Poincaré section we define the action of a regular closed curve C as the signed area:

$$A(C) = \int_C p \, dq \,, \tag{153}$$

where the sign of $A(C)$ (the direction of the path integral) is chosen in such a way that $A(C)$ increases when the curve C approaches the boundary of the regular domain D_i.

With such a definition we can characterize the regular domains D_i by their maximum action:

$$A_i(\lambda) = \int_{\Gamma_i} p \, dq \,, \tag{154}$$

where Γ_i is the boundary of the regular domain D_i with the stochastic domain D_S. The sign of $A_i(\lambda)$ is taken accordingly to the sign of the action in the domain.

We shall assume in what follows that for $\lambda \in I$ the number of regular regions is constant and furthermore that each of them grows ($dA_i/d\lambda > 0$) or becomes smaller ($dA_i/d\lambda < 0$) monotonically with λ. Let us call S^+ the set of indices (i) such that $dA_i/d\lambda > 0$ and S^- the set of indices such that $dA_i/d\lambda < 0$. We shall denote by $A^+(\lambda)$ (resp. $A^-(\lambda)$) the sum of the actions of the growing (resp. decreasing) regular domains:

$$A^+(\lambda) = \sum_{i \in S^+} A_i(\lambda) \qquad A^-(\lambda) = \sum_{i \in S^-} A_i(\lambda) \,. \tag{155}$$

4.3 The Slowly Varying System

We shall now assume that the parameter λ of the Hamiltonian function (151) is slowly changing with the time:

$$\lambda = \varepsilon t \,. \tag{156}$$

The Poincaré section and the Poincaré map are defined as previously. The Poincaré map is still area-preserving, but of course the dynamical system defined by the Poincaré map will be different although we may expect that it will not be very much different for time intervals small compared to ε^{-1}. Our goal is of course to get information about the dynamical system for time intervals of the order of ε^{-1}.

First let us show that in the regular domains the action as defined in (153) is adiabatically invariant. By this we mean that the changes in the action is of the order of ε for time intervals of the order of ε^{-1}.

Indeed the image of a regular curve of D_i remains adiabatically close to a regular curve of D_i as long as this image remains in D_i. To show this let us remark that, in a regular domain, we can define approximate angle-action variables (ψ, J) such that for a fixed value of the parametrer λ, the Hamiltonian (151) is transformed into

$$H = K(J; \lambda) + \eta P(\psi, J, t; \lambda) , \qquad (157)$$

where the "small parameter" η measures the non-integrability of the system in the regular domain. We assume that it can be made as small as ε^2.

If we consider now that $\lambda = \varepsilon t$, the Hamiltonian of the system is no longer given by (157) but by:

$$H' = K(J; \varepsilon t) + \varepsilon R(\psi, J, t; \varepsilon t) + \eta P(\psi, J, t; \varepsilon t) , \qquad (158)$$

where R is the remainder function of the time dependant canonical transformation defining the action-angle variables.

A further averaging transformation brings the Hamiltonian (158) under the form:

$$H' = K(\bar{J}; \varepsilon t) + \varepsilon \bar{R}(\bar{J}; \varepsilon t) + \eta \bar{P}(\bar{\psi}, \bar{J}, t; \varepsilon t) + \varepsilon^2 \mathcal{R}(\bar{\psi}, \bar{J}, t; \varepsilon t) , \qquad (159)$$

which shows that the averaged action $\bar{J}$ is an adiabatic invariant:

$$\frac{d\bar{J}}{dt} = \mathcal{O}(\varepsilon^2) . \qquad (160)$$

The action J itself, which differs from $\bar{J}$ by periodic terms of the order of ε is also an adiabatic invariant.

Now if we consider at time t_0 a closed regular curve C_1 corresponding to a given value of J, its image by an iterate of the return map will form a closed curve C_2. All the points on C_2 will correspond within ε to the same value of J because J is an adiabatic invariant. Thus C_2 is again a regular curve of the frozen system and:

$$\int_{C_1} p \, dq = \int_{C_2} p \, dq . \qquad (161)$$

Hence the action as defined in (153) is adiabatically conserved.

4.4 Transition Between Domains

We wish to estimate statistically when and how a trajectory makes a transition from one domain (regular or stochastic) of the frozen system to another one. We shall consider that the Poincaré section is covered by particles with a density $\varrho(q,p,n)$ where n is the number of the return map. The density ϱ is assumed to depend only upon the action in the regular domains and not on the phase and to have a constant value $\varrho_S(n)$ in the stochastic domain.

Particles starting with an action A in one of the regular domain D_i remain in this regular domain, with the same action, as long as $A < A_i(\varepsilon t)$. But if $i \in S^-$ (i.e. if the domain D_i is one which is decreasing in area), the domain D_i will loose particles to the stochastic domain at a rate of:

$$-\varrho_i \frac{dA_i}{d\lambda}\varepsilon ,\qquad (162)$$

where ϱ_i is the density of particles at the boundary of the domain D_i.

Indeed the particles contained between the regular curves of action $A_i(\varepsilon(n+1)T)$ and $A_i(\varepsilon nT)$ at time $t = nT$ cannot remain in the regular domain at $t = (n+1)T$.

On the other hand, the number of particles leaving the stochastic domain D_S and entering the regular domain D_j (with $j \in S^+$) at each iteration is

$$\varrho_S(n) \frac{dA_j}{d\lambda}\varepsilon ,\qquad (163)$$

where ϱ_S is the density of the stochastic domain at time $t = nT$. Indeed the particles contained between the regular curves of action $A_j(\varepsilon nT)$ and $A_j(\varepsilon(n+1)T)$ at time $t = (n+1)T$ cannot come from elsewhere than the stochastic domain. Their density (which is preserved because the map is area-preserving) was at time $t = n$ equal to the density of the stochastic domain.

The above estimates are based upon the assumption that in the time εT a particle cannot jump directly from one regular domain to another one. It is assumed further that for most particles it takes many iterates of the Poincaré map to cross the stochastic domain. By "many" iterates we mean a number large enough that the mixing character of the stochastic domain has the time to uniformize the density of particles inside D_S. It is difficult to translate quantitatively this assumption because we do not have a quantitative estimate of the mixing character of D_S. But certainly this assumption will be violated if the exchange of area between regular domains in one iteration of the mapping is of the order of the area of the stochastic domain. Hence we assume that:

$$\frac{dA^+}{d\lambda}\varepsilon T \ll A_S \quad , \qquad \frac{dA^-}{d\lambda}\varepsilon T \ll A_S .\qquad (164)$$

Now let us follow the fate of a set of particles entering at time $t = t_0$ the stochastic domain coming from one of the domain D_i which is loosing area. Let us designate by $k(t)$ the fraction of this set of particles which have left the stochastic domain at time $t > t_0$. If $t - t_0$ is large enough, the particles remaining in the stochastic domain are spread uniformly and we can estimate the number of them which are leaving the stochastic domain between t and $t + T$, by using (163):

$$k(t+T) - k(t) = \frac{1 - k(t)}{A_S} \frac{dA^+}{d\lambda} \varepsilon T \, . \tag{165}$$

Indeed $(1 - k(t))/A_S(t)$ is the fractional density of the set of particles we are considering and $\varepsilon T dA^+/d\lambda$ measures the area lost by the stochastic domain to the growing domains.

Converting (165) into a differential equation:

$$\frac{1}{1-k} \frac{dk}{dt} = \frac{\varepsilon}{A_S(t)} \frac{dA^+}{d\lambda} \, , \tag{166}$$

and integrating, we find:

$$k(t) = 1 - \exp(-F^+(t)) \, , \tag{167}$$

with

$$F^+(t) = \varepsilon \int_{t_0}^{t} \frac{1}{A_S(t)} \frac{dA^+}{d\lambda} \, dt \, . \tag{168}$$

The fraction $k_i(t)$ of this set of particles which have entered the regular domain D_i $(i \in S^+)$ at time t is given by:

$$k_i(t) = \varepsilon \int_{t_0}^{t} \frac{1 - k(t)}{A_S(t)} \frac{dA_i}{d\lambda} \, dt \, . \tag{169}$$

In the application described in the following sections we have that $A_S(t) = A_S$ is a constant and so are the quantities:

$$B = \frac{dA^+}{d\lambda} \qquad C = -\frac{dA^-}{d\lambda} \qquad B_i = \frac{dA_i}{d\lambda} \quad (i \in S^+) \, . \tag{170}$$

In this case formulae (167) and (169) are easy to evaluate and we obtain:

$$k(t) = 1 - \exp\left[-\frac{\varepsilon B(t - t_0)}{A_S(t_0)} \right] \, , \tag{171}$$

$$k_i(t) = \frac{B_i}{B} k(t) \, . \tag{172}$$

We conclude that the probability for one particle to enter a particular domain D_i is proportional to the growing rate B_i of this domain.

From (171) we can evaluate the distribution of the values of the action of the particle in the regular domain they have jumped into. The probability of reaching the domain D_i with a value of the action larger than $A_i(0) + \Delta A$ is equal to:

$$P_r(A_i \geq A_i(0) + \Delta A) = \exp\left[-\frac{B}{B_i} \frac{\Delta A}{A_S} \right] \, . \tag{173}$$

In the limit $A_S \to 0$, these formulae agree with the formulae obtained by considering a separatrix crossing and not a chaotic layer crossing. In that case, as we recalled in the introduction, we have:

$$k_i = B_i/B \, , \qquad A_i = A_i(0) \, . \tag{174}$$

4.5 The "MSySM"

As a test of the ideas developed in the previous sections we shall consider as "frozen system" the Modulated Symmetric Standard Map (in short the $MSySM$). Let us first describe the Symmetric Standard Map (in short the $SySM$):

$$(SySM) \qquad \begin{cases} I^{(n+1)} = I^{(n)} - K \sin\left[\varphi^{(n)} + I^{(n)}/2\right] , \\ \varphi^{(n+1)} = \varphi^{(n)} + \left[I^{(n+1)} + I^{(n)}\right]/2 , \end{cases} \qquad (175)$$

which can be interpreted as the application of a first order symplectic integrator, with a time step ε, to the integration of the pendulum. The parameter $K = b\varepsilon^2$ is a scaled value of the restoring force b of the pendulum and $I = p\varepsilon$) is a scaled value of the momentum p.

We have shown in (Henrard and Morbidelli, 1992) how one can construct a formal power series which is a formal invariant for the sequence of points generated by the Symmetric Standard Map and we have shown how to compute it. Applying this technique we found that the action of the perturbed pendulum can be approximated by:

$$\mathcal{J}_{\text{lib}} = \frac{8\sqrt{K}}{\pi} \left\{ \mu_1 \mathbb{E}(\alpha) - (\mu_1 + \mu_2)(1 - \alpha)\mathbb{K}(\alpha) \right\} , \qquad (176)$$

$$\mathcal{J}_{\text{circ}} = \frac{8\sqrt{\alpha K}}{\pi} \left\{ \mu_1 \mathbb{E}(\beta) + \mu_2(1 - \beta)\mathbb{K}(\beta) \right\} , \qquad (177)$$

where $\mathbb{K}$ and $\mathbb{E}$ are the usual elliptic function (see for instance Abramowicz and Stagun, 1968). The parameter $\alpha = \beta^{-1}$ is equal to $(\mathcal{H} + b)/2b$ and is equal to zero at the central stable equilibrium and one on the separatrix. The coefficient μ_1 and μ_2 are given as truncated series in ε by:

$$\mu_1 = 1 + \frac{K}{72}\left[1 - 2\alpha\right] \qquad (178)$$

$$- \frac{K^2}{5\,400}\left[\frac{79}{16} + 11\alpha(1 - \alpha)\right]$$

$$+ \frac{K^3}{7\,938}\left[\frac{3\,593}{2\,560} - \frac{1\,205\,\alpha}{256} + \frac{19\,\alpha^2}{10}(3 - 2\alpha)\right]$$

$$- \frac{K^4}{17\,010}\left[\frac{1\,208\,087}{1\,228\,800} - \frac{1\,553\,\alpha}{9\,600} - \frac{9\,461\,\alpha^2}{3\,200} + \frac{1\,871\,\alpha^3}{600}(2 - \alpha)\right]$$

$$+ \frac{K^5}{22\,869}\left[\frac{181\,980\,143}{294\,912\,000} - \frac{676\,926\,221\,\alpha}{442\,368\,000} - \frac{13\,699\,639\,\alpha^2}{6\,912\,000}\right.$$

$$\left. - \frac{17\,166\,013\,\alpha^3}{3\,456\,000} + \frac{2\,953\,\alpha^4}{2\,700}(5 - 2\alpha)\right]$$

$$\mu_2 = \frac{\alpha K}{36} + \frac{11\alpha K^2}{10\,800}\,[1 - 2\alpha] \tag{179}$$

$$+ \frac{\alpha K^3}{7\,938}\left[\frac{565}{256} - \frac{19}{5}\frac{\alpha}{}(1 - \alpha)\right]$$

$$+ \frac{\alpha K^4}{17\,010}\left[\frac{89}{4\,800} - \frac{1\,277\,\alpha}{800} + \frac{1\,871\,\alpha^2}{1\,200}(3 - 2\alpha)\right]$$

$$+ \frac{\alpha K^5}{76\,230}\left[\frac{2\,344\,901}{1\,638\,400} - \frac{3\,226\,493\,\alpha}{1\,036\,800} + \frac{3\,595\,391\,\alpha^2}{345\,600} - \frac{2\,953\,\alpha^3}{405}(2 - \alpha)\right]$$

In order to obtain a model with a rather large and clean "stochastic layer", we have imposed a slow modulation to the $SySM$ by making K a function of the index n,

$$K_n = \alpha\Delta^2\left[1 + \beta\cos\left(\frac{\pi(2n - 1)}{N}\right)\right]. \tag{180}$$

This is the (normalized) second order symplectic integrator with time-step Δ (we shall reserve the symbol ε for a better use) for the modulated pendulum described by the two degrees of freedom Hamiltonian,

$$H = \frac{1}{2}p^2 + \Lambda + \alpha\left[1 + \beta\cos\frac{2\pi\lambda}{N}\right]\cos q, \tag{181}$$

where λ is the time in disguise and Λ is its associated momentum. We call "modulated symmetric standard map" the N step map from $t = \lambda = 0$ to $t = \lambda = N$, i.e. the symplectic approximate integration of the pendulum over the full period of the modulation.

For trajectories which do not cross the slowly moving separatrix of the pendulum, the action $\mathcal{J}$ (see equations 176 and 177) is a second order (with respect to $2\pi/N$) adiabatic invariant (see for instance Arnold, 1963). Indeed the first order correction is proportional to $(\partial H/\partial\lambda)$ which in this case vanishes at the time the mapping is evaluated (i.e. when $\lambda = 0$ mod 2π).

On the other hand, the trajectories which are forced to cross the slowly moving separatrix are engulfed in a large and "clean" chaotic layer (see figure 13). As shown by Elskens and Escande (1991), it is "clean" (i.e. has sharp boundaries and contains only very thin islands) because the "slowly pulsating separatrix sweep homoclinic tangles where islands must be small". The extend of the chaotic layer can be easily approximated analytically. It corresponds (up to terms of order $2\pi/N$) to the interval of values of the action which are assumed by the separatrix during its pulsation.

Inside the chaotic layer, the dynamics can be described (at least in a first approximation) as a diffusive process (Bruwhiler and Cary, 1989) on the action $\mathcal{J}$ together with a fast "phase mixing" on the angle variable (let us call it Ψ) conjugated to it. The diffusion coefficient of the Fokker-Planck equation for the density $P(\mathcal{J}, t)$ of particles inside the chaotic layer

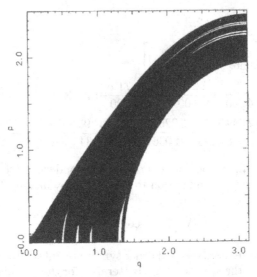

Fig. 13. The chaotic layer of the modulated symmetric standard map ($MSySM$) for $\Delta = 0.02$, $N = 50$, $\alpha = 1$ and $\beta = 0.5$. Notice the thin elongated "islands" and the sharpness of the boundaries

$$\frac{\partial P}{\partial t} - \frac{\partial}{\partial \mathcal{J}}\left[D(\mathcal{J})\frac{\partial P}{\partial \mathcal{J}}\right] = 0 , \tag{182}$$

is the averaged mean square spreading of the adiabatic invariant; the average being performed over the initial phase Ψ and over many iteration of the map

A first order approximation of this diffusion coefficient can be evaluated by neglecting the correlations between iterations of the map (i.e. by taking the average over one period only of the modulation of the pendulum)

$$D_0(\mathcal{J}_0) = \frac{1}{N} \oint (\mathcal{J}^* - \mathcal{J}_0)^2 \, d\Psi_0 , \tag{183}$$

where $(\mathcal{J}_0, \Psi_0)$ are initial conditions and $\mathcal{J}^*$ is the value of the action after one period of the modulation.

Following Bruhwiler and Cary (1989), this integral can be evaluated analytically (neglecting the correlations between the two consecutive separatrix crossings involved in the full period of modulation) as

$$D_0(\mathcal{J}) \approx \frac{2(4\pi)^2}{3N^3} \frac{(\mathcal{J}^2 - \mathcal{J}_{\min}^2)(\mathcal{J}_{\max}^2 - \mathcal{J}^2)}{\mathcal{J}^4} . \tag{184}$$

The function (184) is shown in figure 14 for a typical value of N. Also shown on the same diagrams are direct numerical evaluations of (183). As pointed out by Bruhwiler and Cary we see that, although (184) gives a correct idea of the order of magnitude ($\sim 1/N^3$) of the diffusion coefficient, it is not a very good approximation of it because of the neglect of the correlations and also

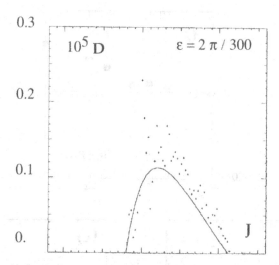

Fig. 14. The diffusion coefficient for $N = 3000$. The curve is given by equation 184 and the crosses by direct numerical evaluation of the integral 183.

presumably because the asymptotic approximation on which (184) is based does not take into account the presence of small islands in the chaotic sea.

The time scale associated with this diffusion coefficient, which is proportional to the *cube* of N, should not be confused and is much larger than the time scale associated with the Lyapunov characteristic exponent which is proportional to N

4.6 Slow Crossing of the Stochastic Layer

In order to simulate a slow evolution of the modulated pendulum (see eq. 181), let us make the coefficient α time-dependent, $\alpha = (1 + \varepsilon t)^2$, and replace p by $p + 3\varepsilon t$. In this way the "cat-eye" of the pendulum is opening up and moving downward. The regular region above the cat-eye and the regular region inside it are growing at about the same rate while the region below it is shrinking.

A rough estimate based upon a pure pendulum approximation gives $8\varepsilon/\pi\sqrt{1/2}$ and $\varepsilon(3 - 4/\pi\sqrt{3/2})$ as the growth rates of the libration and of the positive circulation regular domains, predicting a 55% probability of capture by the libration region for particles uniformly distributed in the stochastic layer.

We conducted several numerical experiments with various values of the deformation parameter ε while keeping N (the modulation parameter) fixed to 50. The results are summarized in figure 15a which reports the ratio of the number of particles captured by the libration region (n_3) to the total number of particles captured ($n_2 + n_3$) after a time equal to $0.45/\varepsilon$ for $\varepsilon = 10^{-3}$ and $0.225/\varepsilon$ for the other cases. We start with 1.000 particles uniformly distributed in the chaotic layer.

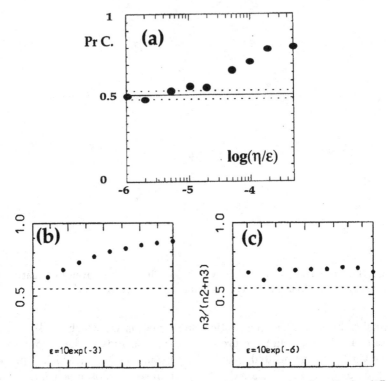

Fig. 15. (a): Probability of capture into the libration regular domain for different values of the evolution parameter ε and of the time step (Δ) of the symplectic integrator. (b) and (c): time evolution of this probability in two cases. The abscissa is the ratio of the area gained by the libration domain over its initial area; it is approximately proportional to the time.

We show also in figure 15b and 15c the evolution with time of this ratio. For very small values of the evolution parameter ($\varepsilon = 10^{-6}$), this probability remains more or less constant with a value (65%) somewhat larger than the 55% estimation. This is due to the roughness of our estimate of the growth rates and of not much concern. On the other hand, for larger values ($\varepsilon = 10^{-3}$) of the evolution parameter, the computed probability shows a systematic increase with time, up to almost 90%.

Figure 16 gives the explanation for this unexpected behavior. We plot there the distribution of particles inside the chaotic layer at four instant of the simulation. For the small value of the evolution rate ε (figure 7a) the distribution remains uniform, but for the larger value of ε (figure 7b) the distribution shows a systematic evolution. Particles keep a constant density along the inside boundary of the chaotic layer (the one next to the libration domain, on the left of the diagrams) and desert the outside boundary (the one next to the circulation domain, on the right of the diagrams). This reflects a

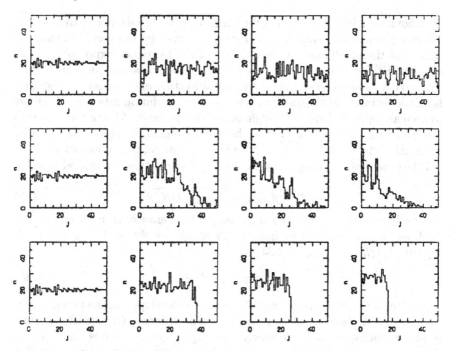

Fig. 16. Distribution of the particles inside the chaotic layer at four moment of the evolution (for $\Delta = 2\pi/50$). The particles inside the chaotic layer, i.e. in the changing $\mathcal{J}$-interval $[\mathcal{J}_{\min}(t), \mathcal{J}_{\max}(t)]$, are distributed into 50 bins according to the value of the action $\mathcal{J}$. Figure (a) shows the evolution of the distribution for a small value of the evolution parameter $\varepsilon = 10^{-6}$. the distribution remains uniform. Figure (b) shows the evolution for a larger value of the parameter ($\varepsilon = 10^{-3}$). The density of particles remains more or less constant close to the inside boundary of the chaotic layer (bin 1) but goes to zero close to the outside boundary (bin 50). Figure (c) shows the theoretical distribution when the diffusion coefficient goes to zero.

lack of diffusion of the action; the boundaries of the chaotic layer move too fast for the diffusion to be able to replenish the areas of phase space which have been depleted. If there was no diffusion at all (i.e. if the action was kept constant), we would see the evolution shown in figure 16c. Indeed the value of $\mathcal{J}$ which marks the outer boundary of the chaotic layer, say $\mathcal{J}_{\max}(t)$, grows with the time. Initially we do not have any particle with $\mathcal{J}$ larger than $\mathcal{J}_{\max}(0)$ as the distribution we have considered has zero density outside the chaotic layer. It means that later on, if $\mathcal{J}$ does not diffuse, the range $[\mathcal{J}_{\max}(0), \mathcal{J}_{\max}(t)]$ would be completely depleted as shown in figure 7c.

One could object that the Fokker-Planck equation (182) is characterized by an infinite speed of propagation. In particular an initially uniform distribution of particles which diffuse in an expanding box, will stay uniform if the box expand linearly with time, regardless of the speed of expansion. However, one should not forget that the diffusion process we are dealing with here is a *discrete* phenomenon with a basic time-scale given by the period of modulation N of the pendulum (i.e. the inverse of the Lyapunov exponent). In our case, the Fokker-Planck equation is valid only on time-scale much larger than this period of modulation. From this consideration one can get a rough and heuristic estimate of the maximum value of the evolution rate ε which allows to keep an uniform density throughout the chaotic layer. After a time equal to the modulation period the limit of the chaotic region $\mathcal{J}_{\max}(N)$ is changed by a quantity $\Delta\mathcal{J} \approx 8\varepsilon N \sqrt{\alpha(1+\beta/\pi}$ which, in our case, amounts to $1.5\,10^2\varepsilon$. On the other hand, during the same period, the density of an interval of width

$$\delta\mathcal{J} \approx \eta(\mathcal{J}_{\max} - \mathcal{J}_{\min})\sqrt{DN/\pi}\,, \qquad (185)$$

on the boundary will become uniform (with tolerance η) according to the Fokker-Plank equation. If we impose $\Delta\mathcal{J} \ll \delta\mathcal{J}$, we obtain (taking $\eta = 10^{-1}$, $D = 10^{-4}$, $(\mathcal{J}_{\max} - \mathcal{J}_{\min}) = 1.3$)

$$\varepsilon \ll 3\,10^{-5}\,. \qquad (186)$$

It does seems that the asymptotic estimate developed in the previous section for the probability of capture in regular domains for particles coming from the stochastic layer of a slowly evolving symplectic map is confirmed by the numerical experiments on the modulated symmetric standard map. But we see that the asymptotic limit is reached only for rate of evolution much smaller than expected *a priori*. The reason for this is now identified. It is the fact that the value of the action diffuses on a time scale (proportional to the cube of the modulation coefficient N) much longer than the time scale of the Lyapunov exponent (which is proportional to N).

References

1. Abramowitz, M. and Segun, I.A.: 1968, *Handbook of Mathematical Functions*, Dover Pub.
2. Alfven, H.: 1950, *Cosmical Electrodynamics*, Clarendon Press, Oxford.
3. Andronov, A.A., Vitt, A.A. and Khaikin, S.E.: 1966, *Theory of Oscillators*, Addison-Wesley, Reading, Mass.
4. Arnold, V.I.: 1963, Small Denominators and Problems of Stability of Motion in Classical and Celestial Mechanics, *Russian Math. Survey*, **18**, 85-191
5. Arnold, V.I., 1964, Small denominators and problems of stability of motion in classical and celestial mechanics, *Russian Math. Survey*, **18**, 85-191.
6. Arnold, V.I.: 1978, *Mathematical Methods of Classical Mechanics*, Springer-Verlag.
7. Arnold, V.I.: 1985, *Dynamical Systems III*, Springer-Verlag
8. Best, R.W.B.: 1968, On the motion of charged particles in a slightly damped sinusoidal potential wave, *Physica 40*, 182-196.
9. Cary, J.R., Escande, D.F. and Tennyson, J.L.: 1986, Adiabatic invariant change due to separatrix crossing, *Physical Review*, **A 34**, 4256-4275.

10. Chirikov, B.V.: 1979, A universal instability of many-dimensional oscillator systems, *Physics Reports*, **52**, 263-379.

11. Birkhoff, G.: 1927, *Dynamical Systems*, Am. Math. Soc. Coll. Pub. IX.

12. Bruhwiler, D.L. and Cary, J.R.: 1989, Diffusion of Particles in a Slowly Modulated Wave, *Physica D*, **40**, 265

13. Burns, T.J.: 1979, On the rotation of Mercury, *Celestial Mechanics*, **19**, 297-313.

14. Dobrott, D. and Greene, J.M.: 1971, Probability of trapping-state transitions in a toroidal device, *Phys. of Fluids*, **14**, 1525-1531.

15. Dubrovin, B.A., Krichever, I.M. and Novikov, S.P.: 1985, Integrable Systems. I, in *Dynamical systems IV*, Arnold and Novikov (eds), Springer-Verlag

16. Elskens, Y. and Escande, D.F.: 1991, Slowly pulsating separatrices sweep homoclinic tangles where island must be small: An extension of classical adiabatic theory, *Nonlinearity*, **4**, 615-667

17. Escande, D.F.: 1985, Change of adiabatic invariant at separatrix crossing: Application to slow Hamiltonian chaos, in *Advances in Nonlinear Dynamics and Stochastic Processes*, (R. Livi and A. Politi eds.), World Scientific Singapore, 67-79.

18. Ferraz-Mello, S.: 1990, Averaging Hamiltonian Systems, in *Modern Methods in Celestial Mechanics*, Benest and Froeschlé (eds), Éditions Fronti'eres

19. Freidberg, J.P.: 1982, Ideal magnetohydrodynamic theory of magnetic fusion systems, *Rev. of Modern Physics*, **54**, 801-902.

20. Goldreich, P.: 1965, An explanation of the frequent occurrence of commensurable mean motions in the Solar System, *M.N.R.A.S.*, **130**, 159-181.

21. Goldreich, P.: 1986, Final spin states of planets and satellites, *Astron. J.*, **71**, 1-7.

22. Goldreich, P. and Peale, S.: 1966, Spin-orbit coupling in the Solar System, *Astron. J.*, **71**, 425-437.

23. Hagihara, Y: 1970, *Celestial Mechanics, Vol I*, Mit Press, Cambridge

24. Hannay, J.H.: 1986, Accuracy loss of action invariance in adiabatic change of a one degree of freedom Hamiltonian, *J. Phys. A*, **19**, 1067-1072.

25. Hénon, M. and Heiles, C.: 1964, The Applicability of the Third Integral of Motion: some Numerical Experiments, *Astron. Journal*, **69**, 73-79

26. Henrard, J., 1982, Capture into resonance: An extension of the use of the adiabatic invariants, *Celestial Mechanics*, **27**, 3-22.

27. Henrard, J.: 1990, Action-Angle Variables, in *Modern Methods in Celestial Mechanics*, Benest and Froeschlé (eds), Éditions Fronti'eres

28. Henrard, J.: 1993, The Adiabatic Invariant in Classical Mechanics, in *Dynamics Reported*, Jones, Kirchgraber and Walther (eds), **2** new series, 117–235

29. Henrard, J. and Henrard, M.: 1991, Slow Crossing of a Stochastic Layer, *Physica D*, **54**, 135-146

30. Henrard, J. and Morbidelli, A.: 1993, Slow Crossing of a Stochastic Layer, *Physica D*, **68**, 187-200

31. Kovrizhnykh, L.M.:1984, Progress in stellarator theory, *Plasma Phys.*, **26**, 195-207.

32. Kruskal, M.: 1952, U.S. Atomic Energy Commission Report N40-998 (PM-S-5).

33. Landau, L.L. and Lifchitz, E.M.: 1960, *Mécanique*, Édition en langues étrangères, Moscou

34. Malhotra , R.: 1994, Nonlinear Resonances in the Solar System, *Physica D*, **77**, 289-304

35. Menyuk, C.R.: 1985, Particle motion in the field of a modulated wave, *Phys. Rev.*, **A 31**, 3282-3290.
Neishtadt, A.I.: 1975, Passage through a separatrix in a resonance problem with a slowly-varying parameter, *Prikl. Matem. Mekhun*, **39**, 621-632.

36. Neishtadt, A.I.: 1986, Change in adiabatic invariant at a separatrix, *Sov. J. Plasma Phys.*, **12**, 568-573

37. Siegel, C.L. and Moser, J.K.: 1971, *Lectures on Celestial Mechanics*, Springer-Verlag.

38. Stäckel.: 1905, *Enc. d. math. Wiss.*, **4**, 494-498

39. Timofeev, A.V.: 1978, On the constancy of the adiabatic invariant when the nature of the motion changes, *Sov. Phys. JETP 48*, 656-659.

40. Urabe, M.: 1954, Infinitesimal deformation of the periodic solution of the second kind and its application to the equation of a pendulum, *J. Sci. Hiroshima Univ.*, **A18**, 183.

41. Urabe, M.:, 1955, The least upper bound of a damping coefficient ensuring the existence of a periodic motion of a pendulum under constant torque, *J. Sci. Hiroshima Univ.*, **A18**, 379.

42. Yoder, C.F.: 1973, *On the establishment and evolution of orbit-orbit resonances*, Thesis, University of California, Santa-Barbara.

43. Yoder, C.F.: 1979a, Diagrammatic theory of transition of Pendulum like systems, *Celestial Mechanics*, **19**, 3-29.

Lectures on Hamiltonian Methods in Nonlinear PDEs

Sergei Kuksin

Department of Mathematics, Heriot-Watt University, Edinburgh
EH14 4AS United Kingdom and
Steklov Institute of Mathematics, 8 Gubkina St. 111966 Moscow, Russia
kuksin@ma.hw.ac.uk

Notations

By $\mathbb{T}^n$ we denote the torus $\mathbb{T}^n = \mathbb{R}^n/2\pi\mathbb{Z}^n$ and write $\mathbb{T}^1 = S^1$. By $\mathbb{R}^n_+$ we denote the open octant $\{x \mid x_j > 0 \ \forall j\}$ and by $\mathbb{Z}_0$ – the set of nonzero integers. Abusing notations, we denote by x both the space-variable and an element of an abstract Banach space X. For an invertible linear operator J we denote $\overline{J} = -J^{-1}$ (so $\overline{\overline{J}} = J$).

1 Symplectic Hilbert Scales and Hamiltonian Equations

1.1 Hilbert Scales and Their Morphisms

Let X be a real Hilbert space with a scalar product $\langle \cdot, \cdot \rangle = \langle \cdot, \cdot \rangle_X$ and a Hilbert basis $\{\varphi_k \mid k \in \widetilde{\mathbb{Z}}\}$, where $\widetilde{\mathbb{Z}}$ is a countable subset of some $\mathbb{Z}^n$. Let us take a positive sequence $\{\vartheta_k \mid k \in \widetilde{\mathbb{Z}}\}$ which goes to infinity with k. For any s we define X_s as a Hilbert space with the Hilbert basis $\{\varphi_k \vartheta_k^{-s} \mid k \in \widetilde{\mathbb{Z}}\}$. By $\| \cdot \|_s$ and $\langle \cdot, \cdot \rangle_s$ we denote the norm and the scalar product in X_s (in particular, $X_0 = X$ and $\langle \cdot, \cdot \rangle_0 = \langle \cdot, \cdot \rangle$). The totality $\{X_s\}$ is called a *Hilbert scale*, the basis $\{\varphi_k\}$ — the *basis of the scale* and the scalar product $\langle \cdot, \cdot \rangle$ — the *basic scalar product of the scale*.

A Hilbert scale may be continuous or discrete, depending on whether $s \in \mathbb{R}$ or $s \in \mathbb{Z}$. The objects we define below and the theorems we discuss are valid in both cases.

A Hilbert scale $\{X_s\}$ possesses the following properties:

1) X_s is compactly embedded in X_r if $s > r$ and is dense there;

2) the spaces X_s and X_{-s} are conjugated with respect to the scalar product $\langle \cdot, \cdot \rangle$. That is, for any $u \in X_s \cap X_0$ we have

$$\|u\|_s = \sup\{\langle u, u' \rangle \mid u' \in X_{-s} \cap X_0, \|u'\|_{-s} = 1\};$$

3) the norms $\| \cdot \|_s$ satisfy the interpolation inequality; linear operators in the spaces X_s satisfy the interpolation theorem

Concerning these and other properties of the scales see [14] and [12].

For a scale $\{X_s\}$ we denote by $X_{-\infty}$ and X_∞ the linear spaces $X_{-\infty} = \bigcup X_s$ and $X_\infty = \bigcap X_s$.

Scales of Sobolev functions are the most important for this work:

Examples

1) Basic for us is the Sobolev scale of functions on an n-torus $\{H^s(\mathbb{T}^n; \mathbb{R}) = H^s(\mathbb{T}^n)\}$. A space $H^s(\mathbb{T}^n)$ is formed by all functions $u \colon \mathbb{T}^n \to \mathbb{R}$ such that

$$u = \sum_{l \in \mathbb{Z}^n} u_l e^{il \cdot x}, \quad \mathbb{C} \ni u_l = \bar{u}_{-l}, \ \|u\|_s^2 = \sum_l (1 + |l|)^{2s} |u_l|^2 < \infty. \quad (1)$$

The basis $\{\varphi_k\}$ is formed by properly normalised functions $\mathrm{Re}\, e^{il \cdot x}$ and $\mathrm{Im}\, e^{il \cdot x}$, $l \in \mathbb{Z}^n$.

2) The Sobolev scales $\{H^s(\mathbb{T}^n; \mathbb{R}^N)\}$ are formed by vector-valued maps and are defined similarly.

3) The scale $\{H_0^s(\mathbb{T}^n)\}$ is formed by functions with zero mean-value, so that in (1) $l \in \mathbb{Z}^n \setminus \{0\}$. In this case in definition of the norm $\| \cdot \|_s$ we replace the factor $(1 + |l|)^{2s}$ by $|l|^{2s}$ (thus defined norm is equivalent and is slightly more convenient). $\square$

Given two scales $\{X_s\}$, $\{Y_s\}$ and a linear map $L \colon X_\infty \to Y_{-\infty}$, we denote by $\|L\|_{s_1, s_2} \le \infty$ its norm as a map $X_{s_1} \to Y_{s_2}$. We say that L defines a *morphism of order d* of the two scales for $s \in [s_0, s_1]$, $s_0 \le s_1$, [1] if $\|L\|_{s, s-d} < \infty$ for every $s \in [s_0, s_1]$. If in addition the inverse map L^{-1} exists and defines a morphism of order $-d$ of the scales $\{Y_s\}$ and $\{X_s\}$ for $s \in [s_0 + d, s_1 + d]$, we say that L defines an *isomorphism of order d* for $s \in [s_0, s_1]$. If $\{X_s\} = \{Y_s\}$, then an isomorphism is called an *automorphism*.

Example 1. Multiplication by a non-vanishing C^r-smooth function defines a zero-order automorphism of the Sobolev scale $\{H^s(\mathbb{T}^n)\}$ for $-r \le s \le r$. $\square$

If L is a morphism of scales $\{X_s\}$, $\{Y_s\}$ of order d for $s \in [s_0, s_1]$, then adjoint maps L^* form a morphism of the scales $\{Y_s\}$ and $\{X_s\}$ of the same order d for $s \in [-s_1 + d, -s_0 + d]$. It is called the *adjoint morphism*.

If $L = L^*$ $(L = -L^*)$ on the space X_∞, then the morphism L is called symmetric (antisymmetric).

If L is a symmetric morphism of $\{X_s\}$ of order d for $s \in [s_0, d - s_0]$, where $s_0 \ge d/2$, then the adjoint morphism L^* is defined for $s \in [s_0, d - s_0]$ and coincide with L on X_∞; hence, $L^* = L$. We call L a *selfadjoint morphism*. Anti-selfadjoint morphisms are defined similarly.

Example 2. The operator Δ defines a selfadjoint morphism of order 2 of the Sobolev scale $\{H^s(\mathbb{T}^n)\}$ for $-\infty < s < \infty$. The operators $\partial/\partial x_j$, $1 \le j \le n$, define anti-selfadjoint morphisms of order one. The automorphism in Example 1.1 is selfadjoint. $\square$

---

[1] or $s \in (s_0, s_1)$, etc.

Let $\{Y_s\}$, $\{Y_s\}$ be two scales and $O_s \subset X_s$, $s \in [a, b]$, be a system of (open) domains, compatible in the following sense:

$$O_{s_1} \cap O_{s_2} = O_{s_2} \quad \text{if } a \leq s_1 \leq s_2 \leq b.$$

Let $F: O_a \to Y_{-\infty}$ be a map such that for every $s \in [a, b]$ its restriction to O_s defines an analytic (C^k-smooth) map $F: O_s \to Y_{s-d}$. Then F is called an analytic (C^k-smooth) morphism of order d for $s \in [a, b]$.

Example 3. Let $\{X_s\}$ be the Sobolev scale $\{H^s(S^1)\}$ and $F(u, x)$ be a C^r-smooth function. Then the map $u(x) \mapsto F(u(x), x)$ defines a zero-order C^r-smooth morphism of the scale $\{X_s\}$ for $s \in (1/2, r]$ (now $O_s = X_s$). If the function F is analytic in u, then the morphism is analytic. $\square$

Given a C^k-smooth function $H: X_d \supset O_d \to \mathbb{R}$, $k \geq 1$, we consider its *gradient map* with respect to the basic scalar product $\langle \cdot, \cdot \rangle$:

$$\nabla H: O_d \to X_{-d}, \qquad \langle \nabla H(u), v \rangle = H_*(u)v \quad \forall v \in X_d,$$

where $H_*(u)$ stands for the linearization of the map H at a point u. The map ∇H is C^{k-1}-smooth.

If O_d belongs to a system of compatible domains O_s, $a \leq s \leq b$, and the gradient map ∇H defines a C^{k-1}-smooth morphism of order d_H for $a \leq s \leq b$, we write that $\operatorname{ord} \nabla H = d_H$.

1.2 Symplectic Structures

For simplicity we restrict ourselves to constant-coefficient symplectic structures. For the general case see [12].

Let $\{X_s\}$ be a Hilbert scale and J be its anti-selfadjoint automorphism of order d for $-\infty < s < \infty$. Then the operator

$$\overline{J} = -J^{-1}$$

defines an anti-selfadjoint automorphism of order $-d$. We define a two-form α_2 as

$$\alpha_2 = \overline{J} \, dx \wedge dx,$$

where by definition

$$\overline{J} \, dx \wedge dx \, [\xi, \eta] = \langle \overline{J}\xi, \eta \rangle.$$

Clearly, $\overline{J} \, dx \wedge dx$ defines a continuous skew-symmetric bilinear form on $X_r \times X_r$ if $r \geq -d/2$. Therefore any space X_r, $r \geq -d/2$, becomes a *symplectic (Hilbert) space* and we shall write it as a pair (X_r, α_2).

The pair $(\{X_s\}, \alpha_2)$ is called a *symplectic (Hilbert) scale*. [2]

---

[2] In [8, 12] we consider symplectic Hilbert scales $(\{X_s\}, \alpha_2)$ such that $d \geq 0$, and work with symplectic spaces (X_r, α_2) with $r \geq 0$. It was done since the relations $d \geq 0$ and $r \geq 0$ hold for most examples and since this assumption simplifies statements of some results, especially if the symplectic form is not constant-coefficient.

Let $(\{X_s\}, \alpha_2 = \overline{J}\,dx \wedge dx)$ and $(\{Y_s\}, \beta_2 = \overline{T}\,dy \wedge dy)$ be two symplectic Hilbert scales and $O_s \subset X_s$, $a \leq s \leq b$, be a system of compatible domains. A C^1-smooth morphism of order d_1

$$F: O_s \to Y_{s-d_1}, \qquad a \leq s \leq b,$$

is *symplectic* if $F^*\beta_2 = \alpha_2$. That is, if $\langle \overline{T} F_*(x)\xi, F_*(x)\eta \rangle_Y \equiv \langle \overline{J}\xi, \eta \rangle_X$, or

$$F^*(x)\overline{T}F_*(x) = \overline{J} \quad \forall x.$$

A symplectic morphism F as above is called a *symplectomorphism* if it is a diffeomorphism.

1.3 Hamiltonian Equations

To a C^1-smooth function h on a domain $O_d \subset X_d$, the symplectic form α_2 as above corresponds the *Hamiltonian vector field* V_h, defined by the usual relation (cf. [1, 5]):

$$\alpha_2[V_h(x), \xi] = -h_*(x)\xi \quad \forall \xi.$$

That is, $\langle \overline{J}V_h(x), \xi \rangle \equiv -\langle \nabla h(x), \xi \rangle$ and

$$V_h(x) = J\nabla h(x).$$

The vector field V_h defines a continuous map $O_d \to X_{-d-d_J}$. Usually we shall assume that V_h is smoother than that and defines a smooth morphism of order $d_1 \leq 2d + d_J$ for all s from some segment.

For any C^1-smooth function h on $O_d \times \mathbb{R}$ we denote by V_h the non-autonomous vector field $V_h(x, t) = J\nabla_x h(x, t)$, where ∇_x is the gradient in x, and consider the corresponding *Hamiltonian equation* (or *Hamiltonian system*)

$$\dot{x} = J\nabla_x h(x, t) = V_h(x, t). \tag{2}$$

A partial differential equation (PDE), supplemented by some boundary conditions, is called a *Hamiltonian PDE* if under a suitable choice of a symplectic Hilbert scale $(\{X_s\}, \alpha_2)$, a domain $O_d \subset X_d$ and a Hamiltonian h, it can be written in the form (2). In this case the vector field V_h is unbounded, $\mathrm{ord}\, V_h = d_1 > 0$. That is,

$$V_h: O_d \times \mathbb{R} \to X_{d-d_1}.$$

Usually O_d belongs to a system of compatible domains O_s, $s \geq d_0$, and V_h (as a function of x) defines an analytic morphism of order d_1 for $s \geq d_0$.

A continuous curve $x: [t_0, t_1] \to O_d$ is called a *solution of* (2) *in the space* X_d if it defines a C^1-smooth map $x: [t_0, t_1] \to X_{d-d_1}$ and both parts of (2) coincide as curves in X_{d-d_1}. A solution x is called *smooth* if it defines a smooth curve in each space X_s.

If a solution $x(t)$, $t \geq t_0$, of (2) such that $x(t_0) = x_0$ exists and is unique, we write $x(t_1) = S_{t_0}^{t_1} x_0$, or $x(t_1) = S^{t_1-t_0} x_0$ if the equation is autonomous (we do not assume that $t_1 \geq t_0$). The operators $S_{t_0}^{t_1}$ and S^t are called *flow-maps* of the equation. Often the flow-map operators have non-trivial domains of definition, where a point $x \in X_d$ belongs to a domain of definition of an operator $S_{t_0}^{t_1}$, if for every $x' \in X_d$, sufficiently close to x, equation (2) has a unique solution in X_d, defined for $t \in [t_0, t_1]$ and equal x' for $t = t_0$.

Clearly, $S_{t_0}^{t_1}$ equals $(S_{t_1}^{t_0})^{-1}$ on a joint domain of definition of the two operators.

1.4 Quasilinear and Semilinear Equations

A nonlinear PDE is called *strongly nonlinear* if its nonlinear part contains as many derivatives as the linear part. Strongly nonlinear Hamiltonian PDEs may possess rather unpleasant properties. In particular, for some of them, every non-zero solution develops a singularity in finite time, see an example in Section 1.4 of [12].

If the nonlinear part contains less derivatives then the linear one, an equation is called *quasilinear*. A quasilinear equation can be written in the form (2) with

$$h(x,t) = \tfrac{1}{2}\langle Ax, x\rangle + h_0(x,t), \tag{3}$$

where A is a linear operator which defines a selfadjoint morphism of the scale (so $\nabla h(x,t) = Ax + \nabla h_0(x,t)$) and $\operatorname{ord} \nabla h_0 < \operatorname{ord} A$.

The class of Hamiltonian PDEs contains many important equations of mathematical physics, some of them are discussed below. The first difficulty one comes across when studies this class is absence of a general theorem which would guarantee that (locally in time) an equation has a unique solution. Such a theorem exists for semilinear equations, where an equation (2) is called *semilinear* if its Hamiltonian has the form (3) and $\operatorname{ord} J\nabla h_0 \leq 0$ (see [13] and Section 1.4 of [12]).

Example 4 (equations of the Korteweg–de Vries type). Let us take for $\{X_s\}$ the scale of zero-mean-value Sobolev spaces $H_0^s(S^1)$ as in Subsection 1.1 and choose $J = \partial/\partial x$, so $d_J = 1$. For a Hamiltonian h we take $h(u) = \int_0^{2\pi} (-\tfrac{1}{8} u'(x)^2 + f(u))\, dx$ with some analytic function $f(u)$. Then $\nabla h(u) = \tfrac{1}{4} u'' + f'(u)$ and the equation takes the form

$$\dot u(t,x) = \frac{1}{4} u''' + \frac{\partial}{\partial x} f'(u). \tag{4}$$

For $f(u) = \tfrac{1}{4} u^3$ we get the classical Korteweg–de Vries (KdV) equation. The map V_h defines an analytic morphism of order 3 of the scale $\{X_s\}$, for $s > 1/2$. The equation has the form (2), (3), where $\operatorname{ord} JA = 3$ and $\operatorname{ord} J\nabla h_0 = 1$. It is quasilinear, but not semilinear. $\square$

Example 5 (nonlinear Schrödinger equations). Let $X_s = H^s(\mathbb{T}^n; \mathbb{C})$, $s \in \mathbb{Z}$, where these Sobolev spaces are treated as *real* Hilbert spaces, and the basic scalar product $\langle \cdot, \cdot \rangle$ is $\langle u, v \rangle = \mathrm{Re} \int u\bar{v}\, dx$. For J we take the operator $Ju(x) = iu(x)$ and choose

$$h(u) = \int_{\mathbb{T}^n} \left(\frac{1}{2} |\nabla u|^2 + g(u, \bar{u}) \right) dx,$$

where $g(u, v)$ is an analytic function, real if $v = \bar{u}$. Then [3] $\nabla h(u) = -\Delta u + 2\frac{\partial}{\partial \bar{u}} g$ and (2) takes the form

$$\dot{u} = -i\Delta u + 2i \frac{\partial}{\partial \bar{u}} g(u, \bar{u}). \tag{5}$$

This is a semilinear Hamiltonian PDE.

2 Basic Theorems on Hamiltonian Systems

Basic theorems from the classical Hamiltonian formalism (see [1, 5]) remain true for equations (2) in Hilbert scales, provided that the theorems are properly formulated. In this section we present three corresponding results. Their proofs can be found in [8, 12].

Let $(\{X_s\}, \alpha_2 = \bar{J}\, dx \wedge dx)$ and $(\{Y_s\}, \beta_2 = \bar{\Upsilon}\, dy \wedge dy)$ be two symplectic scales and (for simplicity) $\mathrm{ord}\, J = \mathrm{ord}\, \Upsilon = d_J \geq 0$. Let $\Phi \colon Q \to O$ be a C^1-smooth symplectic map, where Q and O are domains in Y_d and X_d, $d \geq 0$. If $d_J > 0$, we have to assume that

(H1) for any $|s| \leq d$ linearised maps $\Phi_*(y)$, $y \in Q$, define linear maps $Y_s \to X_s$ which continuously depend on y.

The first theorem states that symplectic maps transform Hamiltonian equations to Hamiltonian:

Theorem 1. *Let $\Phi \colon Q \to O$ be a symplectic map as above (so (H1) holds if $d_J > 0$). Let us assume that the vector field V_h of equation (2) defines a C^1-smooth map $V_h \colon O \times \mathbb{R} \to X_{d-d_1}$ of order $d_1 \leq 2d$ and that this vector field is tangent to the map Φ (i.e., for every $y \in Q$ and every t the vector $V_h(\Phi(y), t)$ belong to the range of the linearised map $\Phi_*(y)$). Then Φ transforms solutions of the Hamiltonian equation*

$$\dot{y} = \Upsilon \nabla_y H(y, t), \qquad H = h \circ \Phi,$$

to solutions of (2)

---

[3] To understand the factor 2, take $g = |u|^2 = u\bar{u}$.

Corollary 1. *If under the assumptions of Theorem 1 $\{X_s\} = \{Y_s\}$ and $\beta_2 = K\alpha_2$ (i.e., $\Phi^* \alpha_2 = K\alpha_2$) for some $K \neq 0$, then Φ transforms solutions of the equation $\dot{x} = K^{-1} J \nabla h$ to solutions of (2). In particular, Φ preserves the class of solutions for (2) if it preserves the symplectic form α_2*

For Hamiltonian PDEs (and for Hamiltonian equations (2)) Theorem 2.1 plays the same role as its classical finite-dimensional counterpart plays for usual Hamiltonian equations: it is used to transform an equation to a normal form, usually in the vicinity of an invariant set (e.g., of an equilibrium). Cf. Section 7 of [12].

To apply Theorem 1 one needs regular ways to construct symplectic transformations. For classical finite-dimensional systems symplectic transformations usually are obtained either via generating functions, or as Lie transformations (i.e., as flow-maps of additional Hamiltonians), see [1, 5]. For infinite dimensional symplectic spaces generating functions play negligible role, while Lie transformations remain an important tool. An easy but important corresponding result is stated in the theorem below.

Let $(\{X_s\}, \alpha_2)$ be a symplectic Hilbert scale as above and O be a domain in X_d.

Theorem 2. *Let f be a C^1-smooth function on $O \times \mathbb{R}$ such that the map $V_f : O \times \mathbb{R} \to X_d$ is Lipschitz in (x, t) and C^1-smooth in x. Let O_1 be a subdomain of O. Then the flow-maps $S_t^\tau : (O_1, \alpha_2) \to (O, \alpha_2)$ are symplectomorphisms (provided that they map O_1 to O). If the map V_f is C^k-smooth or analytic, then the flow-maps are C^k-smooth or analytic as well.*

The assumption that the map V_f is Lipschitz can be replaced by the much weaker assumption that for a solution $x(t)$ of the equation $\dot{x} = V_f(x)$, the linearised equation $\dot{\xi} = V_{f*}(x(t))\xi$ is such that its flow maps are bounded linear transformations of the space X_d. See [12].

Usually Theorem 2 is applied in the situation when $|f| \ll 1$, or $|t - \tau| \ll 1$. In these cases the flow-maps are closed to the identity and the corresponding transformations of the space of C^1-smooth functions on O, $H \mapsto H \circ S_t^\tau$, can be written as Lie series (cf. [4]). In particular, the following simple result holds:

Theorem 3. *Under the assumptions of Theorem 2, let H be a C^1-smooth function on O. Then*

$$\frac{d}{d\tau} H(S_t^\tau(x)) = \{f, H\}(S_t^\tau(x)), \qquad x \in O_1. \tag{1}$$

In this theorem $\{f, H\}$ denotes the *Poisson bracket* of the two functions:

$$\{f, H\}(x) = \langle J\nabla f(x), \nabla H(x) \rangle.$$

It is well defined since $J\nabla f = V_f \in X_d$ by assumptions.

Theorem 2 and formula (1) make from symplectic flow-maps S_t^τ a tool which suits well to prove KAM-theorems for Hamiltonian PDEs, see [8, 12, 6].

An immediate consequence of Theorem 3 is that for an autonomous Hamiltonian equation $\dot{x} = J\nabla f(x)$ such that $\mathrm{ord}\, J\nabla f = 0$, a C^1-smooth function H is an integral of motion [4] if and only if $\{f, H\} \equiv 0$.

If $d' = \mathrm{ord}\, J\nabla f > 0$ and $O = O_d$ belongs to a system of compatible domains $O_s \subset X_s$, $s \in [d_0, d]$, where $d_0 = d - d'$, then H such that $\{f, H\} \equiv 0$ is an integrable of motion for the equation $\dot{x} = J\nabla f(x)$, provided that

$$\mathrm{ord}\, J\nabla f = d' \quad \text{and} \quad \mathrm{ord}\, \nabla H = d_H \quad \text{for} \quad s \in [d_0, d],$$

where $d' + d_H \leq 2d$. Indeed, since $d_0 - d_H \geq -d_0$, then H is a C^1-smooth function on O_{d_0}. Since any solution $x(t)$ is a C^1-smooth curve in O_{d_0} by the definition of a solution, then

$$\frac{d}{dt}\, H(x) = \langle \nabla H(x), \dot{x} \rangle = \langle \nabla H(x), J\nabla f(x) \rangle = \{f, H\}(x) = 0.$$

In particular, f is an integral of motion for the equation $\dot{x} = J\nabla f(x)$ in O_d if we have $\mathrm{ord}\, J = d_J$ and $\mathrm{ord}\, \nabla f = d_f$ for $s = d$ and for $s \in [d, d - d_f - d_J]$, where $d \geq d_f + d_J/2$. That is, if the equation is being considered in sufficiently smooth spaces.

Example 6. Let us consider a nonlinear Schrödinger equation (5) such that $g(u, \overline{u}) = g_0(|u|^2)$, and take $H(u) = \|u\|_0^2 = |u|_{L_2}^2$. Now $d' := \mathrm{ord}\, J\nabla f = 2$ for $s \in (n/2, \infty)$, and $\mathrm{ord}\, \nabla H = 0$. Elementary calculations show that $\{f, H\} \equiv 0$. So L_2-norm is an integral of motion for solutions of (5) in X_s if $s > n/2 + 2$. (In fact this result holds true for solutions of much lower smoothness). □

3 Lax-Integrable Equations

3.1 General Discussion

Let us take a Hamiltonian PDE and write it as a Hamiltonian equation in a suitable symplectic Hilbert scale $(\{Z_s\}, \alpha_2 = \overline{J}\, du \wedge du)$

$$\dot{u} = J\nabla H(u) \tag{1}$$

This equation is called Lax-integrable if there exists an additional Hilbert scale $\{X_s\}$ (real or complex), and finite order linear morphisms $\mathcal{L}_u$ and $\mathcal{A}_u$ of this scale which depend on the parameter $u \in Z_\infty$, such that a curve $u(t)$ is a smooth solution for (1) if and only if

$$\frac{d}{dt}\, \mathcal{L}_{u(t)} = [\mathcal{A}_{u(t)}, \mathcal{L}_{u(t)}]. \tag{2}$$

---

[4] That is, $H(x(t))$ is a time-independent quantity for any solution $x(t)$.

The operators $\mathcal{A}_u$ and $\mathcal{L}_u$, treated as morphisms of the scale $\{X_s\}$, are assumed to depend smoothly on $u \in Z_d$ where d is sufficiently large, so the left-hand side of (2) is well defined (for details see [12]). The pair of operators $\mathcal{L}$, $\mathcal{A}$ is called the *Lax pair*.

In most known examples of Lax-integrable equations relation between the scales $\{Z_s\}$ and $\{X_s\}$ is the following: spaces Z_s are formed by T-periodic Sobolev vector-functions, while $\mathcal{A}$ and $\mathcal{L}$ are differential or integro-differential operators with u-dependent coefficients, acting in a scale $\{X_s\}$ of TL-periodic Sobolev vector-functions. Here L is any fixed integer, so *the scale $\{X_s\}$ is not uniquely defined.*

Let $u(t)$ be a smooth solution for (1). We set $\mathcal{L}_t = \mathcal{L}_{u(t)}$ and $\mathcal{A}_t = \mathcal{A}_{u(t)}$.

Lemma 1. *Let $\chi_0 \in X_\infty$ be a smooth eigenvector of $\mathcal{L}_0$, i.e., $\mathcal{L}_0 \chi_0 = \lambda \chi_0$. Let us assume that the initial-value problem*

$$\dot{\chi} = \mathcal{A}_t \chi, \qquad \chi(0) = \chi_0, \tag{3}$$

has a unique smooth solution $\chi(t)$. Then

$$\mathcal{L}_t \chi(t) = \lambda \chi(t) \quad \forall t. \tag{4}$$

Proof. Let us denote the left-hand side of (4) by $\xi(t)$, the right-hand side — by $\eta(t)$ and calculate their derivatives. We have:

$$\frac{d}{dt} \xi = \frac{d}{dt} \mathcal{L}\chi = [\mathcal{A}, \mathcal{L}]\chi + \mathcal{L}\mathcal{A}\chi = \mathcal{A}\mathcal{L}\chi = \mathcal{A}\xi$$

and

$$\frac{d}{dt} \eta = \frac{d}{dt} \lambda \chi = \lambda \mathcal{A}\chi = \mathcal{A}\eta.$$

Thus, both $\xi(t)$ and $\eta(t)$ solve the problem (3) with χ_0 replaced by $\lambda \chi_0$ and coincide by the uniqueness assumption.

Due to this lemma, a set $\mathcal{T}$ formed by all smooth vectors $u \in Z_\infty$ such that the operator $\mathcal{L}_u$ has a prescribed set of smooth eigenvalues (i.e., the eigenvalues, corresponding to eigenvectors from the space X_∞), is invariant for the flow of equation (1). A remarkable fact is that for many Lax-integrable Hamiltonian PDEs some sets $\mathcal{T}$ as above are finite dimensional symplectic submanifolds $\mathcal{T}^{2n}$ of Z_∞ and restriction of equation (1) to every $\mathcal{T}^{2n}$ is an integrable Hamiltonian equation. Moreover, union of all these manifolds $\mathcal{T}^{2n}$ is dense in every space Z_s. Below we discuss this construction for some Lax-integrable equations.

3.2 Korteweg–de Vries Equation

The KdV equation

$$\dot{u} = \frac{1}{4}\frac{\partial}{\partial x}(u_{xx} + 3u^2), \qquad u(t,x) \equiv u(t, x + 2\pi), \qquad \int_0^{2\pi} u\, dx \equiv 0, \qquad \text{(KdV)}$$

takes the form (1) in the symplectic Hilbert scale $(\{Z_s\}, \alpha_2 = \bar{J}\, du \wedge du)$, where Z_s is the Sobolev space $H_0^s(S^1)$ and $Ju = (\partial/\partial x)u$, see Example 4. Due to Lax himself, this equation is Lax-integrable and the corresponding Lax pair is

$$\mathcal{L}_u = -\frac{\partial^2}{\partial x^2} - u, \qquad \mathcal{A}_u = \frac{\partial^3}{\partial x^3} + \frac{3}{2}u\frac{\partial}{\partial x} + \frac{3}{4}u_x.$$

Taking for $\{X_s\}$ the Sobolev scale of 4π-periodic functions and applying Lemma 1 we obtain that smooth 4π-periodic spectrum of the operator $\mathcal{L}_u$ is an integral of motion. It is well known that the spectrum of $\mathcal{L}_u$ is formed by eigenvalues

$$\lambda_0 < \lambda_1 \le \lambda_2 < \lambda_3 \le \lambda_4 < \cdots \nearrow \infty,$$

and that the corresponding eigenfunctions are smooth, provided that the potential u is. Let us take any integer n-vector $\mathbf{V}$,

$$\mathbf{V} = (V_1, \ldots, V_n) \in \mathbb{N}^n, \qquad V_1 < \cdots < V_n.$$

Denoting $\Delta_j = \lambda_{2j} - \lambda_{2j-1} \ge 0$, $j = 1, 2, \ldots$, we define the set $\mathcal{T}_{\mathbf{V}}^{2n}$ as

$$\mathcal{T}_{\mathbf{V}}^{2n} = \{u(x) \mid \Delta_j \ne 0 \text{ iff } j \in \{V_1, \ldots, V_n\}\}.$$

Clearly $\mathcal{T}_{\mathbf{V}}^{2n}$ equals to the union

$$\mathcal{T}_{\mathbf{V}}^{2n} = \bigcup_{r \in \mathbb{R}_+^n} \mathcal{T}_{\mathbf{V}}^n(r),$$

where $\mathbb{R}_+^n = \{r \mid r_j > 0\ \forall j\}$ and

$$\mathcal{T}_{\mathbf{V}}^n(r) = \{u(x) \in \mathcal{T}_{\mathbf{V}}^{2n} \mid \Delta_j = r_j\ \forall j\}.$$

Since the 4π-periodic spectrum $\{\lambda_j\}$ is an integral of motion for (KdV), then the sets $\mathcal{T}_{\mathbf{V}}^n(r)$ are invariant for the KdV-flow. Due to the classical theory of the Sturm–Liouville operator $\mathcal{L}_u$, the set $\mathcal{T}_{\mathbf{V}}^{2n}$ is a smooth submanifold of any space Z_s, foliated to the smooth n-tori $\mathcal{T}_{\mathbf{V}}^n(r)$. There exists an analytic map $\Phi: \{(r, \mathfrak{z})\} = \mathbb{R}_+^n \times \mathbb{T}^n \to Z_s$ such that $\mathcal{T}_{\mathbf{V}}^n(r) = \Phi(\{r\} \times \mathbb{T}^n)$. One of the most remarkable results of the theory of KdV equation — the *Its–Matveev formula* — explicitly represents the map Φ [5] in terms of theta-functions. Moreover, the Its–Matveev map Φ analytically extends to the closed octant

---

[5] more specially, a possible choice of this map.

$\{r \mid r_j \geq 0 \ \forall j\}$ and integrates (KdV) in the following sense: there is an analytic function $h = h^n(r)$ such that for any r and any $\mathfrak{z}_0 \in \mathbb{T}^n$, the curve $u(t) = \Phi(r, \mathfrak{z}_0 + t\nabla h(r))$ is a smooth solution for (KdV). We note that as a function of t, this solution is a quasi-periodic curve. [6]

3.3 Other Examples

Sine-Gordon. The Sine-Gordon equation on the circle

$$\ddot{u} = u_{xx}(t,x) - \sin u(t,x), \qquad x \in S^1 = \mathbb{R}/2\pi\mathbb{Z}, \qquad \text{(SG)}$$

is another example of a Lax-integrable PDE.

First the equation has to be written in a Hamiltonian form. The most straightforward was to do this is to write (SG) as the system

$$\dot{u} = -v, \qquad \dot{v} = -u_{xx} + \sin u(t,x).$$

One immediately sees that this system is a semilinear Hamiltonian equation in the symplectic scale $(\{Z_s = H^s(S) \times H^s(S)\}, \alpha_2 = \bar{J} \, d\xi \wedge d\xi)$, where $\xi = (u, v)$ and $J(u, v) = (-v, u)$.

Now we derive another Hamiltonian form of (SG), more convenient for its analysis. To do this we consider the shifted Sobolev scale $\{Z_s = H^{s+1}(S^1) \times H^{s+1}(S^1)\}$, where the space Z_0 is given the scalar product

$$\langle \xi_1, \xi_2 \rangle = \int_{S^1} (\xi'_{1x} \cdot \xi'_{2x} + \xi_1 \cdot \xi_2) \, dx,$$

and any space Z_s – the product $\langle \xi_1, \xi_2 \rangle_s = \langle A^s \xi_1, \xi_2 \rangle$. Here A is the operator $A = -\partial^2/\partial x^2 + 1$. Obviously, A defines a selfadjoint automorphism of the scale of order one. The operator $J(u, w) = (-\sqrt{A}\, w, \sqrt{A}\, v)$ defines an anti-selfadjoint automorphism of the same order. We provide the scale with the symplectic form $\beta_2 = \bar{J} \, d\xi \wedge d\xi$. We note that (SG) can be written as the system

$$\dot{u} = -\sqrt{A}\, w, \qquad \dot{w} = \sqrt{A}\,(u + A^{-1}f'(u(x))), \qquad (5)$$

where $f(u) = -\cos u - \frac{1}{2}u^2$, and that (5) is a semilinear Hamiltonian equation in the symplectic scale as above with the Hamiltonian $H(\xi) = \frac{1}{2}\langle \xi, \xi \rangle + \int f(u(x)) \, dx$, $\xi = (u, v)$.

Let us denote by Z_s^o (Z_s^e) subspaces of Z_s formed by odd (even) vector functions $\xi(x)$. Then $(\{Z_s^o\}, \beta_2)$ and $(\{Z_s^e\}, \beta_2)$ are symplectic subscales of the scale above. The space Z_s^o and Z_s^e (with $s \geq 0$) are invariant for the flow of equation (5). The restricted flows correspond to the SG equation under the odd periodic and even periodic boundary conditions, respectively.

---

[6] A continuous curve $u : \mathbb{R} \to X$ is quasiperiodic if there exist $n \in \mathbb{N}$, $\varphi \in \mathbb{T}^n$, $\omega \in \mathbb{R}^n$ and a continuous map $U : \mathbb{T}^n \to X$ such that $u(t) = U(\varphi + t\omega)$.

The SG equation is Lax-integrable under periodic, odd periodic and even periodic boundary conditions. That is, equation (5) is Lax-integrable in the all three symplectic scales defined above.

Zakharov–Shabat equation. Let us take the symplectic Hilbert scale $(X_s = H^s(S^1, \mathbb{C}), \bar{J}\, du \wedge du)$ as in the example 5. Choosing the Hamiltonian

$$h^{\pm}(u) = \int_{S^1} \left(\frac{1}{2} |\nabla u|^2 \pm \frac{1}{4} |u|^4 \right) dx,$$

we get the Zakharov–Shabat equations:

$$\dot{u} = i(-u_{xx} \pm |u|^2 u).$$

The sign '$-$' corresponds to the focusing equation and the sign '$+$' — to the defocusing one. Both these equations are Lax-integrable, see [15].

4 KAM for PDEs

Exact statements of abstract 'KAM for PDEs' theorems are rather long and technical (nothing to say about their proofs!). In this section we restrict ourselves to short discussion of the theorems and give some examples. For extended discussion see [9]. For proofs see [8, 12, 6].

4.1 Perturbations of Lax-Integrable Equation

The 'KAM for PDEs' theory implies that for 'many' Lax-integrable equations, most of time-quasiperiodic solutions that feel the invariant symplectic submanifolds $\mathcal{T}^{2n}$ (see the end of Subsection 3.1) persist under small quasilinear Hamiltonian perturbations of the equation. Here 'most' means 'most in the sense of the Lebesgue measure'.

As an example, we consider the perturbed KdV equation

$$\dot{u} = \frac{1}{4} \frac{\partial}{\partial x} (u_{xx} + 3u^2 + \varepsilon f(u, x)),$$

$$u(t, x) \equiv u(t, x + 2\pi), \quad \int u\, dx \equiv 0,$$

$$(1)$$

where f is a smooth function, 2π-periodic in x and analytic in u. By K we denote any compact set $K \subset \mathbb{R}^n_+$ of a positive Lebesgue measure, and set

$$\mathcal{T}^{2n}_K = \bigcup_{r \in K} T^n_{\mathbf{V}}(r).$$

This is a compact part of the finite-gap manifold $\mathcal{T}^{2n}_{\mathbf{V}}$, defined in Subsection 3.2. Below we present a KAM-theorem for equation (1). For its proof see [7, 12, 6].

Theorem 4. *There exists a Borel subset $K_\varepsilon \subset K$ such that $\mathrm{mes}(K \setminus K_\varepsilon) \to 0$ as $\varepsilon \to 0$, and for every $r \in K_\varepsilon$ equation (1) (treated as a Hamiltonian system in a Sobolev space $H_0^s(S^1)$, $s \ge 1$) has an invariant torus $T_\varepsilon^n(r) \subset H_0^s(S^1)$ which is ε^ϱ-close to $T_V^n(r)$. This torus is filled with smooth time-quasiperiodic solutions of (1).*

In the theorem the exponent ϱ is any fixed number $\varrho \in (0, 1/3)$.

Similar result holds if f depends on t and is a quasiperiodic function of t, see [12].

Proof of Theorem 4, given in [12], is obtained by applying an abstract KAM-theorem. The same theorem applies to perturbations of many other integrable equations (Sine-Gordon, Sinh-Gordon, focusing and defocusing Zakharov–Shabat equations, etc.). See [12] concerning the perturbed Sine-Gordon equation

$$\ddot{u} - u_{xx} + a\sin bu + \varepsilon f(u, x) = 0, \qquad a, b > 0 \tag{2}$$

(for $\varepsilon = 0$ (2) is a scaled Sine-Gordon equation). At the same time the abstract KAM-theorem cannot be used to study perturbations of some other Lax-integrable equations, e.g., of the Kadomtsev–Petviashvili equation.

4.2 Perturbations of Linear Equations

The KAM-theory implies that solutions of a parameter-depending linear Hamiltonian PDE persist under Hamiltonian perturbations for most values of the parameter. This is a vast subject. See theorems, examples, discussions and references in [8, 12, 9, 6].

4.3 Small Oscillation in Nonlinear PDEs

Let us consider the so-called φ^4-equation

$$\ddot{u} - u_{xx} + u - u^3 = 0.$$

One can find positive constants a and b such that $u - u^3 = a\sin bu + O(|u|^5)$. Accordingly, small solutions of the φ^4-equation can be treated as perturbations of a scaled Sine-Gordon equation. That is, as small solutions for (2). So they can be treated using the theory described in Subsection 4.1. Similarly, small solutions for a nonlinear Schrödinger equation

$$\dot{u} - i(u_{xx} + f(|u|^2)u) = 0,$$

where $f(0) = 0$, $f'(0) \ne 0$, can be interpreted as perturbations of solutions for a Zakharov–Shabat equation and can be treated similarly.

For details see joint works of the author with A. Bobenko in Comment. Math. Helv. 70:1 and with J. Pöschel in Annals of Math. 143:1 (for the φ^4-equation and the nonlinear Schrödinger equation, respectively).

5 The Non-squeezing Phenomenon and Symplectic Capacity

5.1 The Gromov Theorem

Let $(\mathbb{R}^{2n}, \beta_2)$ be the space $\mathbb{R}^{2n} = \{x_1, x_{-1}, \ldots, x_{-n}\}$ with the Darboux symplectic form $\beta_2 = \sum dx_j \wedge dx_{-j}$. By $B_r(x) = B_r(x; \mathbb{R}^{2n})$ and $C_\varrho^j = C_\varrho^j(\mathbb{R}^{2n})$, $1 \le j \le n$, we denote the following balls and cylinders in $\mathbb{R}^{2n}$:

$$B_r(x) = \{y \mid |y - x| < r\}, \qquad C_\varrho^j = \{y = (y_1, \ldots, y_{-n}) \mid y_j^2 + y_{-j}^2 < \varrho^2\}.$$

The famous *(non-) squeezing theorem* by M. Gromov states that if $f\colon B_r(x) \to \mathbb{R}^{2n}$ is a symplectomorphism such that its range belongs to a cylinder $x_1 + C_\varrho^j$, $x_1 \in \mathbb{R}^{2n}$, then $\varrho \ge r$. For a proof, references and discussions see [5].

5.2 Infinite-Dimensional Case

Let us consider a symplectic Hilbert scale $(\{Z_s\}, \alpha_2 = \bar{J} \, du \wedge du)$ with a basis $\{\varphi_j \mid j \in \mathbb{Z}_0 = \mathbb{Z} \setminus \{0\}\}$. We assume that this basis can be renormalised to a basis $\{\tilde{\varphi}_j \mid j \in \mathbb{Z}_0\}$ (each $\tilde{\varphi}_j$ is proportional to φ_j) which is a Darboux basis for the form α_2 and a Hilbert basis of some space Z_d. That is,

$$\langle \tilde{\varphi}_j, \tilde{\varphi}_k \rangle_d = \delta_{j,k}, \qquad \alpha_2[\tilde{\varphi}_j, \tilde{\varphi}_{-k}] = \operatorname{sgn} j \, \delta_{j,k} \qquad \forall j, k. \tag{1}$$

These relations imply that

$$\alpha_2[\xi, \eta] = \langle \bar{J}\xi, \eta \rangle_d, \qquad \bar{J}\tilde{\varphi}_j = \operatorname{sgn} j \, \tilde{\varphi}_{-j} \quad \forall j. \tag{2}$$

In particular, $\bar{J} = J$.

Below we skip the tildes and re-denote the new basis back to $\{\varphi_j\}$.

In this scale we consider a semilinear Hamiltonian equation with the Hamiltonian $H(u) = \frac{1}{2}\langle Au, u \rangle_d + h(u, t)$. Due to (2) it can be written in the following way:

$$\dot{u} = JAu + J\nabla^d h(u, t), \tag{3}$$

where ∇^d signifies the gradient in u with respect to the scalar product of Z_d.

If a Hamiltonian PDE is written in the form (3), then the symplectic space (Z_d, α_2) is called the *(Hilbert) Darboux phase space* for this PDE. Below we study properties of flow-maps of equation (3) in its Darboux phase space.

Let us assume that the operator A has the form

(H1) $Au = \sum_{j=1}^\infty \lambda_j(u_j\varphi_j + u_{-j}\varphi_{-j}) \quad \forall u = \sum u_j\varphi_j$,

where λ_j's are some real numbers.

Then $JAu = \sum_{j=1}^\infty \lambda_j(u_{-j}\varphi_{-j} - u_j\varphi_j)$, so the linear operators e^{tJA} are direct sums of rotations in the planes $\mathbb{R}\varphi_j + \mathbb{R}\varphi_{-j} \subset Z_d$, $j = 1, 2, \ldots$.

We also assume that the gradient map $\nabla^d h$ is smoothing:

(H2) there exists $\gamma > 0$ such that $\operatorname{ord} \nabla^d h = -\gamma$ for $s \in [d - \gamma, d + \gamma]$. Moreover, the maps

$$\nabla^d h \colon Z_s \times \mathbb{R} \to Z_{s+\gamma}, \qquad s \in [d - \gamma, d + \gamma],$$

are C^1-smooth and bounded. [7]

For any t and T we denote by O_t^T any open subset of the domain of definition of S_t^T in Z_d, such that for each bounded set $Q \subset O_t^T$ the set $\bigcup_{\tau \in [t,T]} S_t^\tau(Q)$ is bounded in Z_d. [8]

In the theorem below the balls B_r and the cylinders C_ϱ^j, $j \geq 1$, are defined in the same way as in Subsection 5.1.

Theorem 5. *Let us assume that the assumptions* (H1) *and* (H2) *hold and that a ball* $B_r = B_r(u_0, Z_d)$ *belongs to* O_t^T *together with some ε-neighbourhood, $\varepsilon > 0$. Then the relation*

$$S_t^T(B_r) \subset v_0 + C_\varrho^j(Z_d) \tag{4}$$

with some $v_0 \in Z_d$ and $j \geq 1$ implies that $\varrho \geq r$.

Proof. Without lost of generality we may assume that

$$v_0 = 0, \qquad j = 1.$$

Arguing by contradiction we assume that in (4) $\varrho < r$ and choose any $\varrho_1 \in (\varrho, r)$.

For $n \geq 1$ we denote by E^{2n} the subspace of Z_d, spanned by the vectors $\{\varphi_j, |j| \leq n\}$, and provide it with the usual Darboux symplectic structure (it is given by the form $\alpha_2|_{E^{2n}}$). By Π_n we denote the orthogonal projection $\Pi_n : Z_d \to E^{2n}$. We set

$$H^n = \tfrac{1}{2}\langle Au, u\rangle_d + h(\Pi_n(u))$$

and denote by $S_{(n)t}^T$ flow-maps of the Hamiltonian vector filed V_{H^n}. Any map $S_{(n)t}^T$ decomposes to the direct sum of a symplectomorphism of E^{2n} and of a linear symplectomorphism of $Z_d \ominus E^{2n}$. So the theorem's assertion with the map S_t^T replaced by $S_{(n)t}^T$ follows from the Gromov theorem, applied to the symplectomorphism

$$E^{2n} \to E^{2n}, \qquad x \mapsto \Pi_n S_{(n)t}^T(i(x) + u_0),$$

where i stands for the embedding of E^{2n} to Z_d.

---

[7] i.e., they send bounded sets to bounded.

[8] this set should be treated as a 'regular part of the domain of definition'.

Lemma 2. *Under the theorem's assumptions the maps $S^T_{(n)t}$ are defined on B_r for $n \geq n'$ with some sufficiently large n', and there exists a sequence $\varepsilon_n \xrightarrow[n\to\infty]{} 0$ such that*

$$\|S^T_t(u) - S^T_{(n)t}(u)\| \leq \varepsilon_n \tag{5}$$

for $n \geq n'$ and for every $u \in B_r$.

We leave a proof of this lemma as an exercise; alternatively see for the proof [10].

Lemma 3. *For any $u \in B_r$ we have*

$$S^T_t(u) = e^{(T-t)JA}u + \widetilde{S}^T_t(u),$$

where $\widetilde{S}^T_t$ is a C^1-smooth map in the scale $\{Z_s\}$ and $\operatorname{ord}\widetilde{S}^T_t = -\gamma$ for $s \in [d-\gamma, d+\gamma]$.

A proof is another exercise (cf. Lemma 1 in [10]).

Now we continue the proof of the theorem. Since its assertion holds for any map $S^T_{(n)t}$ $(n \geq n')$ and since the ball B_r belongs to this map's domain of definition (see Lemma 2), then for each $n \geq n'$ there exists a point $u_n \in B_r$ such that $S^T_{(n)t}(u_n) \notin C^1_{\varrho_1}(0)$. That is,

$$|\Pi_1 S^T_{(n)t}(u_n)| \geq \varrho_1. \tag{6}$$

By the weak compactness of a Hilbert ball, we can find a weakly converging subsequence

$$u_{n_j} \rightharpoonup u \in B_r, \tag{7}$$

so

$$u_{n_j} \to u \quad \text{strongly in } Z_{d-\gamma}.$$

Due to Lemma 3 this implies that $\widetilde{S}^T_t(u_{n_j}) \to \widetilde{S}^T_t(u)$ in Z_d, and using (7) we obtain the convergence:

$$S^T_t(u_{n_j}) \rightharpoonup S^T_t(u). \tag{8}$$

Noting that $|\Pi_1 S^T_t(u_n)| = |\Pi_1 S^T_{(n)t}u_n + \Pi_1(S^T_t - S^T_{(n)t})u_n|$ and using (6), (5) we get:

$$|\Pi_1 S^T_t(u_n)| \geq \varrho_1 - \varepsilon_n, \quad n \geq n'. \tag{9}$$

Since by (8) $\Pi_1 S^T_t(u_{n_j}) \to \Pi_1 S^T_t(u)$ in E^2, then due to (9) we have $|\Pi_1 S^T_t(u)| \geq \varrho_1$. This contradicts (4) because $\varrho_1 > \varrho$. The obtained contradiction proves the theorem.

5.3 Examples

Example 7. Let us consider the nonlinear wave equation

$$\ddot{u} = \Delta u - \tilde{f}(u; t, x), \tag{10}$$

where $u = u(t, x)$, $x \in \mathbb{T}^n$. The function $\tilde{f}$ is a polynomial in u of a degree D such that its coefficients are smooth functions of t and x. We set $f = \tilde{f} - u$, denote by B the linear operator $B = \sqrt{1 - \Delta}$ and write (10) as the system of two equations:

$$\begin{aligned} \dot{u} &= -Bv, \\ \dot{v} &= Bu + B^{-1}f(u; t, x). \end{aligned} \tag{11}$$

Let us take for $\{Z_s\}$ the shifted Sobolev scale $Z_s = H^{s+1/2}(\mathbb{T}^n; \mathbb{R}^2)$, where $\langle \xi, \eta \rangle_s = \int_{\mathbb{T}^n} B^{2s+1}\xi \cdot \eta \, dx$.

Taking for α_2 the Darboux form $\alpha_2 = \overline{J} \, d\xi \wedge d\xi$, where $J\xi = (-v, u)$ for $\xi = (u, v)$, one sees that (11) is a Hamiltonian equation with the Hamiltonian

$$H(u, v) = \frac{1}{2}\langle B(u, v), (u, v) \rangle_0 + \int F(u; t, x) \, dx,$$

where $F_u' = f_0$. Choosing for $\{\psi_j \mid j \in \mathbb{N}\}$ a (properly enumerated) Hilbert basis of the space $H^{1/2}(\mathbb{T}^n)$, formed by functions $C_s \operatorname{Re} e^{is \cdot x}$ and $C_s \operatorname{Im} e^{is \cdot x}$, we set

$$\widetilde{\varphi}_j = (\psi_j, 0), \quad \widetilde{\varphi}_{-j} = (0, \psi_j), \quad j \in \mathbb{N}.$$

The basis $\{\widetilde{\varphi}_j\}$ satisfies (1), so $Z_0 = H^{1/2}(\mathbb{T}^n, \mathbb{R}^2)$ is the Darboux phase space for the nonlinear wave equation, written in the form (11).

To apply Theorem 5 we have to check conditions (H1) and (H2). The first one (with $A = B$) holds trivially since $\widetilde{\varphi}_j$'s are eigenfunctions of the Laplacian. The condition (H2) holds in the following three cases:

a) $n = 1$,

b) $n = 2$, $D \leq 4$,

c) $n = 3$, $D \leq 2$.

The case a) and the case b) with $D \leq 2$ can be checked using elementary tools, see [10]. Arguments in the case b) with $3 \leq D \leq 4$ and in the case c) are based on Strichartz-type inequalities, see [3].

In the cases a)–c), Theorem 5 applies to equation (10) in the form (11) and shows that the flow maps cannot squeeze $H^{1/2}$-balls to narrow cylinders. This result can be interpreted as impossibility of 'locally uniform' energy transition to high modes, see [10].

Example 8. For a nonlinear Schrödinger equation

$$\dot{u} = i\Delta u + if_u'(|u|^2)u, \qquad x \in \mathbb{T}^n \tag{12}$$

(cf. Example 4), the Darboux phase space is the L_2-space $L_2(\mathbb{T}^n; \mathbb{C})$. It is very unlikely that the flow-maps of (12) satisfy in this space assumption (H2). So we smooth out the Hamiltonian of (12) and replace it by

$$H_\xi = \frac{1}{2} \int (|\nabla u|^2 + f(|U|^2)) \, dx, \qquad U = u * \xi,$$

where $u * \xi$ is the convolution of u with a function $\xi \in C^\infty(\mathbb{T}^n, \mathbb{R})$. The corresponding Hamiltonian equation is

$$\dot{u} = i \Delta u + i(f'(|U|^2)U) * \xi.$$

This smoothed equation satisfies (H1), (H2) and Theorem 5 applies to its flow-maps.

5.4 Symplectic Capacity

Another way to prove Theorem 5 uses a new object — symplectic capacity — which is interesting on its own.

Symplectic capacity in a Hilbert Darboux space (Z_d, α_2) as in Subsection 5.2 (below we abbreviate Z_d to Z), is a map c which corresponds to any open subset $O \subset Z$ a number $c(O) \in [0, \infty]$ and satisfies the following properties:

1) *translational invariance*: $c(O) = c(O + \xi)$ for any $\xi \in Z$;
2) *monotonicity*: if $O_1 \supset O_2$, then $c(O_1) \geq c(O_2)$;
3) *2-homogeneity*: $c(\tau O) = \tau^2 c(O)$;
4) *normalisation*: for any ball $B_r = B_r(x; Z)$ and any cylinder $C_r^j = C_r^j(Z)$ we have

$$c(B_r) = c(C_r^j) = \pi r^2.$$

(We note that for $x = 0$ the cylinder contains the ball and is 'much bigger', but both sets have the same capacity.)

5) *Symplectic invariance*: for any symplectomorphism $\Phi: Z \to Z$ and any domain O, $c(\Phi(O)) = c(O)$.

If (Z, α_2) is a finite-dimensional Darboux space, then existence of a capacity with properties 1)–5) is equivalent to the Gromov theorem. Indeed, if a capacity exists, then the squeezing (4) with $\varrho < r$ is impossible due to 2), 4) and 5). On the opposite, the quantity

$$\tilde{c}(O) = \sup\{\pi r^2 \mid \text{there exists a symplectomorphism which sends } B_r \text{ in } O\}$$

obviously satisfies 1)–3) and 5). Using the Gromov theorem we see that $\tilde{c}$ satisfies 4) as well.

If (Z, α_2) is a Hilbert Darboux space, then the finite-dimensional symplectic capacity, obtained in [5], can be used to construct a capacity c which meets 1)–4). This capacity turns out to be invariant under symplectomorphisms, which are flow-maps S_t^T as in Theorem 5, see [10]. This result also implies Theorem 5.

6 The Squeezing Phenomenon

Example 7 shows that flow-maps of the nonlinear wave equation (11) satisfy the Gromov property. This means (more or less) that *flow of generalised solutions for a nonlinear wave equation cannot squeeze a ball to a narrow cylinder.* On the contrary, behaviour of the flow formed by *classical* solutions for the nonlinear wave equation in sufficiently smooth Sobolev spaces exhibits 'a lot of squeezing', at least if we put a small parameter δ in front of the Laplacian. Corresponding results apply to a bigger class of equations. Below we discuss them for nonlinear Schrödinger equations; concerning the nonlinear wave equation (10) see the author's paper in GAFA 5:4.

Let us consider the nonlinear Schrödinger equation:

$$\dot{u} = -i\delta\Delta u + i|u|^{2p}u, \tag{1}$$

where $\delta > 0$ and $p \in \mathbb{N}$. To present results of this section it is more convenient to consider the equation under the odd periodic boundary conditions:

$$\begin{aligned} u(t,x) &= u(t,x_1,\ldots,x_j+2,\ldots,x_n) \\ &= -u(t,x_1,\ldots,-x_j,\ldots,x_n), \qquad j = 1,\ldots,n, \end{aligned} \tag{2}$$

where $n \leq 3$. Clearly, any function which satisfies (2) vanishes at the boundary of the cube K^n of half-periods, $K^n = \{0 \leq x_j \leq 1\}$. The problem (1), (2) can be written in the Hamiltonian form (2) if for the symplectic Hilbert scale $(\{X_s\}, \alpha_2)$ one takes a scale formed by odd periodic complex Sobolev functions, $X_s = H^s_{\text{odd}}(\mathbb{R}^n/2\mathbb{Z}^n; \mathbb{C})$, and $\alpha_2 = i\, du \wedge du$ (cf. Example 5).

Due to a nontrivial result of J. Bourgain (which can be extracted from [2]), flow-maps S^t for (1), (2) are well defined in the spaces X_s, $s \geq 1$. In particular, they are well defined in the space C^∞ of smooth odd periodic functions. Denoting by $|\cdot|_m$ the C^m-norm, $|u|_m = \sup_{|\alpha|=m}\sup_x |\partial_x^\alpha u(x)|$, we define below the set $\mathfrak{A}_m \subset C^\infty$ which we call the essential part of the smooth phase-space for the problem (1), (2) with respect to the C^m-norm, or just the *essential part of the phase-space*:

$$\mathfrak{A}_m = \{u \in C^\infty \mid u \text{ satisfies (2) and the condition (3)}\},$$

where

$$|u|_0 \leq K_m \delta^\mu |u|_m^{1/(2pm\varkappa+1)}, \tag{3}$$

with a suitable $K_m = K_m(\varkappa)$ and $\mu = m\varkappa/(2pm\varkappa+1)$. Here $\varkappa$ is any fixed constant $\varkappa \in (0, 1/3)$.

Intersection of the set $\mathfrak{A}_m$ with the R-sphere in the C^m-norm (i.e., with the set $\{|u|_m = R\}$) has the C^0-diameter $\leq 2K_m\delta^\mu R^{1/(2pm\varkappa+1)}$. Asymptotically (as $\delta \to 0$ or $R \to \infty$) this is much smaller than the C^0-diameter of the sphere, which equals $C_m R$. Thus, $\mathfrak{A}_m$ is an 'asymptotically narrow' subset of the smooth phase space.

The theorem below states that for any $m \geq 2$ the set $\mathfrak{A}_m$ is a recursion subset for the dynamical system, and gives a control for the recursion time:

Theorem 6. *Let $u(t) = u(t, \cdot)$ be a smooth solution for (1), (2) and $|u(t_0)|_0 = U$. Then there exists $T \leq t_0 + \delta^{-1/3}U^{-4p/3}$ such that $u(T) \in \mathfrak{A}_m$ and $\frac{1}{2}U \leq |u(T)|_0 \leq \frac{3}{2}U$.*

Since L_2-norm of a solution is an integral of motion (see Example 6) and $|u(t)|_0 \geq |u(t)|_{L_2(K^n)}$, then we obtain the following

Corollary 2. *Let $u(t)$ be a smooth solution for (1), (2) and $|u(t)|_{L_2(K^n)} \equiv W$. Then for any $m \geq 2$ this solution cannot stay outside $\mathfrak{A}_m$ longer than the time $\delta^{-1/3}W^{-4p/3}$.*

For the theorem's proof we refer the reader to Appendix 3 in [11]. Here we explain why 'something like this result' should be true. Presenting the arguments it is more convenient to operate with the Sobolev norms $\| \cdot \|_m$. Let us denote $\|u(t_0)\|_0 = A$. Arguing by contradiction, we assume that for all $t \in [t_0, t_1] = L$, where $t_1 = t_0 + \delta^{-1/3}U^{-4p/3}$, we have

$$C\delta^a \|u\|_m^b < \|u\|_0. \tag{4}$$

Since $\|u(t)\|_0 \equiv A$, then (4) and the interpolation inequality imply upper bounds

$$\|u(t)\|_l \leq C(l, \delta), \quad 0 \leq l \leq m, \ t \in L. \tag{5}$$

If this estimate with $l = 3$ implies that

$$\delta \|\Delta u\|_1 \leq \delta^c \tag{6}$$

with some $c > 0$, then for $t \in L$ equation (1) treated as a dynamical system in H^1_{odd}, is a perturbation of the trivial equation

$$\dot{u} = i|u|^{2p}u. \tag{7}$$

Elementary arguments show that H^1-norm of solutions for (7) grow linearly with time. This implies a lower estimate for $\|u(t_1)\|_1$, where $u(t)$ is the solution for (1), (2) which we discuss. It turns out that one can choose a, b and A in such a way that (6) holds and the lower estimate we obtained contradicts (5) with $l = 1$. This contradiction shows that (4) cannot hold for all $t \in L$. In other words, $\|u(\tau)\|_0 \leq C\delta^a\|u(\tau)\|_m^b$ for some $\tau \in L$. At this moment τ the solution enters a domain, similar to the essential part $\mathfrak{A}_m$. $\square$

Let us consider any trajectory $u(t)$ for (1), (2) such that $|u(t)|_{L_2(K^n)} \equiv W \sim 1$, and discuss the time-averages $\langle |u|_m \rangle$ and $\langle \|u\|_m^2 \rangle^{1/2}$ of its C^m-norm $|u|_m$ and its Sobolev norm $\|u\|_m$, where we set

$$\langle |u|_m \rangle = \frac{1}{T} \int_0^T |u|_m \, dt, \qquad \langle \|u\|_m^2 \rangle^{1/2} = \left(\frac{1}{T} \int_0^T \|u\|_m^2 \, dt \right)^{1/2},$$

and the time T of averaging is specified below. While the trajectory stays in $\mathfrak{A}_m$, we have

$$|u|_m \geq (WK_m^{-1}\delta^{-\mu})^{1/(1-2p\mu)}.$$

One can show that this inequality implies that each visit to $\mathfrak{A}_m$ increases the integral $\int |u|_m \, dt$ by a term bigger than δ to a negative degree. Since these visits are sufficiently frequent by the Corollary, then we obtain a lower estimate for the quantity $\langle |u|_m \rangle$. Details can be found in the author's paper in CMPh 178, pp. 265–280. Here we present a better result which estimates the time-averaged Sobolev norms. For a proof see Subsection 4.1 of [11].

Theorem 7. *Let $u(t)$ be a smooth solution for the equation* (1), (2) *such that* $|u(t)|_{L_2(K^n)} \geq 1$. *Then there exists a sequence* $k_m \nearrow 1/3$ *and constants* $C_m > 0$, $\delta_m > 0$ *such that* $\langle \|u\|_m^2 \rangle^{1/2} \geq C_m \delta^{-2mk_m}$, *provided that* $m \geq 4$, $\delta \leq \delta_m$ *and* $T \geq \delta^{-1/3}$.

The results stated in Theorems 6, 7 remain true for equations (1) with dissipation. I.e., for the equations with δ replaced by $\delta\nu$, where ν is a unit complex number such that $\mathrm{Re}\,\nu \geq 0$ and $\mathrm{Im}\,\nu \geq 0$. [9] If $\mathrm{Im}\,\nu > 0$, then smooth solutions for (1), (2) converge to zero in any C^m-norm. Since the essential part $\mathfrak{A}_m$ clearly contains a sufficiently small C^m-neighbourhood of zero, then eventually any smooth solution enter $\mathfrak{A}_m$ and stays there forever. Theorem (1) states that the solution will visit the essential part much earlier, before its norm decays.

References

1. V. I. Arnold. *Mathematical methods in classical mechanics.* Springer-Verlag, Berlin, 3rd edition, 1989.
2. J. Bourgain. Fourier transform restriction phenomenona for certain lattice subsets and applications to nonlinear evolution equations. *Geometric and Functional Analysis*, 3:107–156 and 209–262, 1993.
3. J. Bourgain. Aspects of long time behaviour of solutions of nonlinear Hamiltonian evolution equations. *Geometric and Functional Analysis*, 5:105–140, 1995.
4. G. E. Giacaglia. *Perturbation methods in non-linear systems.* Springer-Verlag, Berlin, 1972.
5. H. Hofer and E. Zehnder. *Symplectic invariants and Hamiltonian dynamics.* Birkhäuser, Basel, 1994.
6. T. Kappeler and J. Pöschel. Perturbed KdV equation, 2001.
7. S. B. Kuksin. The perturbation theory for the quasiperiodic solutions of infinite-dimensional hamiltonian systems and its applications to the Korteweg – de Vries equation. *Math. USSR Sbornik*, 64:397–413, 1989.
8. S. B. Kuksin. *Nearly integrable infinite-dimensional Hamiltonian Systems.* Springer-Verlag, Berlin, 1993.
9. S. B. Kuksin. KAM-theory for partial differential equations. In *Proceedings of the First European Congress of Mathematics*, volume 2, pages 123–157. Birkhäuser, 1994.

---

[9] The only correction is that if $\mathrm{Im}\,\nu > 0$, then in Theorem 7 one should take $T = \delta^{-1/3}$.

10. S. B. Kuksin. Infinite-dimensional symplectic capacities and a squeezing theorem for Hamiltonian PDEs. *Comm. Math. Physics*, 167:531–552, 1995.

11. S. B. Kuksin. Spectral properties of solutions for nonlinear PDEs in the turbulent regime. *Geometric and Functional Analysis*, 9:141–184, 1999.

12. S. B. Kuksin. *Analysis of Hamiltonian PDEs*. Oxford University Press, Oxford, 2000.

13. A. Pazy. *Semigroups of linear operators and applications to partial differential equations*. Springer-Verlag, Berlin, 1983.

14. M. Reed and B. Simon. *Methods of modern mathematical physics*, volume 2. Academic Press, New York - London, 1975.

15. V. E. Zakharov, S. V. Manakov, S. P. Novikov, and L. P. Pitaevskij. *Theory of solitons*. Plenum Press, New York, 1984.

List of Participants

1. Berretti Alberto
   Dipartimento di Matematica, II Universita' di Roma (Tor Vergata),
   via della Ricerca scientifica, 00133 Roma (Italy)
   berretti@mvxgl1.fis.uniroma2.it
2. Benettin Giancarlo
   Dipartimento di Matematica Pura ed Applicata,
   Universita' di Padova,
   via Belzoni 7, 35131 Padova (Italy)
   benettin@math.unipd.it
3. Bertini Massimo
   Dipartimento di Matematica, Universita' Statale di Milano,
   via Saldini 50, 20133 Milano (Italy)
   bertini@berlioz.mat.unimi.it
4. Bertotti Maria Letizia
   Dipartimento di Matematica e Applicazioni c/o Ingegneria,
   Viale delle Scienze, 90128 Palermo (Italy) and:
   Dipartimento Ingegneria Meccanica e Strutturale, Ingegneria,
   via Mesiano 77, 38050 Trento (Italy)
   bertotti@ing.unitn.it bertotti@dipmat.math.unipa.it
5. Camyshev Andrei
   Institute of Mathematics,
   Akademijas lauk. 1, Riga, LV 1524 (Latvia)
   camysh@lanet.nv
6. Castella Enric
   Departament de Matematica Aplicada i Analisi,
   Universitat de Barcelona,
   Gran Via 585, 08007 Barcelona (Spain)
   enric@maia.ub.es
7. Cellina Arrigo
   Dipartimento di Matematica e Applicazioni,
   Universita' di Milano Bicocca,
   via degli Arcimboldi 8, 20126 Milano, (Italy)
   cellina@mat.unimi.it

8. Cherubini Anna Maria
   Dipartimento di Matematica, Universita' degli Studi di Lecce,
   via per Arnesano, 73100 Lecce (Italy)
   ANNA.CHERUBINI@unile.it

9. Conti Monica
   Dipartimento di Matematica del Politecnico di Milano,
   Piazza Leonardo da Vinci 32, Milano (Italy)
   moncon@mate.polimi.it monica@socrates.mat.unimi.it

10. Degiovanni Luca
    Dipartimento di Matematica, Universita' di Torino,
    Palazzo Campana, via Carlo Albrto, Torino (Italy)
    degio@dm.unito.it

11. Eliasson Hakan
    Department of Mathematics, Royal Inst. of Techn.
    S-10044 Stockolm (Sweden)
    hakane@math.kth.se

12. Fasso Francesco
    Dipartimento di Matematica Pura ed Applicata, Universita' di Padova,
    via Belzoni 7, 35131 Padova (Italy)
    fasso@math.unipd.it

13. Finco Domenico
    Dipartimento di Matematica, Universita' "La Sapienza" di Roma
    piazza A. Moro 5, 00185 Roma (Italy)
    finco@mat.uniroma1.it

14. Firpo Marie Christine
    PIIM - UMR 6633, Equipe Turbulece Plasma,
    Universite' Aix-Marseille I
    Centre S. Jerome, Case 321-F-13397,
    Marseille Cedex 20 (France)
    firpo@newsup.univ-mrs.fr

15. Gabern Frederic
    Departament de Matematica Aplicada i Analisi, Universitat de Barcelona,
    Gran Via 585, 08007 Barcelona (Spain)
    gabern@mat.ub.es

16. Galgani Luigi
    Dipartimento di Matematica, Universita' Statale'di Milano,
    via Saldini 50, 20133 Milano (Italy)
    galgani@mi.infn.it

17. Gentile Guido
    Dipartimento di Matematica, Universita' di Roma 3,
    Largo S. Leonardo Murialdo 1, 00146 Roma (Italy)
    gentile@matrm3.mat.uniroma3.it

18. Giorgi Giordano
    Department: Dipartimento di Fisica, Universita' "La Sapienza"
    Personal Post Address: via G. Sirtori 69, 00149 Roma (Italy)
    giordagi@tin.it

19. Giorgilli Antonio
    Dipartimento di Matematica e Applicazioni,
    Universita' di Milano Bicocca,
    via degli Arcimboldi 8, 20126 Milano (Italy)
    antonio@matapp.unimib.it

20. Gonzalez Maria Alejandra
    Departament de Matematica Aplicada i Analisi,
    Universitat de Barcelona,
    Gran Via 585, 08007 Barcelona (Spain)
    gonzalea@maia.ub.es

21. Henrard Jacques
    Departement de Mathematique FUNDP 8,
    Rempart de la Vierge, B-5000 Namur, (Belgium)
    Jacques.Henrard@fundp.ac.be

22. Kuksin Sergei
    Department of Mathematics, Heriott-Watt University,
    Edinburgh EH14 4AS, Scotland (United Kingdom)
    S.B.Kuksin@ma.hw.ac.uk

23. Lazaro Ochoa J.Tomas
    Departament de Matematica Aplicada I,
    Universitat Politecnica de Catalunya,
    Diagonal 647, 08028 Barcelona (Spain)
    lazaro@ma1.upc.es

24. Locatelli Ugo
    School of Cosmic Physics, Dublin Institut for Advanced Studies,
    5 Merrion Square, Dublin 2, (Ireland)
    ugo@cp.dias.ie

25. Macri' Marta
    Dipartimento di Matematica e Applicazioni "R. Cacciopoli",
    Monte S. Angelo, via Cinthia, Napoli (Italy)
    macrima@matna3.dma.unina.it

26. Mastropietro Vieri
    Dipartimento di Matematica,
    II Universita' di Roma (Tor Vergata),
    via della Ricerca scientifica, 00133 Roma (Italy)
    vieri@ipparco.roma1.infn.it

27. Naselli Franz
    Departament de Matematica Aplicada i Analisi,
    Universitat de Barcelona,
    Gran Via 585, 08007 Barcelona (Spain)
    naselli@socrates.mat.unimi.it

28. Nekhoroshev Nikolai
   Department of Mechanics and Mathematics, Moscow State University,
   119899 Moscow (Russia)
   root@corvette.math.msu.su

29. Pacha Andujar Juan Ramon
   Departament de Matematica Aplicada I,
   Universitat Politecnica de Catalunya,
   Diagonal 647, 08028 Barcelona (Spain)
   joanr@vilma.upc.es

30. Paleari Simone
   Dipartimento di Matematica, Universita' Statale di Milano,
   via Saldini 50, 20133 Milano, (Italy)
   paleari@berlioz.mat.unimi.it

31. Panati Gianluca
   Mathematical Physics Sector, SISSA/ISAS,
   via Beirut 2, 34014 Trieste (Italy)
   panati@sissa.it

32. Prykarpatsky Yarema
   Department of ordinary differential equations,
   Institute of Mathematics at MAS of Ukraine,
   Tereshchenkirska str., 252601 Kiev (Ukraine)
   yarchyk@imath.kiev.ua

33. Puig Joaquim
   Departament de Matematica Aplicada i Analisi,
   Universitat de Barcelona,
   Gran Via 585, 08007 Barcelona (Spain)
   jpuig@eic.ictnet.es

34. Pyke Randall
   Department of Mathematics, University of Toronto,
   Toronto, Ontario, M5S 3G3 (Canada)
   pyke@math.toronto.edu

35. Sama Cami Anna
   Departament de Matematiques, Facultat de Ciencies,
   Universitat Autonoma de Barcelona
   08290 Cerdanyola del Valles (Spain)
   sama@manwe.mat.uab.es

36. Shirikyan Armen
   Department of Mathematics, Heriott-Watt University,
   Edinburgh EH14 4AS, Scotland (United Kingdom)
   A.Shirikyan@ma.hw.ac.uk

37. Simo' Carles
   Departament de Matematica Aplicada i Analisi,
   Universitat de Barcelona,
   Gran Via 585, 08007 Barcelona (Spain)
   carles@maia.ub.es

38. Slijepcevic Sinisa
    Department of Mathematics, PMF,
    Bijenicka 30, 10000 Zagreb (Croatia)
    S.Slijepcevic@damtp.cam.ac.uk

39. Sommer Britta
    Inst. Reine und Angewandte Mathematik,
    RWTH-Aachen Templergraben 55, 52062 Aachen (Germany)
    Britta.Sommer@post.rwth-aachen.de

40. Terracini Susanna
    Dipartimento di Matematica del Politecnico di Milano,
    Piazza Leonardo da Vinci 32, Milano (Italy)
    suster@mate.polimi.it

41. Villanueva Jordi
    Departament de Matematica Aplicada I,
    Universitat Politecnica de Catalunya,
    Diagonal 647, 08028 Barcelona (Spain)
    jordi@tere.upc.es

42. Vitolo Renato
    Department of Mathematics, University of Groningen,
    P.O. Box 800, 9700 AV Groningen (Netherlands)
    R.Vitolo@math.rug.nl

43. Vittot Michel
    Centre de Physique theorique - CNRS
    Luminy, Case 907, 13288 Marseille, Cedex 9 (France)
    vittot@cpt.univ.mrs.fr

LIST OF C.I.M.E. SEMINARS

Fondazione C.I.M.E.

Centro Internazionale Matematico Estivo
International Mathematical Summer Center
http://www.cime.unifi.it
cime@math.unifi.it

2005 COURSES LIST

Enumerative Invariants
in Algebraic Geometry and String Theory

June 6–11, Cetraro

Course Directors:

Prof. Kai Behrend (University of British Columbia, Vancouver, Canada)
Prof. Barbara Mantechi (SISSA, Trieste, Italy)

Calculus of Variations
and Non-linear Partial Differential Equations

June 27–July 2, Cetraro

Course Directors:

Prof. Bernard Dacorogna (EPFL, Lousanne, Switzerland)
Prof. Paolo Marcellini (Università di Firenze, Italy)

SPDE in Hydrodynamics:
Recent Progress and Prospects

August 29–September 3, Cetraro

Course Directors:

Prof. Giuseppe Da Prato (Scuola Normale Superiore, Pisa, Italy)
Prof. Michael Rockner (Bielefeld University, Germany)

Printing and Binding: Strauss GmbH, Mörlenbach

4. Manuscripts should in general be submitted in English. Final manuscripts should contain at least 100 pages of mathematical text and should always include
   - a general table of contents;
   - an informative introduction, with adequate motivation and perhaps some historical remarks: it should be accessible to a reader not intimately familiar with the topic treated;
   - a global subject index: as a rule this is genuinely helpful for the reader.

5. Lecture Notes volumes are, as a rule, printed digitally from the authors' files. We strongly recommend that all contributions in a volume be written in the same LaTeX version, preferably LaTeX2e. To ensure best results, authors are asked to use the LaTeX2e style files available from Springer's web-pages at

   www.springeronline.com

   [on this page, click on <Mathematics>, then on <For Authors> and look for <Macro Packages for books>]. Macros in LaTeX2.09 and TeX are available on request from: lnm@springer.de. Careful preparation of the manuscripts will help keep production time short besides ensuring satisfactory appearance of the finished book in print and online. After acceptance of the manuscript authors will be asked to prepare the final LaTeX source files (and also the corresponding dvi-, pdf- or zipped ps-file) together with the final printout made from these files. The LaTeX source files are essential for producing the full-text online version of the book. For the existing online volumes of LNM see: http://www.springerlink.com .
   The actual production of a Lecture Notes volume takes approximately 8 weeks.

6. Volume editors receive a total of 50 free copies of their volume to be shared with the authors, but no royalties. They and the authors are entitled to a discount of 33.3 % on the price of Springer books purchased for their personal use, if ordering directly from Springer.

7. Commitment to publish is made by letter of intent rather than by signing a formal contract. Springer-Verlag secures the copyright for each volume. Authors are free to reuse material contained in their LNM volumes in later publications: A brief written (or e-mail) request for formal permission is sufficient.

Addresses:

Professor J.-M. Morel, CMLA,
École Normale Supérieure de Cachan,
61 Avenue du Président Wilson, 94235 Cachan Cedex, France
E-mail: Jean-Michel.Morel@cmla.ens-cachan.fr

Professor F. Takens, Mathematisch Instituut,
Rijksuniversiteit Groningen, Postbus 800,
9700 AV Groningen, The Netherlands
E-mail: F.Takens@math.rug.nl

Professor B. Teissier, Université Paris 7
Institut Mathématique de Jussieu, UMR 7586 du CNRS
Équipe "Géométrie et Dynamique", 175 rue du Chevaleret
75013 Paris, France
E-mail: teissier@math.jussieu.fr

Springer-Verlag, Mathematics Editorial, Tiergartenstr. 17,
69121 Heidelberg, Germany,
Tel.: +49 (6221) 487-8410
Fax: +49 (6221) 487-8355
E-mail: lnm@springer.de